Instructor's Manual with Solutions

for

Business Mathematics

Second Edition

Instructor's Manual with Solutions

for

Business Mathematics

Second Edition

Richard N. Aufmann
Palomar College

Vernon C. Barker
Palomar College

Joanne S. Lockwood
Plymouth State College

Business Consultant:
Diane Coleman
Department of Business
Hutchinson Community College

HOUGHTON MIFFLIN COMPANY   BOSTON   TORONTO
Geneva, Illinois   Palo Alto   Princeton, New Jersey

Sponsoring Editor: Maureen O'Connor
Manager, Basic Books: Sue Warne
Production Coordinator: Lucille Belmonte
Senior Manufacturing Coordinator: Marie Barnes
Marketing Manager: Mike Ginley

Printed in the U.S.A.

ISBN: 0-395-67533-2
Business Mathematics: 0-395-67531-6

123456789-PO-97 96 95 94 93

CONTENTS

INTRODUCTION

Changes to the Contents of the Textbook

Business Mathematics, Second Edition, provides a unified and comprehensive introduction to those math skills needed for success in business. The first chapters of the text cover basic skills involving operations with whole numbers, fractions, decimals, and percent. The remaining chapters are devoted to applications of those skills, including purchasing, pricing, payroll, simple and compound interest, annuities, business and consumer loans, inventory, depreciation, taxes, insurance, investments, and financial statements. These chapters give the student a sound background in the application of business math concepts to the world of business today.

New to this edition are Chapter 4, which is devoted to topics related to banking, and Chapter 5, which presents solving equations and using formulas to solve problems. The topics of pricing and purchasing are now presented in two separate chapters, and the pricing of perishables has been added to this material. The chapter on inventory has been expanded to include the calculation of the rate of turnover, and the topic of partnerships has been added to the chapter on investments. Also new to this edition is Chapter 16, International Business. In light of today's growing global economy, exposure to topics related to international trade is a vital part of any business student's background.

The entire text has been updated and much of the material rewritten. However, for those instructors who taught from the first edition, the following chart provides a list of the contents of the second edition and the location of the same topical coverage in the first edition.

Correlation of Content in First and Second Editions

Contents of Business Mathematics, Second Edition	Location of Material in the First Edition
1. Whole Numbers and Business Applications	Chapter 1
2. Fractions and Business Applications	Chapter 2
3. Decimals and Business Applications	Chapter 3, Sections 1, 2, 3
4. Banking	Chapter 3, Section 4 (Expanded coverage in second edition)
5. Equations	Chapter 4, Objective 2A (Expanded coverage in second edition)

Contents of Business Mathematics, Second Edition	Location of Material in the First Edition
6. Percent and Business Applications	Chapter 4
7. Purchasing	Chapter 5, Sections 2, 3
8. Pricing	
Section 1 Markup and Markdown	Chapter 5, Section 1
Section 2 Perishables	New to second edition
9. Payroll	Chapter 6
10. Simple and Compound Interest	Chapter 7
11. Annuities	Chapter 8
12. Business and Consumer Loans	Chapter 9
13. Inventory	
Section 1 The Specific Identification Method and the Average Cost Method	Chapter 11, Section 1
Section 2 The First-in, First-out Method and the Last-in, First-out Method	Chapter 11, Section 2
Section 3 Inventory Turnover	New to second edition
14. Depreciation	Chapter 10
15. Taxes and Insurance	Chapter 14
16. International Business	New to second edition
17. Investments	
Section 1 Stocks	Chapter 12, Section 1 (Expanded coverage in second edition)
Section 2 Bonds	Chapter 12, Section 2 (Expanded coverage in second edition)
Section 3 Mutual Funds	Chapter 12, Section 3
Section 4 Partnerships	New to second edition
18. Financial Statements	Chapter 13
19. Statistics	
Section 1 Circle Graphs, Bar Graphs, and Line Graphs	Chapter 15, Section 1
Section 2 Frequency Distributions, Histograms, and Frequency Polygons	Chapter 15, Section 2 (Expanded coverage in second edition)
Section 3 Mean, Median, and Mode	Chapter 15, Section 3 (Expanded coverage in second edition)

Alternate Sequencing of Content

Not all instructors will wish to cover every topic presented in the text or to cover the topics in the sequence provided. With this in mind, many of the chapters in *Business Mathematics,* Second Edition, have been written as self-contained units so instructors can develop a sequence to meet individual course needs. The following chart shows the prerequisite skills or topics needed for each chapter. Note that with an understanding of the material presented in Chapters 1, 2, 3, 5, and 6, Chapters 7, 8, 9, 10, 13, 14, 15, 16, 18, and 19 can be covered in any order.

Chapter	Prerequisite Skills	Chapters Containing Prerequisite Skills
1. Whole Numbers and Business Applications	None	
2. Fractions and Business Applications	Whole numbers	Chapter 1
3. Decimals and Business Applications	Whole numbers, fractions	Chapters 1, 2
4. Banking	Decimals	Chapter 3
5. Equations	Whole numbers, fractions, decimals	Chapters 1, 2, 3
6. Percent and Business Applications	Whole numbers, fractions, decimals, equations	Chapters 1, 2, 3, 5
7. Purchasing	Decimals, equations, percent	Chapters 3, 5, 6
8. Pricing	Decimals, equations, percent	Chapters 3, 5, 6
9. Payroll	Fractions, decimals, percent	Chapters 2, 3, 6
10. Simple and Compound Interest	Fractions, decimals, equations, percent	Chapters 1, 2, 3, 5, 6
11. Annuities	Compound interest	Chapter 10
12. Business and Consumer Loans	Simple and compound interest, annuities	Chapters 10, 11
13. Inventory	Decimals	Chapter 3
14. Depreciation	Fractions, decimals, percent	Chapters 2, 3, 6
15. Taxes and Insurance	Fractions, decimals, percent	Chapters 2, 3, 6
16. International Business	Decimals, percent	Chapters 3, 6
17. Investments	Fractions, decimals, equations, percent, ratio, simple interest	Chapters 2, 3, 5, 6, 10
18. Financial Statements	Decimals, percent, ratio	Chapters 3, 6
19. Statistics	Decimals, percent, ratio	Chapters 3, 6

Instructional Features

Interactive Approach

Instructors have long realized the need for a text that requires the student to use a skill as it is being taught. *Business Mathematics,* Second Edition, uses an interactive technique that meets this need. The exposition of every objective is followed by one or more pairs of examples in which one example is worked. The second example in the pair, the You-Try-It example, is not worked so that the students may "interact" with the text by solving it, using the first example as a model. The complete worked-out solutions to these examples are in the Appendix at the back of the book, so the students can obtain immediate feedback on and reinforcement of the skill being learned. (The reference at the bottom right side of each example box provides the page number on which the solution can be found.) By comparing their solutions with the one provided, students can determine exactly where any errors were made. A benefit of this interactive approach is that students can check their understanding of a concept before attempting a homework assignment.

Emphasis on Problem-Solving Strategies

The solution of an application problem in *Business Mathematics,* Second Edition, is always accompanied by two parts: **Strategy** and **Solution**. The strategy is a written description of the steps that are necessary to solve the problem; the solution is the implementation of the strategy. This format provides students with a structure for solving each type of problem. It also encourages students to write strategies for solving problems which, in turn, fosters "thinking through" a problem situation in a logical manner.

Completely Integrated Learning System Organized by Objectives

Business Mathematics is organized into nineteen chapters. Each chapter is divided into sections. Each section is labeled by chapter and section; for example, Section 9.3 is the third section in Chapter 9. Each section contains related objectives. The objective label designates the chapter and section in the text where that objective can be found. For example, Objective 9.3B is the second objective (B) in Chapter 9, Section 3.

Each chapter begins with a list of the learning objectives included within that chapter. Each of the objectives is then restated in the chapter to remind the student of the current topic of discussion. The same objectives that organize the lessons are used as the structure for the exercise sets, tests, and the testing programs. The answers to the questions on the Review/Tests at the end of each chapter are provided in the Appendix, where they are keyed to the objective in the textbook. Therefore, the student is referred to the objective to restudy if a question on the Review/Test is answered incorrectly.

The advantage of this objective-by-objective organization is that it enables the student who is uncertain at any step in the learning process to refer easily to the original presentation and review that material. This approach also allows the instructor greater control over the management of student progress. The Computerized Testing Program and the Printed Testing Program are organized by the same objectives as the text. These references are provided with the answers to the test items. This allows the instructor to determine quickly those objectives for which a student may need additional instruction.

Content Features

Business Case Studies

Every chapter concludes with one or more cases describing a real-world business situation. Students use the skills they have learned to answer questions about the situation. These cases can be used for individual assignments, extra credit, or cooperative learning exercises like small group projects and class discussion. Answers to the business case studies are provided in the Solutions Manual.

Calculator Procedures

Each chapter, except for Chapter 2 (Fractions), includes a feature entitled "Calculators." The student is provided with instruction and practice on the efficient use of a hand-held calculator in solving business problems.

Chapter Introductions

Each chapter opens with a discussion of the material presented in the chapter and of its importance to the study of business-related topics.

Chapter Review/Tests

A Review/Test is found at the end of each chapter. These exercises are selected to help the student integrate all of the topics presented in the chapter. The answers to all review exercises are given in the answer section. Along with the answer to each exercise is a reference that keys the exercise to the corresponding textbook objective.

Chapter Summaries

A Chapter Summary is provided at the end of each chapter. Included are the key terms and essential rules presented in that chapter. An objective reference provided with each entry enables a student to refer back to the place in the text where that concept is presented.

Glossary

The glossary provided at the back of the book includes all of the terms defined in the text and listed in the Chapter Summaries.

Study Skills

The "To the Student" preface provides the student with suggestions for studying for college courses in general and the effective use of this business mathematics text in particular.

Supplements

Instructor's Annotated Edition (IAE)

The Instructor's Annotated Edition is an exact replica of the student text except that answers to all problems in the text are printed in color on the answer lines of each exercise page. Answers to the student You Try Its, which follow the exposition in each objective, are also provided in the IAE. In addition, marginal notes to the instructor provide teaching tips and address such issues as student pitfalls, points that might be emphasized, and use of the features of the textbook.

Instructor's Manual with Solutions

This manual provides complete worked-out solutions for all exercise sets, business case study questions, and Review/Tests.

Test Bank

The Test Bank includes two forms of each of the following printed tests: chapter tests for every chapter; cumulative tests for Chapters 1–5, 6–10, 11–15, and 16–19; and final examinations covering all nineteen chapters of the text.

The Testing Program also includes a data base of over 1200 test items that are organized around the same hierarchy of objectives that organize the lessons of the text. The data base can be used for selecting specific questions when preparing a test using the Instructor's Computerized Test Generator, or for selecting questions to be included on an exam prepared by hand.

Instructor's Computerized Test Generator

The Instructor's Computerized Test Generator is designed to produce free-response, objective-referenced tests for each chapter of the text. Cumulative tests and final examinations may also be created on the test generator. The questions contained in the Test Generator are unique to it and do not repeat items provided in the printed tests. The Instructor's Computerized Test Generator is available for IBM® PC and Macintosh®.

Computer Tutor

The Computer Tutor, an interactive instructional program for student use, covers basic skills involving whole numbers, fractions, decimals, and percent. The lesson objectives of the Computer Tutor correspond exactly to the lesson objectives contained within the corresponding chapters of the text. The Computer Tutor can be used in several ways: (1) to provide initial instruction to a student who has missed a class; (2) to reinforce instruction on a concept that the student has not yet mastered; (3) to review material in preparation for an exam; (4) to provide review and extra practice on material in these early chapters of the text that is considered assumed knowledge and not covered by the instructor during the course. The Computer Tutor is available for the IBM® PC and compatible computers.

The following chart provides the correlation between lessons on the Computer Tutor and the objectives in the textbook. For Chapters 1–3, the Computer Tutor lessons correspond to the textbook objectives of the same number (that is, lesson 1.1A corresponds to objective 1.1A). For Chapters 4–6, the correspondence is:

Objective in the Textbook	Corresponding Computer Tutor Lesson	
Objective 4.1B	Disk 3	Lesson 3.4A
Objective 4.2A		Lesson 3.4B
Objective 5.1B	Disk 4	Lesson 4.2A
Objective 6.1A	Disk 4	Lesson 4.1A
Objective 6.1B		Lesson 4.1B
Objective 6.2A		Lesson 4.2B
Objective 6.2B		Lesson 4.2C
Objectives 6.3A and 6.3B		Lesson 4.3A
Objective 6.4A		Lesson 4.4A
Objective 6.4B		Lesson 4.4B
Objective 6.4C		Lesson 4.4C

CHAPTER 1
Whole Numbers and Business Applications

Section 1.1, pages 5-6

1. eight hundred five   2. six hundred nine   3. four hundred eighty-five

4. five hundred seventy-six   5. two thousand six hundred seventy-five

6. three thousand seven hundred ninety

7. forty-two thousand nine hundred twenty-eight

8. fifty-eight thousand four hundred seventy-three

9. eighty thousand one hundred six   10. sixty thousand nine hundred thirty

11. three hundred fifty-six thousand nine hundred forty-three

12. four hundred ninety-eight thousand five hundred twelve

13. three million six hundred ninety-seven thousand four hundred eighty-three

14. six million eight hundred forty-two thousand seven hundred fifteen

15. 85	16. 357	17. 406	18. 2390
19. 3456	20. 63,780	21. 52,148	22. 70,971
23. 609,948	24. 7,024,709	25. 4,003,002	26. 6,005,008
27. 9,463,000	28. 16,830,000,000	29. 930	30. 850
31. 1400	32. 4000	33. 7000	34. 8000
35. 44,000	36. 92,000	37. 254,000	38. 648,000
39. 60,000	40. 30,000	41. 930,000	42. 380,000
43. 4,000,000	44. 10,000,000	45. 5,569,000	46. 8,436,000
47. 6,850,000	48. 7,380,000	49. 39,876,000	50. 24,120,000

1

Section 1.2, pages 13–16

1.
```
    421
  +308
───────
    729
```

2.
```
   8092
  +6307
───────
 14,399
```

3.
```
  71,092
 +85,407
────────
 156,499
```

4.
```
   923,571
  +863,117
──────────
 1,786,688
```

5.
```
     1
    859
   +725
───────
   1584
```

6.
```
   1 1 1
   1897
  +3246
───────
   5143
```

7.
```
   1 1 1
  36,925
 +69,392
────────
 106,317
```

8.
```
    2 2
    878
    737
   +189
───────
   1804
```

9.
```
    1 1
    482
    309
   +551
───────
   1342
```

10.
```
    1 2
   9409
   3253
  +7078
───────
 19,740
```

11.
```
   1 1  1 1
   67,428
   32,171
  +20,971
─────────
  120,570
```

12.
```
    1 2
    439
    332
    589
   +528
───────
   1888
```

13.
```
   2 12
   2,709
     658
 +10,935
────────
  14,302
```

14.
```
   1   1
   8,707
     216
 +90,714
────────
  99,637
```

15.
```
   1 1 1
  20,958
   3,218
  +   42
────────
  24,218
```

16.
```
   1 1 2
  80,973
   5,168
  +   29
────────
  86,170
```

17.
```
   1 1 1
    392
     37
  10,924
  +  621
────────
  11,974
```

18.
```
   1 2 2
     694
      62
  70,129
  +  217
────────
  71,102
```

19.
```
   1 2 1
    692
   2107
   3196
  +  92
───────
   6087
```

20.
```
   1 2 2
    294
   1029
   7935
  +  65
───────
   9323
```

21.
```
  1 1 2 1
      97
   7,234
  69,552
  +  276
────────
  77,159
```

22.
```
   1 2 2
      87
   1,698
  27,317
  +  727
────────
  29,829
```

23.
```
   1 2 1
      62
     329
    8954
  +1072
───────
  10,417
```

24.
```
   1 2 1
    654
   7293
    237
  +  33
───────
   8217
```

25.
```
   1 2 1
     87
    946
   6571
  +2103
───────
   9707
```

26.
```
  1 2  2 1
     994
  91,764
   6,571
  + 2,103
────────
 101,432
```

27.
```
    89
   -23
──────
    66
```

28.
```
   1202
  - 701
───────
    501
```

29.
```
   8974
  -3972
───────
   5002
```

30.
```
   8976
  -7463
───────
   1513
```

31.
```
   7 18
    8̸8̸
   -79
──────
     9
```

32.
```
    8 13
    9̸9̸3̸
   -537
───────
    456
```

33.
```
    6 16
    7̸6̸8
   -194
───────
    574
```

34.
```
    8 13
    8̸9̸3̸
   -874
───────
     19
```

35.
```
       10
    2 0 12
    3̸1̸2̸9
   -1785
───────
    1344
```

36.
```
    3 9 13
    7̸4̸0̸3̸
   - 294
───────
    7109
```

37.
$$
\begin{array}{r}
\overset{15}{}\\
\overset{1\ \cancel{5}\ 9\ 10}{\cancel{2}\cancel{6}\cancel{0}\cancel{0}}\\
-1972\\
\hline
628
\end{array}
$$

38.
$$
\begin{array}{r}
\overset{7\ 9\ 9\ 13}{\cancel{8}\cancel{0}\cancel{0}\cancel{3}}\\
-1735\\
\hline
6268
\end{array}
$$

39.
$$
\begin{array}{r}
\overset{16}{}\\
\overset{3\ \cancel{5}\ 10}{\cancel{4}\cancel{7}\cancel{0}}\\
-\ 92\\
\hline
378
\end{array}
$$

40.
$$
\begin{array}{r}
\overset{6\ 14}{\cancel{6}\cancel{7}\cancel{4}}\\
-337\\
\hline
337
\end{array}
$$

41.
$$
\begin{array}{r}
\overset{3\ 13\ 4\ 10}{\cancel{4}\cancel{3}\cancel{5}\cancel{0}}\\
-\ 729\\
\hline
3621
\end{array}
$$

42.
$$
\begin{array}{r}
\overset{11\ 12}{}\\
\overset{6\ \cancel{2}\ \cancel{2}\ 16}{\cancel{7}\cancel{2}\cancel{3}\cancel{6}}\\
-1978\\
\hline
5258
\end{array}
$$

43.
$$
\begin{array}{r}
\overset{6\ 9\ 10}{\cancel{3}\cancel{7}\cancel{0}\cancel{0}}\\
-\ 58\\
\hline
3642
\end{array}
$$

44.
$$
\begin{array}{r}
\overset{7\ 10\ 4\ 12}{\cancel{8}\cancel{0}\cancel{5}\cancel{2}}\\
-2709\\
\hline
5343
\end{array}
$$

45.
$$
\begin{array}{r}
\overset{6\ 10\ 6\ 9\ 12}{7\cancel{0},\cancel{7}\cancel{0}\cancel{2}}\\
-\ 4,239\\
\hline
66,463
\end{array}
$$

46.
$$
\begin{array}{r}
\overset{9\ 10\ 1\ 14}{\cancel{1}\cancel{0},\cancel{0}\cancel{2}\cancel{4}}\\
-\ 9,306\\
\hline
718
\end{array}
$$

47.
$$
\begin{array}{r}
\overset{6\ 9\ 11}{12,\cancel{7}\cancel{0}\cancel{1}}\\
-\ 8,624\\
\hline
4,077
\end{array}
$$

48.
$$
\begin{array}{r}
\overset{12}{}\\
\overset{3\ \cancel{2}\ 11}{14,\cancel{3}\cancel{1}\cancel{6}}\\
-\ \ 942\\
\hline
13,374
\end{array}
$$

49.
$$
\begin{array}{r}
\overset{7\ 9\ 10\ 4\ 13}{\cancel{8}\cancel{0},\cancel{0}\cancel{5}\cancel{3}}\\
-27,649\\
\hline
52,404
\end{array}
$$

50.
$$
\begin{array}{r}
\overset{14\ 13\ 12}{}\\
\overset{8\ \cancel{4}\ \cancel{3}\ \cancel{2}\ 12}{\cancel{9}\cancel{5},\cancel{4}\cancel{3}\cancel{2}}\\
-87,857\\
\hline
7,575
\end{array}
$$

51.
$$
\begin{array}{r}
\overset{7\ 9\ 16}{13,\cancel{8}\cancel{0}\cancel{6}}\\
-\ 9,439\\
\hline
4,367
\end{array}
$$

52.
$$
\begin{array}{r}
\overset{17\ \ 11}{}\\
\overset{5\ 7\ \cancel{9}\ \cancel{2}\ 13}{\cancel{6}\cancel{8},\cancel{0}\cancel{2}\cancel{3}}\\
-29,174\\
\hline
38,849
\end{array}
$$

53. Strategy
To find the number of days left, subtract the number of days worked (43) from the number of days specified in the contract (90).

Solution
$$
\begin{array}{r}
90\\
-43\\
\hline
47
\end{array}
$$

The construction company has 47 days to complete the job.

54. Strategy
To find the amount that remains to be paid, subtract the payment ($85) from the outstanding bill ($175).

Solution
$$
\begin{array}{r}
175\\
-\ 85\\
\hline
90
\end{array}
$$

$90 remains to be paid by the customer.

55. Strategy
To find the current inventory, subtract the number shipped (550) from the previous inventory (3000).

Solution
$$
\begin{array}{r}
3000\\
-\ 550\\
\hline
2450
\end{array}
$$

The current inventory includes 2450 sports jackets.

56. Strategy
To find the current inventory, subtract the number in the order (325) from the previous inventory (2750).

Solution
$$
\begin{array}{r}
2750\\
-\ 325\\
\hline
2425
\end{array}
$$

The current inventory includes 2425 tennis rackets.

57. Strategy
    To find the amount the customer would
    have to pay, subtract the trade-in
    allowance ($3500) from the selling
    price ($18,500).

    Solution
    ```
      18,500
    -  3,500
      ------
      15,000
    ```

    The customer would have to pay $15,000
    in order to purchase the car.

59. Strategy
    To find how many miles the car was
    driven, subtract the odometer reading
    at the beginning of the month (28,479)
    from the odometer reading at the end
    of the month (30,362).

    Solution
    ```
      30,362
    -28,479
     ------
       1883
    ```

    The car was driven 1883 miles during
    the month.

61. Strategy
    To find the current number of boxes in
    the supply room:
    • Subtract the number distributed
      (242) from the number on hand
      (473).
    • Add the difference to the shipment
      received (500).

    Solution
    ```
      473            500
     -242           +231
     ----           ----
      231            731
    ```

    The current number of boxes in the
    supply room is 731.

58. Strategy
    To find the amount that remains to be
    paid, subtract the down payment
    ($1249) from the cost ($12,490).

    Solution
    ```
      12,490
    -  1,249
      ------
      11,241
    ```

    $11,241 remains to be paid on the
    computer system.

60. Strategy
    To find the number of pencils in the
    supply room:
    • Find the sum of the numbers in the
      two orders (1 dozen + 2 dozen = 12
      + 24).
    • Subtract the sum from the number of
      pencils in the supply room before
      the orders were filled (120).

    Solution
    ```
       12            120
      +24           - 36
      ---           ----
       36             84
    ```

    After the orders were filled, 84
    pencils were in the supply room.

62. Strategy
    To find the number of shovels:
    • Subtract the number sold (73) from
      the number in the store (150).
    • Add the number returned (5) to the
      difference.

    Solution
    ```
      150             77
    -  73            + 5
      ---            ---
       77             82
    ```

    The hardware store had 82 shovels at
    the end of the month.

63. Strategy
    To find the number of pairs of shoes
    in inventory:
    • Subtract the number sold (162) from
      the number in inventory at the
      beginning of the week (453).
    • Add the number returned (18) to the
      difference.

    Solution
    ```
         453            291
        -162           + 18
         ----          -----
         291            309
    ```

    At the end of the week, 309 pairs of
    shoes were in inventory.

64. Strategy
    To find the difference, subtract the
    1929 quota (150,000) from the 1921
    quota (357,803).

    Solution
    ```
     357,803
    -150,000
    --------
     207,803
    ```

    The difference is 207,803.

65. Strategy
    To find the difference, subtract the
    1952 quota (158,361) from the 1921
    quota (357,803).

    Solution
    ```
     357,803
    -158,361
    --------
     199,442
    ```

    The difference is 199,442.

66. Strategy
    To find the total sales expected, add
    the sales quotas for the five
    territories ($75,000 + $87,500 +
    $68,000 + $96,000 + $82,500).

    Solution
    ```
      75,000
      87,500
      68,000
      96,000
    +82,500
    -------
     409,000
    ```

    The total sales expected from the five
    territories are $409,000.

67. Strategy
    To find the total sales expected, add
    the sales quotas for the four
    territories ($165,000 + $195,000 +
    $155,000 + $130,000).

    Solution
    ```
     165,000
     195,000
     155,000
    +130,000
    --------
     645,000
    ```

    The total sales expected from the four
    territories are $645,000.

68. Strategy
    To find the total sales expected, add
    the sales quotas for the four
    territories ($1,750,000 + $2,250,000 +
    $2,500,000 + $2,750,000).

    Solution
    ```
     1,750,000
     2,250,000
     2,500,000
    +2,750,000
    ---------
     9,250,000
    ```

    The total sales expected from the four
    territories are $9,250,000.

69. Strategy
To find the number of potential
customers that must be contacted:
• Find the total number of customers
  contacted during the first three
  days of the week by adding the
  number contacted on Monday (46),
  the number contacted on Tuesday
  (43), and the number contacted on
  Wednesday (39).
• Subtract the sum from the minimum
  number of customers that must be
  contacted (200).

Solution

```
  46
  43        200
 +39       -128
 ───       ────
 128         72
```

The sales representative must contact
72 potential customers on Thursday and
Friday.

71. Strategy
To find the number of units that must
be sold in April:
• Find the total number sold during
  the first three months by adding
  the number sold in January (247),
  the number sold in February (293),
  and the number sold in March (208).
• Subtract the sum from the four-
  month sales quota (1000).

Solution

```
 247
 293       1000
+208      - 748
────      ─────
 748        252
```

The representative must sell 252 units
in April.

70. Strategy
To find the number of units that must
be sold during the fourth quarter:
• Find the total number sold during
  the first three quarters by adding
  the number sold during the first
  quarter (859), the number sold
  during the second quarter (836),
  and the number sold during the
  third quarter (924).
• Subtract the sum from the annual
  sales quota (3500).

Solution

```
  859
  836       3500
 +924      -2619
 ────      ─────
 2619        881
```

The sales representative must sell 881
units during the fourth quarter.

72. Strategy
To find the total sales for the fourth
quarter:
• Find the total sales for the first
  three quarters by adding the sales
  for the first quarter ($87,700),
  the sales for the second quarter
  ($92,600), and the sales for the
  third quarter ($79,800).
• Subtract the sum from the annual
  sales quota ($350,000).

Solution

```
 87,700
 92,600     350,000
+79,800    -260,100
───────    ────────
260,100      89,900
```

The representative's total sales for
the fourth quarter must be $89,900.

Section 1.3, pages 25–28

1.
```
   6
  89
 x 7
 ───
 623
```
2.
```
   4
  45
 x 9
 ───
 405
```
3.
```
   1
 623
 x 4
 ────
2492
```
4.
```
   1
 802
 x 5
 ────
4010
```
5.
```
   6
 607
 x 9
 ────
5463
```
6.
```
  3 3
 4,780
 x   4
 ──────
19,120
```
7.
```
 5 1 3 2
 48,253
 x     7
 ───────
337,771
```
8.
```
    27
   x72
   ───
    54
   189
  ────
  1944
```

9.
```
        95
      x 33
      ────
       285
      285
      ────
      3135
```

10.
```
       727
     x  60
     ──────
     43,620
```

11.
```
        588
      x  75
      ──────
      2 940
      41 16
      ──────
      44,100
```

12.
```
       8279
     x   46
     ──────
     49 674
     331 16
     ───────
     380,834
```

13.
```
       6938
     x   78
     ──────
      55 504
     485 66
     ───────
     541,164
```

14.
```
       3009
     x   35
     ──────
      15 045
      90 27
     ───────
     105,315
```

15.
```
       6003
     x   57
     ──────
      42 021
     300 15
     ───────
     342,171
```

16.
```
       3987
     x   29
     ──────
      35 883
      79 74
     ───────
     115,623
```

17.
```
       4765
     x   37
     ──────
      33 355
     142 95
     ───────
     176,305
```

18.
```
        607
      x  406
      ──────
       3 642
     242 80
     ───────
     246,442
```

19.
```
        809
      x  503
      ──────
       2 427
     404 50
     ───────
     406,927
```

20.
```
        312
      x  134
      ──────
       1 248
        9 36
       31 2
      ───────
      41,808
```

21.
```
        423
      x  427
      ──────
       2 961
         8 46
       169 2
      ───────
      180,621
```

22.
```
        386
      x  759
      ──────
       3 474
      19 30
     270 2
     ───────
     292,974
```

23.
```
        2675
      x   487
      ──────
      18 725
     214 00
     1 070 0
     ───────
     1,302,725
```

24.
```
        3985
      x   364
      ──────
      15 940
     239 10
     1 195 5
     ────────
     1,450,540
```

25. $2^3 = 2 \cdot 2 \cdot 2 = 8$ 26. $5^2 = 5 \cdot 5 = 25$ 27. $9^2 = 9 \cdot 9 = 81$

28. $4^3 = 4 \cdot 4 \cdot 4 = 64$ 29. $0^4 = 0 \cdot 0 \cdot 0 \cdot 0 = 0$

30. $1^6 = 1 \cdot 1 \cdot 1 \cdot 1 \cdot 1 \cdot 1 = 1$ 31. $3^4 = 3 \cdot 3 \cdot 3 \cdot 3 = 81$

32. $6^3 = 6 \cdot 6 \cdot 6 = 216$ 33. $10^2 = 10 \cdot 10 = 100$

34. $10^4 = 10 \cdot 10 \cdot 10 \cdot 10 = 10,000$ 35. $10^3 = 10 \cdot 10 \cdot 10 = 1000$

36. $10^5 = 10 \cdot 10 \cdot 10 \cdot 10 \cdot 10 = 100,000$

37.
```
         3,209
      6 | 19,254
        -18
        ────
          1 2
         -1 2
         ────
           05
          -0
          ───
            54
           -54
           ────
             0
```

38.
```
         9,800
      4 | 39,200
        -36
        ────
          3 2
         -3 2
         ────
           00
          -0
          ───
            00
           -0
           ───
             0
```

39.
```
         90r2
      7 | 632
        -63
        ────
          02
         -0
         ───
          2
```

40.
```
         90r3
      4 | 363
        -36
        ────
          03
         -0
         ───
          3
```

8 Chapter 1

41.
```
      204r3
  8 ) 1635
     -16
     ----
      03
     - 0
     ----
      35
     -32
     ----
       3
```

42.
```
      1347r3
  7 ) 9432
     -7
     ----
      24
     -21
     ----
      33
     -28
     ----
      52
     -49
     ----
       3
```

43.
```
      778r2
  9 ) 7004
     -63
     ----
      70
     -63
     ----
      74
     -72
     ----
       2
```

44.
```
      857r2
  7 ) 6001
     -56
     ----
      40
     -35
     ----
      51
     -49
     ----
       2
```

45.
```
       3,825
  4 ) 15,300
     -12
     ----
      3 3
     -3 2
     ----
       10
      - 8
      ----
       20
      -20
      ----
        0
```

46.
```
       6,214r2
  7 ) 43,500
     -42
     ----
      1 5
     -1 4
     ----
       10
      - 7
      ----
       30
      -28
      ----
        2
```

47.
```
       3r15
  27 ) 96
      -81
      ----
       15
```

48.
```
       1r38
  44 ) 82
      -44
      ----
       38
```

49.
```
       21r36
  41 ) 897
      -82
      ----
       77
      -41
      ----
       36
```

50.
```
       21r21
  32 ) 693
      -64
      ----
       53
      -32
      ----
       21
```

51.
```
       200r21
  44 ) 8821
      -88
      ----
       02
      - 0
      ----
       21
      - 0
      ----
       21
```

52.
```
       203r2
  19 ) 3859
      -38
      ----
       05
      - 0
      ----
       59
      -57
      ----
        2
```

53.
```
       4,483r18
  22 ) 98,644
      -88
      ----
       10 6
      - 8 8
      ----
        1 84
       -1 76
       -----
         84
        -66
        ----
         18
```

54.
```
       1,086r7
  77 ) 83,629
      -77
      ----
        6 6
       - 0
       ----
        6 62
       -6 16
       -----
         469
        -462
        ----
           7
```

55.
```
        15r7
  206 ) 3097
       -206
       -----
        1037
       -1030
       -----
           7
```

56.
```
        56r39
  87 ) 4911
      -435
      -----
        561
       -522
       ----
         39
```

57.
```
        50r92
  169 ) 8542
       -845
       -----
         92
        - 0
        ----
         92
```

58.
```
         16r427
  456 ) 7723
       -456
       -----
        3163
       -2736
       -----
         427
```

59.
```
        40r7
  223 ) 8927
       -892
       -----
         07
        - 0
        ----
          7
```

60.
```
        20r4
  467 ) 9344
       -934
       -----
         04
        - 0
        ----
          4
```

61. Strategy
    To find the cost of one sponge, divide
    the cost for 4 sponges (88¢) by 4.

    Solution
    88 ÷ 4 = 22

    The cost of one sponge is 22¢.

62. Strategy
    To find the cost of one box of light
    bulbs, divide the cost for 2 boxes
    (98¢) by 2.

    Solution
    98 ÷ 2 = 49

    The cost of one box of light bulbs is
    49¢.

63. Strategy
    To find the unit cost, divide the
    total cost ($34) by the number of
    units (2).

    Solution
    34 ÷ 2 = 17

    The unit cost is $17.

64. Strategy
    To find the unit cost, divide the
    total cost ($84) by the number of
    units (6).

    Solution
    84 ÷ 6 = 14

    The unit cost is $14.

65. Strategy
    To find the unit cost, divide the
    total cost ($1160) by the number of
    units (8).

    Solution
    1160 ÷ 8 = 145

    The unit cost is $145.

66. Strategy
    To find the unit cost, divide the
    total cost ($8250) by the number of
    units (5).

    Solution
    8250 ÷ 5 = 1650

    The unit cost is $1650.

67. Strategy
    To find the unit cost, divide the
    total cost ($9300) by the number of
    units (775).

    Solution
    $$\begin{array}{r} 12 \\ 775{\overline{\smash{\big)}\,9300}} \\ \underline{-775} \\ 1550 \\ \underline{-1550} \\ 0 \end{array}$$

    The unit cost is $12.

68. Strategy
    To find the unit cost, divide the
    total cost ($12,375) by the number of
    units (825).

    Solution
    $$\begin{array}{r} 15 \\ 825{\overline{\smash{\big)}\,12{,}375}} \\ \underline{-8\ 25} \\ 4\ 125 \\ \underline{-4\ 125} \\ 0 \end{array}$$

    The unit cost is $15.

69. Strategy
    To find the total cost, multiply the
    unit cost ($8) by the number of units
    (275).

    Solution
    $$\begin{array}{r} 275 \\ \times\ 8 \\ \hline 2200 \end{array}$$

    The total cost is $2200.

70. Strategy
    To find the total cost, multiply the
    unit cost ($6) by the number of units
    (350).

    Solution
    $$\begin{array}{r} 350 \\ \times\ 6 \\ \hline 2100 \end{array}$$

    The installer would pay $2100 for 350
    floor tiles.

71. Strategy
    To find the total cost, multiply the
    unit cost ($12) by the number of units
    (150).

    Solution
    ```
      150
    x  12
     ----
      300
      150
     ----
     1800
    ```

    The total cost is $1800.

72. Strategy
    To find the total cost, multiply the
    unit cost ($15) by the number of units
    (250).

    Solution
    ```
      250
    x  15
     ----
     1250
      250
     ----
     3750
    ```

    The total cost is $3750.

73. Strategy
    To find the total cost, multiply the
    unit cost ($85) by the number of units
    (2100).

    Solution
    ```
       2100
    x    85
      ------
      10 500
      16 800
     -------
     178,500
    ```

    The total cost is $178,500.

74. Strategy
    To find the total cost, multiply the
    unit cost ($2575) by the number of
    units (35).

    Solution
    ```
      2575
    x   35
     ------
     12875
      7725
     ------
     90,125
    ```

    The total cost is $90,125.

75. Strategy
    To find the total cost:
    • Find the number of packages ordered
      by dividing the number ordered (50)
      by the number in each package (10).
    • Multiply the cost per package ($40)
      by the number of packages ordered
      (5).

    Solution
    50 ÷ 10 = 5
    40 x 5 = 200

    The total cost is $200.

76. Strategy
    To find the total cost:
    • Find the number of packages ordered
      by dividing the number ordered (15)
      by the number in each package (3).
    • Multiply the cost per package ($16)
      by the number of packages ordered
      (5).

    Solution
    15 ÷ 3 = 5
    16 x 5 = 80

    The total cost is $80.

77. Strategy
    To find the cost for 2 pounds of
    tomatoes:
    • Find the unit cost by dividing the
      cost for 3 pounds (99¢) by the
      number of units (3).
    • Multiply the unit cost by the
      number of units (2).

    Solution
    99 ÷ 3 = 33
    33 x 2 = 66

    The cost for 2 pounds of tomatoes is
    66¢.

78. Strategy
    To find the cost of three tires:
    • Find the unit cost by dividing the
      cost for two tires ($240) by the
      number of units (2).
    • Multiply the unit cost by the
      number of units (3).

    Solution
    240 ÷ 2 = 120
    120 x 3 = 360

    The cost of three tires is $360.

79. Strategy
    To find the total cost:
    • Find the total cost of the first 25 dressers ordered by multiplying the unit cost ($135) by the number of units (25).
    • Find the total cost of the additional dressers ordered by multiplying the unit cost ($115) by the number of units (35 – 25 = 10).
    • Add the total cost of the first 25 dressers ordered to the total cost of the additional dressers ordered.

    Solution

    ```
     135          115          3375
    x 25         x 10        +1150
    ────         ────         ────
     675         1150         4525
     270
    ────
    3375
    ```

    The total cost is $4525.

80. Strategy
    To find the total cost:
    • Find the total cost of the first 50 keyboards ordered by multiplying the unit cost ($185) by the number of units (50).
    • Find the total cost of the additional keyboards ordered by multiplying the unit cost ($145) by the number of units (65 – 50 = 15).
    • Add the total cost of the first 50 keyboards ordered to the total cost of the additional keyboards ordered.

    Solution

    ```
     185          145          9250
    x 50         x 15        +2175
    ────         ────         ─────
    9250          725        11,425
                  145
                 ────
                 2175
    ```

    The total cost is $11,425.

Business Case Study

1. Business Expenses During First Year of Operation:

Rent: $700 per month (700 x 12 = 8400)	$ 8400
Utilities: $115 per month (115 x 12 = 1380)	1380
Telephone bill: $30 per month (30 x 12 = 360)	360
Parts: $150 per month (150 x 12 = 1800)	1800
Insurance coverage	1400
Telephone installation fee	55
Tools	400
Half-page newspaper ad, Week 1	150
5-inch newspaper ad (5 x 4 = 20 per week, 20 x 51 weeks = 1020)	1020
	$14,965

   If you devote 25 hours per week to repairing bicycles:
   Income = $25 per hour x 25 hours per week x 52 weeks = $32,500
   Profit = Income – Expenses = $32,500 – $14,965 = $17,535

   If you devote 15 hours per week to repairing bicycles:
   Income = $25 per hour x 15 hours per week x 52 weeks = $19,500
   Profit = Income – Expenses = $19,500 – $14,965 = $4535

2. Your possible profit is less than your current earnings.

3. Answers may vary. For example:

   If you are the only person running the operation and you take a vacation, the business must close, which results in lost income. As a company employee, you are generally entitled to paid vacation each year; as an entrepreneur, you do not receive income during vacation periods.

   An employer generally provides medical coverage for employees under a group medical plan. As an entrepreneur, you are responsible for providing your own medical coverage, which may be more expensive than a plan offered by an employer.

   Starting a new business is both time consuming and risky. Perhaps the greatest risk is that the business will fail.

   A business such as a bicycle repair business may experience seasonal changes in demand, resulting in fluctuating income levels during the year. Since many personal expenses, such as rent, do not fluctuate, careful budgeting is crucial.

4. Some factors considered to be advantages of going into business for yourself include the independence, the challenge, and the possibility of earning a great deal more money.

Review/Test, pages 33–34

1. two hundred seven thousand sixty-eight

2. 1,204,006

3.
```
              ┌──── Given place value
     74,965
              └──── 6 is greater than 5
```

   74,965 rounded to the nearest hundred is 75,000.

4.
```
    25,492
   +71,306
   ───────
    96,798
```

5.
```
     2  21
    89,756
     9,094
   +37,065
   ───────
   135,915
```

6.
```
    21 21
    87,256
     3,095
   + 9,981
   ───────
   100,332
```

7.
```
    17,495
   − 8,162
   ───────
     9,333
```

8.
```
   19 16 13
   2̶0̶,7̶3̶6
   − 9,854
   ───────
    10,882
```

9.
```
   8 14 9 14
   9̶3̶0̶4̶
   −7819
   ─────
    1685
```

10.
```
     6 5 2
    90,763
   x     8
   ───────
   726,104
```

11.
```
        9736
   x     704
   ─────────
      38 944
   6 815 20
   ─────────
   6,854,144
```

12. 1400 x 20 = 28,000

13. $8^2 = 8 \cdot 8 = 64$

14.
```
      703
  8│ 5624
    -56
    ───
     02
    - 0
     ──
     24
    -24
     ──
      0
```

15.
```
       8,710r2
   7│ 60,972
     -56
     ───
      4 9
     -4 9
      ───
       07
      - 7
      ──
       02
      - 0
       ──
        2
```

16.
```
         1,121r27
  97│ 108,764
      -97
      ───
       11 7
      - 9 7
       ───
        2 06
       -1 94
        ───
         124
        - 97
         ──
          27
```

17. **Strategy**
To find the current inventory, subtract the order (245) from the number in inventory before the order was filled (1890).

Solution
```
  1890
  -245
  ────
  1645
```

The current inventory is 1645 skateboards.

18. **Strategy**
To find the number of units that must be sold:
- Find the total number of units sold during January and February (857 + 796).
- Subtract the sum from the quota (2500).

Solution
```
   857          2500
  +796         -1653
  ────         ─────
  1653          847
```

The salesperson must sell 847 units before the end of the month.

19. **Strategy**
To find the unit cost, divide the total cost ($12,750) by the number of units (750).

Solution
```
            17
  750│ 12,750
      -7 50
      ─────
       5 250
      -5 250
      ──────
           0
```

The unit cost is $17.

20. **Strategy**
To find the total cost, multiply the unit cost ($13) by the number of units (175).

Solution
```
    175
  x  13
  ────
    525
    175
  ────
   2275
```

The total cost is $2275.

CHAPTER 2
Fractions and Business Applications

Section 2.1, pages 41–42

1. $\frac{5}{4}$; $1\frac{1}{4}$

2. $\frac{8}{3}$; $2\frac{2}{3}$

3.
$$4\overline{\smash)11} \quad \frac{11}{4} = 2\frac{3}{4}$$
$$\begin{array}{r} 2 \\ 4\overline{\smash)11} \\ -8 \\ \hline 3 \end{array} \quad \frac{11}{4} = 2\frac{3}{4}$$

4.
$$\begin{array}{r} 2 \\ 3\overline{\smash)7} \\ -6 \\ \hline 1 \end{array} \quad \frac{7}{3} = 2\frac{1}{3}$$

5.
$$\begin{array}{r} 5 \\ 4\overline{\smash)20} \\ -20 \\ \hline 0 \end{array} \quad \frac{20}{4} = 5$$

6.
$$\begin{array}{r} 1 \\ 8\overline{\smash)9} \\ -8 \\ \hline 1 \end{array} \quad \frac{9}{8} = 1\frac{1}{8}$$

7.
$$\begin{array}{r} 2 \\ 10\overline{\smash)23} \\ -20 \\ \hline 3 \end{array} \quad \frac{23}{10} = 2\frac{3}{10}$$

8.
$$\begin{array}{r} 3 \\ 16\overline{\smash)48} \\ -48 \\ \hline 0 \end{array} \quad \frac{48}{16} = 3$$

9.
$$\begin{array}{r} 5 \\ 3\overline{\smash)16} \\ -15 \\ \hline 1 \end{array} \quad \frac{16}{3} = 5\frac{1}{3}$$

10.
$$\begin{array}{r} 14 \\ 2\overline{\smash)29} \\ -2 \\ \hline 09 \\ -8 \\ \hline 1 \end{array} \quad \frac{29}{2} = 14\frac{1}{2}$$

11.
$$\begin{array}{r} 16 \\ 1\overline{\smash)16} \\ -1 \\ \hline 06 \\ -6 \\ \hline 0 \end{array} \quad \frac{16}{1} = 16$$

12.
$$\begin{array}{r} 2 \\ 8\overline{\smash)17} \\ -16 \\ \hline 1 \end{array} \quad \frac{17}{8} = 2\frac{1}{8}$$

13.
$$\begin{array}{r} 1 \\ 16\overline{\smash)31} \\ -16 \\ \hline 15 \end{array} \quad \frac{31}{16} = 1\frac{15}{16}$$

14.
$$\begin{array}{r} 2 \\ 5\overline{\smash)12} \\ -10 \\ \hline 2 \end{array} \quad \frac{12}{5} = 2\frac{2}{5}$$

15.
$$2\frac{1}{3} = \frac{6+1}{3} = \frac{7}{3}$$

16. $4\frac{2}{3} = \frac{12+2}{3} = \frac{14}{3}$

17. $6\frac{1}{2} = \frac{12+1}{2} = \frac{13}{2}$

18. $6\frac{5}{6} = \frac{36+5}{6} = \frac{41}{6}$

19. $7\frac{3}{8} = \frac{56+3}{8} = \frac{59}{8}$

20. $9\frac{1}{4} = \frac{36+1}{4} = \frac{37}{4}$

21. $10\frac{1}{2} = \frac{20+1}{2} = \frac{21}{2}$

22. $15\frac{1}{8} = \frac{120+1}{8} = \frac{121}{8}$

23. $3\frac{7}{9} = \frac{27+7}{9} = \frac{34}{9}$

24. $2\frac{5}{8} = \frac{16+5}{8} = \frac{21}{8}$

25. $1\frac{3}{8} = \frac{8+3}{8} = \frac{11}{8}$

26. $4\frac{5}{9} = \frac{36+5}{9} = \frac{41}{9}$

27. $16 \div 4 = 4$
$$\frac{1 \cdot 4}{4 \cdot 4} = \frac{4}{16}$$

28. $81 + 9 = 9$

$\frac{5 \cdot 9}{9 \cdot 9} = \frac{45}{81}$

29. $33 + 11 = 3$

$\frac{7 \cdot 3}{11 \cdot 3} = \frac{21}{33}$

30. $32 + 8 = 4$

$\frac{5 \cdot 4}{8 \cdot 4} = \frac{20}{32}$

31. $5 = \frac{5}{1}$

$25 + 1 = 25$

$\frac{5 \cdot 25}{1 \cdot 25} = \frac{125}{25}$

32. $9 = \frac{9}{1}$

$4 + 1 = 4$

$\frac{9 \cdot 4}{1 \cdot 4} = \frac{36}{4}$

33. $60 + 15 = 4$

$\frac{11 \cdot 4}{15 \cdot 4} = \frac{44}{60}$

34. $36 + 9 = 4$

$\frac{5 \cdot 4}{9 \cdot 4} = \frac{20}{36}$

35. $45 + 9 = 5$

$\frac{7 \cdot 5}{9 \cdot 5} = \frac{35}{45}$

36. $36 + 12 = 3$

$\frac{11 \cdot 3}{12 \cdot 3} = \frac{33}{36}$

37. $64 + 16 = 4$

$\frac{15 \cdot 4}{16 \cdot 4} = \frac{60}{64}$

38. $54 + 18 = 3$

$\frac{11 \cdot 3}{18 \cdot 3} = \frac{33}{54}$

39. $\frac{2}{14} = \frac{2+2}{14+2} = \frac{1}{7}$

40. $\frac{50}{75} = \frac{50+25}{75+25} = \frac{2}{3}$

41. $\frac{40}{36} = \frac{40+4}{36+4} = \frac{10}{9} = 1\frac{1}{9}$

42. $\frac{75}{25} = \frac{75+25}{25+25} = \frac{3}{1} = 3$

43. $\frac{8}{60} = \frac{8+4}{60+4} = \frac{2}{15}$

44. $\frac{12}{35}$ is in simplest form.

45. $\frac{24}{40} = \frac{24+8}{40+8} = \frac{3}{5}$

46. $\frac{12}{16} = \frac{12+4}{16+4} = \frac{3}{4}$

47. $\frac{4}{32} = \frac{4+4}{32+4} = \frac{1}{8}$

48. $\frac{60}{100} = \frac{60+20}{100+20} = \frac{3}{5}$

49. $\frac{36}{16} = \frac{36+4}{16+4} = \frac{9}{4} = 2\frac{1}{4}$

50. $\frac{80}{45} = \frac{80+5}{45+5} = \frac{16}{9} = 1\frac{7}{9}$

Section 2.2, pages 51–54

1.
$$\begin{array}{r|rr} 3 & 3 & 8 \\ 2 & 1 & 8 \\ 2 & 1 & 4 \\ 2 & 1 & 2 \\ \hline & 1 & 1 \end{array}$$

The LCM = $3 \cdot 2 \cdot 2 \cdot 2 = 24$.

2.
$$\begin{array}{r|rr} 5 & 5 & 7 \\ 7 & 1 & 7 \\ \hline & 1 & 1 \end{array}$$

The LCM is $5 \cdot 7 = 35$.

3.
$$\begin{array}{r|rr} 2 & 6 & 8 \\ 3 & 3 & 4 \\ 2 & 1 & 4 \\ 2 & 1 & 2 \\ \hline & 1 & 1 \end{array}$$

The LCM = $2 \cdot 3 \cdot 2 \cdot 2 = 24$.

4.
$$\begin{array}{r|rr} 2 & 12 & 16 \\ 2 & 6 & 8 \\ 3 & 3 & 4 \\ 2 & 1 & 4 \\ 2 & 1 & 2 \\ \hline & 1 & 1 \end{array}$$

The LCM = $2 \cdot 2 \cdot 3 \cdot 2 \cdot 2$
$\qquad = 48$.

5.
$$\begin{array}{r|rr} 2 & 8 & 14 \\ 2 & 4 & 7 \\ 2 & 2 & 7 \\ 7 & 1 & 7 \\ \hline & 1 & 1 \end{array}$$

The LCM = $2 \cdot 2 \cdot 2 \cdot 7 = 56$.

6.
$$\begin{array}{r|rr} 3 & 3 & 9 \\ 3 & 1 & 3 \\ \hline & 1 & 1 \end{array}$$

The LCM = $3 \cdot 3 = 9$.

7.
```
2│ 4  10
2│ 2   5
5│ 1   5
   1   1
```
The LCM = 2·2·5 = 20.

8.
```
2│14  42
7│ 7  21
3│ 1   3
   1   1
```
The LCM = 2·7·3 = 42.

9.
```
2│ 8  8  12
2│ 2  4   6
2│ 1  2   3
3│ 1  1   3
   1  1   1
```
The LCM = 2·2·2·3 = 24.

10.
```
3│ 3  5  10
5│ 1  5  10
2│ 1  1   2
   1  1   1
```
The LCM = 3·5·2 = 30.

11.
```
5│ 5  12  18
2│ 1  12  18
2│ 1   6   9
3│ 1   3   9
3│ 1   1   3
   1   1   1
```
The LCM = 5·2·2·3·3
= 180.

12.
```
3│ 9  36  64
3│ 3  12  64
2│ 1   4  64
2│ 1   2  32
2│ 1   1  16
2│ 1   1   8
2│ 1   1   4
2│ 1   1   2
   1   1   1
```
The LCM =
3·3·2·2·2·2·2·2 = 576.

13.
$$\frac{2}{7}$$
$$+\frac{1}{7}$$
$$\overline{\frac{3}{7}}$$

14.
$$\frac{3}{8}$$
$$\frac{7}{8}$$
$$+\frac{1}{8}$$
$$\overline{\frac{11}{8}} = 1\frac{3}{8}$$

15.
$$\frac{1}{2} = \frac{3}{6}$$
$$+\frac{2}{3} = \frac{4}{6}$$
$$\overline{\frac{7}{6}} = 1\frac{1}{6}$$

16.
$$\frac{3}{5} = \frac{6}{10}$$
$$+\frac{7}{10} = \frac{7}{10}$$
$$\overline{\frac{13}{10}} = 1\frac{3}{10}$$

17.
$$\frac{1}{6} = \frac{3}{18}$$
$$+\frac{7}{9} = \frac{14}{18}$$
$$\overline{\frac{17}{18}}$$

18.
$$\frac{5}{12} = \frac{20}{48}$$
$$+\frac{5}{16} = \frac{15}{48}$$
$$\overline{\frac{35}{48}}$$

19.
$$\frac{2}{3} = \frac{38}{57}$$
$$+\frac{6}{19} = \frac{18}{57}$$
$$\overline{\frac{56}{57}}$$

20.
$$\frac{1}{3} = \frac{6}{18}$$
$$\frac{5}{6} = \frac{15}{18}$$
$$+\frac{7}{9} = \frac{14}{18}$$
$$\overline{\frac{35}{18}} = 1\frac{17}{18}$$

21.
$$\frac{2}{3} = \frac{8}{12}$$
$$\frac{5}{6} = \frac{10}{12}$$
$$+\frac{7}{12} = \frac{7}{12}$$
$$\overline{\frac{25}{12}} = 2\frac{1}{12}$$

22.
$$\frac{2}{3} = \frac{40}{60}$$
$$\frac{1}{5} = \frac{12}{60}$$
$$+\frac{7}{12} = \frac{35}{60}$$
$$\overline{\frac{87}{60}} = 1\frac{27}{60} = 1\frac{9}{20}$$

23.
$$\frac{2}{3} = \frac{80}{120}$$
$$\frac{3}{5} = \frac{72}{120}$$
$$+\frac{7}{8} = \frac{105}{120}$$
$$\overline{\frac{257}{120}} = 2\frac{17}{120}$$

24.
$$\frac{2}{3} = \frac{48}{72}$$
$$\frac{5}{8} = \frac{45}{72}$$
$$+\frac{7}{9} = \frac{56}{72}$$
$$\overline{\frac{149}{72}} = 2\frac{5}{72}$$

25. $1\frac{1}{2} = 1\frac{3}{6}$
   $+ 2\frac{1}{6} = 2\frac{1}{6}$
   $\overline{ 3\frac{4}{6}} = 3\frac{2}{3}$

26. $2\frac{2}{5} = 2\frac{4}{10}$
   $+ 3\frac{3}{10} = 3\frac{3}{10}$
   $\overline{ 5\frac{7}{10}}$

27. $4\frac{1}{2} = 4\frac{6}{12}$
   $+ 5\frac{7}{12} = 5\frac{7}{12}$
   $\overline{ 9\frac{13}{12}} = 10\frac{1}{12}$

28. $3\frac{3}{8} = 3\frac{6}{16}$
   $+ 2\frac{5}{16} = 2\frac{5}{16}$
   $\overline{ 5\frac{11}{16}}$

29. $2\frac{7}{9} = 2\frac{28}{36}$
   $+ 3\frac{5}{12} = 3\frac{15}{36}$
   $\overline{ 5\frac{43}{36}} = 6\frac{7}{36}$

30. $3\frac{5}{8} = 3\frac{25}{40}$
   $+ 2\frac{11}{20} = 2\frac{22}{40}$
   $\overline{ 5\frac{47}{40}} = 6\frac{7}{40}$

31. $3\frac{1}{2} = 3\frac{6}{12}$
   $2\frac{3}{4} = 2\frac{9}{12}$
   $+ 1\frac{5}{6} = 1\frac{10}{12}$
   $\overline{ 6\frac{25}{12}} = 8\frac{1}{12}$

32. $2\frac{1}{2} = 2\frac{6}{12}$
   $3\frac{2}{3} = 3\frac{8}{12}$
   $+ 4\frac{1}{4} = 4\frac{3}{12}$
   $\overline{ 9\frac{17}{12}} = 10\frac{5}{12}$

33. $7\frac{2}{5} = 7\frac{12}{30}$
   $3\frac{7}{10} = 3\frac{21}{30}$
   $+ 5\frac{11}{15} = 5\frac{22}{30}$
   $\overline{ 15\frac{55}{30}} = 16\frac{25}{30} = 16\frac{5}{6}$

34. $ \frac{11}{15}$
   $- \frac{3}{15}$
   $\overline{ \frac{8}{15}}$

35. $ \frac{11}{12}$
   $- \frac{7}{12}$
   $\overline{ \frac{4}{12}} = \frac{1}{3}$

36. $\frac{2}{3} = \frac{4}{6}$
   $- \frac{1}{6} = \frac{1}{6}$
   $\overline{ \frac{3}{6}} = \frac{1}{2}$

37. $\frac{5}{8} = \frac{35}{56}$
   $- \frac{2}{7} = \frac{16}{56}$
   $\overline{ \frac{19}{56}}$

38. $\frac{5}{7} = \frac{10}{14}$
   $- \frac{3}{14} = \frac{3}{14}$
   $\overline{ \frac{7}{14}} = \frac{1}{2}$

39. $\frac{5}{9} = \frac{25}{45}$
   $- \frac{7}{15} = \frac{21}{45}$
   $\overline{ \frac{4}{45}}$

40. $\frac{7}{9} = \frac{14}{18}$
   $- \frac{1}{6} = \frac{3}{18}$
   $\overline{ \frac{11}{18}}$

41. $\frac{5}{12} = \frac{20}{48}$
   $- \frac{5}{16} = \frac{15}{48}$
   $\overline{ \frac{5}{48}}$

42. $\frac{7}{30} = \frac{14}{60}$
   $- \frac{3}{20} = \frac{9}{60}$
   $\overline{ \frac{5}{60}} = \frac{1}{12}$

43. $\frac{5}{9} = \frac{20}{36}$
   $- \frac{1}{12} = \frac{3}{36}$
   $\overline{ \frac{17}{36}}$

44. $\frac{11}{16} = \frac{33}{48}$
   $- \frac{5}{12} = \frac{20}{48}$
   $\overline{ \frac{13}{48}}$

45. $\frac{53}{70} = \frac{53}{70}$
   $- \frac{13}{35} = \frac{26}{70}$
   $\overline{ \frac{27}{70}}$

46. $\frac{7}{16} = \frac{21}{48}$
   $- \frac{5}{24} = \frac{10}{48}$
   $\overline{ \frac{11}{48}}$

47. $\frac{7}{8} = \frac{63}{72}$
   $- \frac{5}{9} = \frac{40}{72}$
   $\overline{ \frac{23}{72}}$

48. $\frac{5}{6} = \frac{25}{30}$
   $- \frac{3}{5} = \frac{18}{30}$
   $\overline{ \frac{7}{30}}$

49. $ 5\frac{7}{12}$
   $- 2\frac{5}{12}$
   $\overline{ 3\frac{2}{12}} = 3\frac{1}{6}$

50. $ 16\frac{11}{15}$
   $- 11\frac{8}{15}$
   $\overline{ 5\frac{3}{15}} = 5\frac{1}{5}$

51. $ 6\frac{1}{3}$
   $- 2$
   $\overline{ 4\frac{1}{3}}$

52.
$$5\frac{7}{8}$$
$$-\ 1$$
$$\overline{\quad 4\frac{7}{8}\quad}$$

53.
$$10 = 9\frac{3}{3}$$
$$-\ 6\frac{1}{3} = 6\frac{1}{3}$$
$$\overline{\qquad 3\frac{2}{3}}$$

54.
$$3 = 2\frac{9}{9}$$
$$-\ 2\frac{5}{9} = 2\frac{5}{9}$$
$$\overline{\qquad \frac{4}{9}}$$

55.
$$6\frac{2}{5} = 5\frac{7}{5}$$
$$-\ 4\frac{4}{5} = 4\frac{4}{5}$$
$$\overline{\qquad 1\frac{3}{5}}$$

56.
$$16\frac{3}{8} = 15\frac{11}{8}$$
$$-\ 10\frac{7}{8} = 10\frac{7}{8}$$
$$\overline{\qquad 5\frac{4}{8} = 5\frac{1}{2}}$$

57.
$$23\frac{7}{8} = 23\frac{21}{24}$$
$$-\ 16\frac{2}{3} = 16\frac{16}{24}$$
$$\overline{\qquad 7\frac{5}{24}}$$

58.
$$16\frac{2}{5} = 16\frac{18}{45} = 15\frac{63}{45}$$
$$-\ 8\frac{4}{9} = 8\frac{20}{45} = 8\frac{20}{45}$$
$$\overline{\qquad\qquad\qquad 7\frac{43}{45}}$$

59.
$$16\frac{3}{10} = 15\frac{13}{10}$$
$$-\ 7\frac{9}{10} = 7\frac{9}{10}$$
$$\overline{\qquad 8\frac{4}{10} = 8\frac{2}{5}}$$

60.
$$14\frac{3}{5} = 14\frac{27}{45} = 13\frac{72}{45}$$
$$-\ 7\frac{8}{9} = 7\frac{40}{45} = 7\frac{40}{45}$$
$$\overline{\qquad\qquad\qquad 6\frac{32}{45}}$$

61. **Strategy**
To find the difference, subtract the market price one year ago (25) from the market price today ($29\frac{3}{8}$).

Solution
$$29\frac{3}{8}$$
$$-\ 25$$
$$\overline{\quad 4\frac{3}{8}}$$

The difference is $4\frac{3}{8}$.

62. To find the difference, subtract the market price today ($27\frac{3}{8}$) from the market price six months ago (35).

Solution
$$35 = 34\frac{8}{8}$$
$$-\ 27\frac{3}{8} = 27\frac{3}{8}$$
$$\overline{\qquad 7\frac{5}{8}}$$

The difference is $7\frac{5}{8}$.

63. **Strategy**
To find the stockholder's gain per share, subtract the purchase price per share ($37\frac{3}{8}$) from the selling price per share ($48\frac{1}{4}$).

Solution
$$48\frac{1}{4} = 48\frac{2}{8} = 47\frac{10}{8}$$
$$-\ 37\frac{3}{8} = 37\frac{3}{8} = 37\frac{3}{8}$$
$$\overline{\qquad\qquad\qquad 10\frac{7}{8}}$$

The stockholder's gain per share was $10\frac{7}{8}$.

64. **Strategy**
To find the stockholder's loss per share, subtract the selling price per share ($34\frac{1}{4}$) from the purchase price per share ($36\frac{5}{8}$).

Solution
$$36\frac{5}{8} = 36\frac{5}{8}$$
$$-\ 34\frac{1}{4} = 34\frac{2}{8}$$
$$\overline{\qquad 2\frac{3}{8}}$$

The stockholder's loss per share was $2\frac{3}{8}$.

65. Strategy
To find the stock's market price,
subtract $2\frac{7}{8}$ from the purchase price
(25).

Solution
$$\begin{array}{rcl} 25 & = & 24\frac{8}{8} \\ -\ 2\frac{7}{8} & = & 2\frac{7}{8} \\ \hline & & 22\frac{1}{8} \end{array}$$

The market price is $22\frac{1}{8}$.

66. Strategy
To find the stock's market price, add
$3\frac{1}{4}$ to the purchase price ($50\frac{1}{2}$).

Solution
$$\begin{array}{rcl} 50\frac{1}{2} & = & 50\frac{2}{4} \\ +\ 3\frac{1}{4} & = & 3\frac{1}{4} \\ \hline & & 53\frac{3}{4} \end{array}$$

The market price is $53\frac{3}{4}$.

67. Strategy
To find the difference, subtract the
lowest price paid ($28\frac{7}{8}$) from the
highest price paid ($29\frac{3}{4}$).

Solution
$$\begin{array}{rcl} 29\frac{3}{4} & = & 29\frac{6}{8} = 28\frac{14}{8} \\ -\ 28\frac{7}{8} & = & 28\frac{7}{8} = 28\frac{7}{8} \\ \hline & & \frac{7}{8} \end{array}$$

The difference in prices is $\frac{7}{8}$.

68. To find the market price per share,
add the gain ($5\frac{1}{2}$) to the purchase
price ($83\frac{5}{8}$).

Solution
$$\begin{array}{rcl} 83\frac{5}{8} & = & 83\frac{5}{8} \\ +\ 5\frac{1}{2} & = & 5\frac{4}{8} \\ \hline & & 88\frac{9}{8} = 89\frac{1}{8} \end{array}$$

The market price per share was $89\frac{1}{8}$.

69. Strategy
To find the price of the stock, add
the gain per share ($13\frac{3}{4}$) to the
selling price at the beginning of the
year ($26\frac{5}{8}$).

Solution
$$\begin{array}{rcl} 26\frac{5}{8} & = & 26\frac{5}{8} \\ +\ 13\frac{3}{4} & = & 13\frac{6}{8} \\ \hline & & 39\frac{11}{8} = 40\frac{3}{8} \end{array}$$

The price of the stock is $40\frac{3}{8}$.

70. Strategy
To find the price of the stock, add
the gain per share ($28\frac{3}{4}$) to the
selling price at the beginning of the
week ($158\frac{3}{8}$).

Solution
$$\begin{array}{rcl} 158\frac{3}{8} & = & 158\frac{3}{8} \\ +\ 28\frac{3}{4} & = & 28\frac{6}{8} \\ \hline & & 186\frac{9}{8} = 187\frac{1}{8} \end{array}$$

The price of the stock is $187\frac{1}{8}$.

20 *Chapter 2*

71. Strategy
To find the market price, add the gains $(1\frac{1}{2},\ 2\frac{5}{8},$ and $\frac{1}{4})$ to the purchase price $(26\frac{3}{4})$.

Solution

$$26\frac{3}{4} = 26\frac{6}{8}$$
$$1\frac{1}{2} = 1\frac{4}{8}$$
$$2\frac{5}{8} = 2\frac{5}{8}$$
$$+\ \frac{1}{4} = \frac{2}{8}$$
$$\overline{\qquad\qquad 29\frac{17}{8} = 31\frac{1}{8}}$$

The market price was $31\frac{1}{8}$.

73. Strategy
To find the value of 1 share of the stock:
- Add the gain $(5\frac{5}{8})$ to the purchase price $(24\frac{1}{2})$.
- Subtract the loss $(2\frac{1}{4})$ from the sum.

Solution

$$24\frac{1}{2} = 24\frac{4}{8} \qquad\quad 30\frac{1}{8} = 30\frac{1}{8} = 29\frac{9}{8}$$
$$+\ 5\frac{5}{8} = 5\frac{5}{8} \qquad\quad -\ 2\frac{1}{4} = 2\frac{2}{8} = 2\frac{2}{8}$$
$$\overline{\qquad 29\frac{9}{8} = 30\frac{1}{8}} \qquad \overline{\qquad\qquad\qquad 27\frac{7}{8}}$$

The value of 1 share of the stock was $27\frac{7}{8}$.

75. Strategy
To find the market price:
- Subtract the loss $(2\frac{3}{4})$ from the purchase price $(45\frac{5}{8})$.
- Add the gain $(1\frac{1}{2})$ to the difference.

Solution

$$45\frac{5}{8} = 45\frac{5}{8} = 44\frac{13}{8} \qquad\quad 42\frac{7}{8} = 42\frac{7}{8}$$
$$-\ 2\frac{3}{4} = 2\frac{6}{8} = 2\frac{6}{8} \qquad\quad +\ 1\frac{1}{2} = 1\frac{4}{8}$$
$$\overline{\qquad\qquad\qquad 42\frac{7}{8}} \qquad \overline{\qquad\quad 43\frac{11}{8} = 44\frac{3}{8}}$$

The market price was $44\frac{3}{8}$.

72. Strategy
To find the market price, add the gains $(\frac{3}{8},\ 1\frac{1}{2},$ and $\frac{3}{4})$ to the purchase price $(55\frac{3}{8})$.

Solution

$$55\frac{3}{8} = 55\frac{3}{8}$$
$$\frac{3}{8} = \frac{3}{8}$$
$$1\frac{1}{2} = 1\frac{4}{8}$$
$$+\ \frac{3}{4} = \frac{6}{8}$$
$$\overline{\qquad\qquad 56\frac{16}{8} = 58}$$

The market price was 58.

74. Strategy
To find the market price:
- Add the gain $(2\frac{3}{8})$ to the purchase price $(37\frac{1}{2})$.
- Subtract the loss $(1\frac{1}{4})$ from the sum.

Solution

$$37\frac{1}{2} = 37\frac{4}{8} \qquad\qquad 39\frac{7}{8} = 39\frac{7}{8}$$
$$+\ 2\frac{3}{8} = 2\frac{3}{8} \qquad\qquad -\ 1\frac{1}{4} = 1\frac{2}{8}$$
$$\overline{\qquad\qquad 39\frac{7}{8}} \qquad\qquad \overline{\qquad\qquad 38\frac{5}{8}}$$

The market price was $38\frac{5}{8}$.

Section 2.3, pages 59–62

1. $\frac{2}{3} \times \frac{7}{8} = \frac{2 \cdot 7}{3 \cdot 8} = \frac{14}{24} = \frac{14+2}{24+2} = \frac{7}{12}$

2. $\frac{1}{2} \times \frac{2}{3} = \frac{1 \cdot 2}{2 \cdot 3} = \frac{2}{6} = \frac{2+2}{6+2} = \frac{1}{3}$

3. $\frac{1}{2} \times \frac{5}{6} = \frac{1 \cdot 5}{2 \cdot 6} = \frac{5}{12}$

4. $\frac{1}{6} \times \frac{1}{8} = \frac{1 \cdot 1}{6 \cdot 8} = \frac{1}{48}$

5. $\frac{11}{12} \times \frac{3}{5} = \frac{11 \cdot 3}{12 \cdot 5} = \frac{33}{60} = \frac{33+3}{60+3} = \frac{11}{20}$

6. $\frac{2}{5} \times \frac{4}{9} = \frac{2 \cdot 4}{5 \cdot 9} = \frac{8}{45}$

7. $\frac{1}{5} \times \frac{5}{8} = \frac{1 \cdot 5}{5 \cdot 8} = \frac{5}{40} = \frac{5+5}{40+5} = \frac{1}{8}$

8. $\frac{3}{5} \times \frac{3}{10} = \frac{3 \cdot 3}{5 \cdot 10} = \frac{9}{50}$

9. $\frac{5}{6} \times \frac{1}{2} = \frac{5 \cdot 1}{6 \cdot 2} = \frac{5}{12}$

10. $\frac{7}{8} \times \frac{3}{14} = \frac{7 \cdot 3}{8 \cdot 14} = \frac{21}{112} = \frac{21+7}{112+7} = \frac{3}{16}$

11. $\frac{5}{12} \times \frac{6}{7} = \frac{5 \cdot 6}{12 \cdot 7} = \frac{30}{84} = \frac{30+6}{84+6} = \frac{5}{14}$

12. $\frac{12}{5} \times \frac{5}{8} = \frac{12 \cdot 5}{5 \cdot 8} = \frac{60}{40} = \frac{60+20}{40+20} = \frac{3}{2} = 1\frac{1}{2}$

13. $14 \times \frac{5}{7} = \frac{14}{1} \times \frac{5}{7} = \frac{14 \cdot 5}{1 \cdot 7} = \frac{70}{7} = \frac{70+7}{7+7} = \frac{10}{1} = 10$

14. $\frac{2}{3} \times 6 = \frac{2}{3} \times \frac{6}{1} = \frac{2 \cdot 6}{3 \cdot 1} = \frac{12}{3} = \frac{12+3}{3+3} = \frac{4}{1} = 4$

15. $\frac{1}{3} \times 1\frac{1}{3} = \frac{1}{3} \times \frac{4}{3} = \frac{1 \cdot 4}{3 \cdot 3} = \frac{4}{9}$

16. $\frac{2}{5} \times 2\frac{1}{2} = \frac{2}{5} \times \frac{5}{2} = \frac{2 \cdot 5}{5 \cdot 2} = \frac{10}{10} = \frac{10+10}{10+10} = \frac{1}{1} = 1$

17. $4 \times 2\frac{1}{2} = \frac{4}{1} \times \frac{5}{2} = \frac{4 \cdot 5}{1 \cdot 2} = \frac{20}{2} = \frac{20+2}{2+2} = \frac{10}{1} = 10$

18. $9 \times 3\frac{1}{3} = \frac{9}{1} \times \frac{10}{3} = \frac{9 \cdot 10}{1 \cdot 3} = \frac{90}{3} = \frac{90+3}{3+3} = \frac{30}{1} = 30$

19. $\frac{3}{8} \times 4\frac{4}{5} = \frac{3}{8} \times \frac{24}{5} = \frac{3 \cdot 24}{8 \cdot 5} = \frac{72}{40} = \frac{72+8}{40+8} = \frac{9}{5} = 1\frac{4}{5}$

20. $\frac{3}{8} \times 4\frac{1}{2} = \frac{3}{8} \times \frac{9}{2} = \frac{3 \cdot 9}{8 \cdot 2} = \frac{27}{16} = 1\frac{11}{16}$

21. $1\frac{1}{3} \times 2\frac{1}{4} = \frac{4}{3} \times \frac{9}{4} = \frac{4 \cdot 9}{3 \cdot 4} = \frac{36}{12} = \frac{36+12}{12+12} = \frac{3}{1} = 3$

22. $1\frac{1}{2} \times 5\frac{1}{2} = \frac{3}{2} \times \frac{11}{2} = \frac{3 \cdot 11}{2 \cdot 2} = \frac{33}{4} = 8\frac{1}{4}$

23. $2\frac{2}{5} \times 1\frac{7}{12} = \frac{12}{5} \times \frac{19}{12} = \frac{12 \cdot 19}{5 \cdot 12} = \frac{228}{60} = \frac{228+12}{60+12} = \frac{19}{5} = 3\frac{4}{5}$

24. $3\frac{1}{3} \times 6\frac{3}{5} = \frac{10}{3} \times \frac{33}{5} = \frac{10 \cdot 33}{3 \cdot 5} = \frac{330}{15} = \frac{330+15}{15+15} = \frac{22}{1} = 22$

25. $5\frac{3}{7} \times 3\frac{1}{2} = \frac{38}{7} \times \frac{7}{2} = \frac{38 \cdot 7}{7 \cdot 2} = \frac{266}{14} = \frac{266+14}{14+14} = \frac{19}{1} = 19$

26. $2\frac{2}{7} \times 3\frac{1}{2} = \frac{16}{7} \times \frac{7}{2} = \frac{16 \cdot 7}{7 \cdot 2} = \frac{112}{14} = \frac{112+14}{14+14} = \frac{8}{1} = 8$

27. $2\frac{2}{3} \times 3\frac{1}{4} = \frac{8}{3} \times \frac{13}{4} = \frac{8 \cdot 13}{3 \cdot 4} = \frac{104}{12} = \frac{104+4}{12+4} = \frac{26}{3} = 8\frac{2}{3}$

28. $5\frac{1}{5} \times 3\frac{3}{4} = \frac{26}{5} \times \frac{15}{4} = \frac{26 \cdot 15}{5 \cdot 4} = \frac{390}{20} = \frac{390+10}{20+10} = \frac{39}{2} = 19\frac{1}{2}$

29. $\frac{5}{8} \times 5\frac{3}{5} = \frac{5}{8} \times \frac{28}{5} = \frac{5 \cdot 28}{8 \cdot 5} = \frac{140}{40} = \frac{140+20}{40+20} = \frac{7}{2} = 3\frac{1}{2}$

30. $3\frac{1}{5} \times 2\frac{2}{3} = \frac{16}{5} \times \frac{8}{3} = \frac{16 \cdot 8}{5 \cdot 3} = \frac{128}{15} = 8\frac{8}{15}$

31. $\frac{1}{3} \div \frac{2}{5} = \frac{1}{3} \times \frac{5}{2} = \frac{1 \cdot 5}{3 \cdot 2} = \frac{5}{6}$

32. $\frac{3}{7} \div \frac{3}{2} = \frac{3}{7} \times \frac{2}{3} = \frac{3 \cdot 2}{7 \cdot 3} = \frac{6}{21} = \frac{6+3}{21+3} = \frac{2}{7}$

33. $\frac{3}{7} \div \frac{3}{7} = \frac{3}{7} \times \frac{7}{3} = \frac{3 \cdot 7}{7 \cdot 3} = \frac{21}{21} = \frac{21+21}{21+21} = \frac{1}{1} = 1$

34. $\frac{8}{9} \div \frac{4}{5} = \frac{8}{9} \times \frac{5}{4} = \frac{8 \cdot 5}{9 \cdot 4} = \frac{40}{36} = \frac{40+4}{36+4} = \frac{10}{9} = 1\frac{1}{9}$

35. $\frac{2}{5} \div \frac{4}{7} = \frac{2}{5} \times \frac{7}{4} = \frac{2 \cdot 7}{5 \cdot 4} = \frac{14}{20} = \frac{14+2}{20+2} = \frac{7}{10}$

36. $\frac{1}{2} \div \frac{1}{4} = \frac{1}{2} \times \frac{4}{1} = \frac{1 \cdot 4}{2 \cdot 1} = \frac{4}{2} = \frac{4+2}{2+2} = \frac{2}{1} = 2$

37. $\frac{1}{3} \div \frac{1}{9} = \frac{1}{3} \times \frac{9}{1} = \frac{1 \cdot 9}{3 \cdot 1} = \frac{9}{3} = \frac{9+3}{3+3} = \frac{3}{1} = 3$

38. $\frac{5}{8} \div \frac{15}{2} = \frac{5}{8} \times \frac{2}{15} = \frac{5 \cdot 2}{8 \cdot 15} = \frac{10}{120} = \frac{10+10}{120+10} = \frac{1}{12}$

39. $\frac{5}{16} \div \frac{3}{8} = \frac{5}{16} \times \frac{8}{3} = \frac{5 \cdot 8}{16 \cdot 3} = \frac{40}{48} = \frac{40+8}{48+8} = \frac{5}{6}$

40. $\frac{5}{7} \div \frac{2}{7} = \frac{5}{7} \times \frac{7}{2} = \frac{5 \cdot 7}{7 \cdot 2} = \frac{35}{14} = \frac{35+7}{14+7} = \frac{5}{2} = 2\frac{1}{2}$

41. $\frac{5}{6} \div \frac{1}{9} = \frac{5}{6} \times \frac{9}{1} = \frac{5 \cdot 9}{6 \cdot 1} = \frac{45}{6} = \frac{45+3}{6+3} = \frac{15}{2} = 7\frac{1}{2}$

42. $\frac{15}{8} \div \frac{5}{32} = \frac{15}{8} \times \frac{32}{5} = \frac{15 \cdot 32}{8 \cdot 5} = \frac{480}{40} = \frac{480+40}{40+40} = \frac{12}{1} = 12$

43. $\frac{5}{6} \div 25 = \frac{5}{6} \div \frac{25}{1} = \frac{5}{6} \times \frac{1}{25} = \frac{5 \cdot 1}{6 \cdot 25} = \frac{5}{150} = \frac{5+5}{150+5} = \frac{1}{30}$

44. $22 \div \frac{3}{11} = \frac{22}{1} \div \frac{3}{11} = \frac{22}{1} \times \frac{11}{3} = \frac{22 \cdot 11}{1 \cdot 3} = \frac{242}{3} = 80\frac{2}{3}$

45. $6 \div 3\frac{1}{3} = \frac{6}{1} \div \frac{10}{3} = \frac{6}{1} \times \frac{3}{10} = \frac{6 \cdot 3}{1 \cdot 10} = \frac{18}{10} = \frac{18+2}{10+2} = \frac{9}{5} = 1\frac{4}{5}$

46. $5\frac{1}{2} \div 11 = \frac{11}{2} \div \frac{11}{1} = \frac{11}{2} \times \frac{1}{11} = \frac{11 \cdot 1}{2 \cdot 11} = \frac{11}{22} = \frac{11+11}{22+11} = \frac{1}{2}$

47. $3\frac{1}{3} \div \frac{3}{8} = \frac{10}{3} \div \frac{3}{8} = \frac{10}{3} \times \frac{8}{3} = \frac{10 \cdot 8}{3 \cdot 3} = \frac{80}{9} = 8\frac{8}{9}$

48. $6\frac{1}{2} \div \frac{1}{2} = \frac{13}{2} \div \frac{1}{2} = \frac{13}{2} \times \frac{2}{1} = \frac{13 \cdot 2}{2 \cdot 1} = \frac{26}{2} = \frac{26+2}{2+2} = \frac{13}{1} = 13$

49. $\frac{3}{8} \div 2\frac{1}{4} = \frac{3}{8} \div \frac{9}{4} = \frac{3}{8} \times \frac{4}{9} = \frac{3 \cdot 4}{8 \cdot 9} = \frac{12}{72} = \frac{12+12}{72+12} = \frac{1}{6}$

50. $\dfrac{5}{12} \div 4\dfrac{4}{5} = \dfrac{5}{12} \div \dfrac{24}{5} = \dfrac{5}{12} \times \dfrac{5}{24} = \dfrac{5 \cdot 5}{12 \cdot 24} = \dfrac{25}{288}$

51. $1\dfrac{1}{2} \div 1\dfrac{3}{8} = \dfrac{3}{2} \div \dfrac{11}{8} = \dfrac{3}{2} \times \dfrac{8}{11} = \dfrac{3 \cdot 8}{2 \cdot 11} = \dfrac{24}{22} = \dfrac{22+2}{22} = \dfrac{12}{11} = 1\dfrac{1}{11}$

52. $2\dfrac{1}{4} \div 1\dfrac{3}{8} = \dfrac{9}{4} \div \dfrac{11}{8} = \dfrac{9}{4} \times \dfrac{8}{11} = \dfrac{9 \cdot 8}{4 \cdot 11} = \dfrac{72}{44} = \dfrac{72+4}{44+4} = \dfrac{18}{11} = 1\dfrac{7}{11}$

53. $1\dfrac{3}{5} \div 2\dfrac{1}{10} = \dfrac{8}{5} \div \dfrac{21}{10} = \dfrac{8}{5} \times \dfrac{10}{21} = \dfrac{8 \cdot 10}{5 \cdot 21} = \dfrac{80}{105} = \dfrac{80+5}{105+5} = \dfrac{16}{21}$

54. $2\dfrac{5}{6} \div 1\dfrac{1}{9} = \dfrac{17}{6} \div \dfrac{10}{9} = \dfrac{17}{6} \times \dfrac{9}{10} = \dfrac{17 \cdot 9}{6 \cdot 10} = \dfrac{153}{60} = \dfrac{153+3}{60+3} = \dfrac{51}{20} = 2\dfrac{11}{20}$

55. $2\dfrac{1}{3} \div 3\dfrac{2}{3} = \dfrac{7}{3} \div \dfrac{11}{3} = \dfrac{7}{3} \times \dfrac{3}{11} = \dfrac{7 \cdot 3}{3 \cdot 11} = \dfrac{21}{33} = \dfrac{21+3}{33+3} = \dfrac{7}{11}$

56. $4\dfrac{1}{2} \div 2\dfrac{1}{6} = \dfrac{9}{2} \div \dfrac{13}{6} = \dfrac{9}{2} \times \dfrac{6}{13} = \dfrac{9 \cdot 6}{2 \cdot 13} = \dfrac{54}{26} = \dfrac{54+2}{26+2} = \dfrac{27}{13} = 2\dfrac{1}{13}$

57. $7\dfrac{1}{2} \div 2\dfrac{2}{3} = \dfrac{15}{2} \div \dfrac{8}{3} = \dfrac{15}{2} \times \dfrac{3}{8} = \dfrac{15 \cdot 3}{2 \cdot 8} = \dfrac{45}{16} = 2\dfrac{13}{16}$

58. $8\dfrac{1}{4} \div 2\dfrac{3}{4} = \dfrac{33}{4} \div \dfrac{11}{4} = \dfrac{33}{4} \times \dfrac{4}{11} = \dfrac{33 \cdot 4}{4 \cdot 11} = \dfrac{132}{44} = \dfrac{132+44}{44+44} = \dfrac{3}{1} = 3$

59. $6\dfrac{1}{3} \div 5 = \dfrac{19}{3} \div \dfrac{5}{1} = \dfrac{19}{3} \times \dfrac{1}{5} = \dfrac{19 \cdot 1}{3 \cdot 5} = \dfrac{19}{15} = 1\dfrac{4}{15}$

60. $8\dfrac{2}{7} \div 1 = \dfrac{58}{7} \div \dfrac{1}{1} = \dfrac{58}{7} \times \dfrac{1}{1} = \dfrac{58 \cdot 1}{7 \cdot 1} = \dfrac{58}{7} = 8\dfrac{2}{7}$

61. Strategy
To find the hygienist's overtime rate, multiply the regular hourly rate ($16) by $1\dfrac{1}{2}$.

Solution
$16 \times 1\dfrac{1}{2} = \dfrac{16}{1} \times \dfrac{3}{2} = 24$

The hygienist's overtime rate is $24 per hour.

62. Strategy
To find the electrician's overtime rate, multiply the regular hourly rate ($22) by $1\dfrac{1}{2}$.

Solution
$22 \times 1\dfrac{1}{2} = \dfrac{22}{1} \times \dfrac{3}{2} = 33$

The electrician's overtime rate is $33 per hour.

63. Strategy
To find the carpenter's overtime pay:
• Find the overtime rate by multiplying the regular hourly rate ($18) by $1\dfrac{1}{2}$.
• Multiply the overtime rate by the number of hours of overtime worked (5).

Solution
$18 \times 1\dfrac{1}{2} = \dfrac{18}{1} \times \dfrac{3}{2} = 27$
$27 \times 5 = 135$

The carpenter's overtime pay for this week is $135.

64. Strategy
To find the plumber's overtime pay:
• Find the overtime rate by multiplying the regular hourly wage ($20) by $1\dfrac{1}{2}$.
• Multiply the overtime rate by the number of hours of overtime worked (4).

Solution
$20 \times 1\dfrac{1}{2} = \dfrac{20}{1} \times \dfrac{3}{2} = 30$
$30 \times 4 = 120$

The plumber's overtime pay is $120.

65. Strategy
    To find the regular hourly wage, divide the overtime rate ($15) by $1\frac{1}{2}$.

    Solution
    $15 \div 1\frac{1}{2} = 15 \div \frac{3}{2} = 15 \times \frac{2}{3} = \frac{15}{1} \times \frac{2}{3} = 10$

    The regular hourly wage is $10.

66. Strategy
    To find the regular hourly wage, divide the overtime rate ($42) by $1\frac{1}{2}$.

    Solution
    $42 \div 1\frac{1}{2} = 42 \div \frac{3}{2} = 42 \times \frac{2}{3} = \frac{42}{1} \times \frac{2}{3} = 28$

    The regular hourly wage is $28.

67. Strategy
    To find the regular hourly wage:
    - Find the overtime rate by dividing the overtime earned ($96) by the number of hours of overtime worked (8).
    - Divide the overtime rate by $1\frac{1}{2}$.

    Solution
    $96 \div 8 = 12$
    $12 \div 1\frac{1}{2} = 12 \div \frac{3}{2} = 12 \times \frac{2}{3} = \frac{12}{1} \times \frac{2}{3} = 8$

    The regular hourly wage is $8.

68. Strategy
    To find the regular hourly wage:
    - Find the overtime rate by dividing the overtime earned ($126) by the number of hours of overtime worked (7).
    - Divide the overtime rate by $1\frac{1}{2}$.

    Solution
    $126 \div 7 = 18$
    $18 \div 1\frac{1}{2} = 18 \div \frac{3}{2} = 18 \times \frac{2}{3} = \frac{18}{1} \times \frac{2}{3} = 12$

    The regular hourly rate is $12.

69. Strategy
    To find the overtime pay:
    - Find the overtime rate by multiplying the regular hourly wage ($8) by $1\frac{1}{2}$.
    - Find the total number of hours of overtime worked.
    - Multiply the sum by the overtime rate.

    Solution
    $8 \times 1\frac{1}{2} = \frac{8}{1} \times \frac{3}{2} = 12$
    $4 + 5\frac{1}{2} = 9\frac{1}{2}$
    $9\frac{1}{2} \times 12 = \frac{19}{2} \times \frac{12}{1} = 114$

    The overtime pay is $114.

70. Strategy
    To find the overtime earnings:
    - Find the overtime rate by multiplying the regular hourly wage ($6) by $1\frac{1}{2}$.
    - Find the total number of hours of overtime worked.
    - Multiply the sum by the overtime rate.

    Solution
    $6 \times 1\frac{1}{2} = \frac{6}{1} \times \frac{3}{2} = 9$
    8 A.M. - noon = 4 hours
    2 P.M. - 4 P.M. = 2 hours
    $4 + 2 = 6$
    $6 \times 9 = 54$

    The overtime earnings are $54.

71. Strategy
    To find the earnings for the week:
    - Find the earnings for the first 40 hours worked by multiplying 40 by the regular hourly rate ($12).
    - Find the overtime rate by multiplying the regular hourly rate by $1\frac{1}{2}$.
    - Find the overtime earnings by multiplying the hours worked over 40 $\left(42\frac{1}{2} - 40\right)$ by the overtime rate.
    - Add the overtime earnings to the earnings for the first 40 hours.

    Solution
    $12 \times 40 = 480$
    $12 \times 1\frac{1}{2} = \frac{12}{1} \times \frac{3}{2} = 18$
    $2\frac{1}{2} \times 18 = \frac{5}{2} \times \frac{18}{1} = 45$
    $480 + 45 = 525$

    The earnings for the week are $525.

72. Strategy
    To find the earnings for the week:
    - Find the earnings for the first 40 hours worked by multiplying 40 by the regular hourly rate ($8).
    - Find the overtime rate by multiplying the regular hourly rate by $1\frac{1}{2}$.
    - Find the overtime earnings by multiplying the hours worked over 40 $\left(48\frac{1}{4} - 40\right)$ by the overtime rate.
    - Add the overtime earnings to the earnings for the first 40 hours.

    Solution
    $8 \times 40 = 320$
    $8 \times 1\frac{1}{2} = \frac{8}{1} \times \frac{3}{2} = 12$
    $8\frac{1}{4} \times 12 = \frac{33}{4} \times \frac{12}{1} = 99$
    $320 + 99 = 419$

    The earnings for the week are $419.

73. Strategy
    To find the earnings for the week:
    - Find the earnings for the first 40 hours worked by multiplying 40 by the regular hourly rate ($16).
    - Find the overtime rate by multiplying the regular hourly rate by $1\frac{1}{2}$.
    - Find the overtime earnings by multiplying the hours worked over 40 $\left(46\frac{1}{2} - 40\right)$ by the overtime rate.
    - Add the overtime earnings to the earnings for the first 40 hours.

    Solution
    $16 \times 40 = 640$
    $16 \times 1\frac{1}{2} = \frac{16}{1} \times \frac{3}{2} = 24$
    $6\frac{1}{2} \times 24 = \frac{13}{2} \times \frac{24}{1} = 156$
    $640 + 156 = 796$

    Hector's earnings for this week are $796.

74. Strategy
    To find the earnings for the week:
    - Find the total number of hours worked.
    - Find the earnings for the first 40 hours worked by multiplying 40 by the regular hourly rate ($20).
    - Find the overtime rate by multiplying the regular hourly rate by $1\frac{1}{2}$.
    - Find the overtime earnings by multiplying the hours worked over 40 by the overtime rate.
    - Add the overtime earnings to the earnings for the first 40 hours.

    Solution
    $8\frac{1}{4} + 9\frac{1}{2} + 7\frac{3}{4} + 8\frac{1}{2} + 8\frac{1}{2} = 42\frac{1}{2}$
    $20 \times 40 = 800$
    $20 \times 1\frac{1}{2} = \frac{20}{1} \times \frac{3}{2} = 30$
    $42\frac{1}{2} - 40 = 2\frac{1}{2}$ hours of overtime
    $2\frac{1}{2} \times 30 = \frac{5}{2} \times \frac{30}{1} = 75$
    $800 + 75 = 875

    The earnings for the week are $875.

75. Strategy
    To find the machinist's earnings for
    the past week:
    * Find the total number of hours
      worked.
    * Find the earnings for the first 40
      hours worked by multiplying 40 by
      the regular hourly rate ($14).
    * Find the overtime rate by
      multiplying the regular hourly rate
      by $1\frac{1}{2}$.
    * Find the overtime earnings by
      multiplying the hours worked over
      40 by the overtime rate.
    * Add the overtime earnings to the
      earnings for the first 40 hours.

    Solution
    $9\frac{1}{4} + 8\frac{3}{4} + 7 + 9\frac{1}{4} + 8\frac{3}{4} = 43$
    $14 \times 40 = 560$
    $14 \times 1\frac{1}{2} = \frac{14}{1} \times \frac{3}{2} = 21$
    $43 - 40 = 3$ hours of overtime
    $3 \times 21 = 63$
    $560 + 63 = 623$

    The earnings for the week are $623.

Business Case Study

1. Each unit is 30 feet x 50 feet = 1500 square feet.
   40 units x 1500 square feet = 60,000 square feet
   $\frac{3}{4}$ acres = $\frac{3}{4}$ x 43,560 square feet = 32,670 square feet
   Total land needed: 60,000 square feet + 32,670 square feet = 92,670 square feet
   $2\frac{1}{2}$ acres = $2\frac{1}{2}$ x 43,560 square feet = 108,900 square feet
   $3\frac{1}{4}$ acres = $3\frac{1}{4}$ x 43,560 square feet = 141,570 square feet
   108,900 square feet is greater than 92,670 square feet.
   141,570 square feet is greater than 92,670 square feet.
   Either lot is adequate for your building needs.

2. a. $31,800 \div 2\frac{1}{2} = 12,720$

      The asking price per acre of the $2\frac{1}{2}$-acre lot is $12,720.

   b. $39,975 \div 3\frac{1}{4} = 12,300$

      The asking price per acre of the $3\frac{1}{4}$-acre lot is $12,300.

   c. 12,720 - 12,300 = 420
      The difference in asking prices is $420.

3. Price per acre may well be a consideration in deciding which property to purchase.
   Other factors to be taken into account include location, the price each seller might
   be willing to accept for the property, and the quality of the ground upon which the
   buildings will be constructed. The feasibility of selling unused acreage might also
   be considered.

Review/Test, pages 67–68

1.

$$5\overline{)18}$$
$$\underline{-15}$$
$$3$$

$$\frac{18}{5} = 3\frac{3}{5}$$

2. $9\frac{4}{5} = \frac{45 + 4}{5} = \frac{49}{5}$

3. $32 \div 8 = 4$　　$\frac{5\cdot 4}{8\cdot 4} = \frac{20}{32}$

$\frac{20}{32}$ is equivalent to $\frac{5}{8}$.

4. $\frac{20}{32} = \frac{20 \div 4}{32 \div 4} = \frac{5}{8}$

5.

2	10	12
2	5	6
3	5	3
5	5	1
	1	1

The LCM $= 2\cdot 2\cdot 3\cdot 5 = 60$

6. $\frac{7}{12} + \frac{11}{12} + \frac{1}{12} = \frac{19}{12} = 1\frac{7}{12}$

7. The LCD of 6 and 9 is 18.

$$\frac{5}{6} = \frac{15}{18}$$
$$+ \frac{7}{9} = \frac{14}{18}$$
$$\overline{\phantom{+\frac{7}{9}=}\frac{29}{18}} = 1\frac{11}{18}$$

8. The LCD of 4 and 6 is 12.

$$2\frac{3}{4} = 2\frac{9}{12}$$
$$+ 5\frac{1}{6} = 5\frac{2}{12}$$
$$\overline{\phantom{+5\frac{1}{6}=}7\frac{11}{12}}$$

9. $\frac{17}{24} - \frac{11}{24} = \frac{6}{24} = \frac{1}{4}$

10. The LCD of 8 and 4 is 8.

$$\frac{7}{8} = \frac{7}{8}$$
$$- \frac{3}{4} = \frac{6}{8}$$
$$\overline{\phantom{-\frac{3}{4}=}\frac{1}{8}}$$

11.

$$23 = 22\frac{8}{8}$$
$$- 9\frac{1}{8} = 9\frac{1}{8}$$
$$\overline{\phantom{-9\frac{1}{8}=}13\frac{7}{8}}$$

12. $\frac{9}{10} \times \frac{4}{7} = \frac{9\cdot 4}{10\cdot 7} = \frac{36}{70}$

$\phantom{\frac{9}{10} \times \frac{4}{7}} = \frac{36 \div 2}{70 \div 2} = \frac{18}{35}$

13. $2\frac{2}{3} \times 1\frac{1}{4} = \frac{8}{3} \times \frac{7}{4} = \frac{8\cdot 7}{3\cdot 4}$

$\phantom{2\frac{2}{3} \times 1\frac{1}{4}} = \frac{56}{12} = \frac{56 \div 4}{12 \div 4} = \frac{14}{3} = 4\frac{2}{3}$

14. $\frac{5}{9} \div \frac{3}{8} = \frac{5}{9} \times \frac{8}{3} = \frac{5\cdot 8}{9\cdot 3}$

$\phantom{\frac{5}{9} \div \frac{3}{8}} = \frac{40}{27} = 1\frac{13}{27}$

15. $3 \div 4\frac{1}{5} = \frac{3}{1} \div \frac{21}{5} = \frac{3}{1} \times \frac{5}{21}$

$\phantom{3 \div 4\frac{1}{5}} = \frac{3\cdot 5}{1\cdot 21} = \frac{15}{21}$

$\phantom{3 \div 4\frac{1}{5}} = \frac{15 \div 3}{21 \div 3} = \frac{5}{7}$

16. $3\frac{2}{3} \div 3\frac{1}{6} = \frac{11}{3} \div \frac{19}{6} = \frac{11}{3} \times \frac{6}{19}$

$\phantom{3\frac{2}{3} \div 3\frac{1}{6}} = \frac{11\cdot 6}{3\cdot 19} = \frac{66}{57}$

$\phantom{3\frac{2}{3} \div 3\frac{1}{6}} = \frac{66 \div 3}{57 \div 3} = \frac{22}{19} = 1\frac{3}{19}$

17. Strategy
    To find the difference, subtract
    today's market price $\left(37\frac{3}{8}\right)$ from the
    market price one year ago (50).

    Solution

    $$
    \begin{array}{rcl}
    50 &=& 49\frac{8}{8}\\
    -\ 37\frac{3}{8} &=& 37\frac{3}{8}\\
    \hline
    && 12\frac{5}{8}
    \end{array}
    $$

    The difference between the stock's
    market prices is $12\frac{5}{8}$.

18. Strategy
    To find the value of the stock, add
    the gains $\left(\frac{5}{8}\text{ and }1\frac{1}{2}\right)$ to the purchase
    price $\left(42\frac{3}{8}\right)$.

    Solution

    $$
    \begin{array}{rcl}
    42\frac{3}{8} &=& 42\frac{3}{8}\\
    \frac{5}{8} &=& \frac{5}{8}\\
    +\ 1\frac{1}{2} &=& 1\frac{4}{8}\\
    \hline
    43\frac{12}{8} &=& 44\frac{1}{2}
    \end{array}
    $$

    The value of the stock at the end of
    the two months was $44\frac{1}{2}$.

19. Strategy
    To find the regular hourly pay:
    • Divide the earnings ($60) by the
      number of hours of overtime worked
      (5) to find the overtime rate.
    • Divide the overtime rate by $1\frac{1}{2}$.

    Solution
    $60 \div 5 = 12$
    $12 \div 1\frac{1}{2} = \frac{12}{1} \div \frac{3}{2} = \frac{12}{1} \times \frac{2}{3} = \frac{12 \cdot 2}{1 \cdot 3}$
    $\qquad = \frac{24}{3} = \frac{24+3}{3+3} = \frac{8}{1} = 8$

    The employee's regular hourly rate is
    $8.

20. Strategy
    To find the employee's earnings:
    • Multiply the regular hourly rate
      (12) by 40.
    • Multiply the number of hours of
      overtime worked $\left(44\frac{1}{2} - 40 = 4\frac{1}{2}\right)$
      by the regular hourly rate by $1\frac{1}{2}$.
    • Add the two products.

    Solution
    $12 \times 40 = 480$
    $4\frac{1}{2} \times 12 \times 1\frac{1}{2} = \frac{9}{2} \times \frac{12}{1} \times \frac{3}{2} = \frac{9 \cdot 12 \cdot 3}{2 \cdot 1 \cdot 2}$
    $\qquad\qquad = \frac{324}{4} = 81$
    $480 + 81 = 561$

    The employee's earnings are $561.

CHAPTER 3
Decimals and Business Applications

Section 3.1, pages 77–80

1. twenty-seven hundredths

2. ninety-two hundredths

3. one and five thousandths

4. three and sixty-seven thousandths

5. thirty-six and four tenths

6. fifty-nine and seven tenths

7. six and three hundred twenty-four thousandths

8. eight and nine hundred sixteen thousandths

9. one and one hundred-thousandth

10. three and forty-one ten-thousandths

11. 0.762	12. 0.295	13. 8.0304	14. 4.0907
15. 304.07	16. 896.41	17. 5.36	18. 9.24
19. 362.048	20. 3048.2002	21. 5,230,000	22. 12,400,000,000
23. 7,900	24. 6,850,000,000,000		

25.
```
   1.007
  +2.1
 ──────
   3.107
```

26.
```
   7.3
  +9.005
 ──────
  16.305
```

27.
```
  1 1 1
   8.962
 +10.599
 ───────
  19.561
```

28.
```
  1 1 1 1
  11.957
 + 9.374
 ───────
  21.331
```

29.
```
   1 1
  27.42
 + 9.765
 ──────
  37.185
```

30.
```
  1 1 1
   7.85
 +29.762
 ──────
  37.612
```

31.
```
  2   1 1
   4.9257
  27.05
 + 9.0063
 ───────
  40.9820
```

32.
```
  2 1 1
   8.72
  99.073
 + 2.9763
 ────────
 110.7693
```

33.
```
  1 1 1
  62.4
   9.827
 +692.44
 ───────
 764.667
```

34.
```
  2
    8.
   89.43
 +  7.0659
 ────────
  104.4959
```

35.
```
  1
  17.32
   1.0579
 +16.5
 ───────
  34.8779
```

36.
```
  1   1
   1.792
  67.
 +27.0526
 ───────
  95.8446
```

37.
```
      1
    3.02
   62.7
 +  3.94
 ───────
   69.66
```

38.
```
   2 1  1
   9.06
   4.976
 +59.6
 ───────
  73.636
```

39.
```
   2.9 million
 +6.5 million
 ─────────────
   9.4 million
```

40.
```
   4.6 billion
 +3   billion
 ─────────────
   7.6 billion
```

41.
```
  82.6 thousand
 +9.9 thousand
 ──────────────
  92.5 thousand
```

42.
```
   7.1 trillion
 +7.2 trillion
 ──────────────
  14.3 trillion
```

43.
```
   0.675
  -0.32
 ───────
   0.355
```

44.
```
   2 9 9 10
   3.000
  -1.296
 ────────
   1.704
```

45.
```
    4 9 17
   7.307
  -3.419
 ───────
   4.088
```

46.
```
   116  10810
   27.090
  - 7.265
 ─────────
   19.825
```

47.
```
   7 11 10 6 10
   82.070
  - 7.354
 ─────────
   74.716
```

48.
```
   7 12 10 14
   18.314
  - 9.785
 ─────────
   8.529
```

49.
```
   5 10 11 13
   16.123
  - 7.457
 ─────────
   8.666
```

50.
```
   2 9 10
   3.005
  -1.982
 ───────
   1.023
```

51.
```
        8 10
   123.790
  - 92.456
 ─────────
   31.334
```

52.
```
   2 13 9 10
   23.400
  - 0.921
 ─────────
   22.479
```

53.
```
   1 13 10
   24.037
  -18.410
 ────────
   5.627
```

54.
```
   1 15 10
   26.029
  -19.310
 ────────
   6.719
```

55.
```
   0 13 9 9 10
   214.000
  -  7.143
 ──────────
   206.857
```

56.
```
   5 14 9 9 10
   16.3000
  - 9.7902
 ──────────
   6.7098
```

57.
```
   2 11 9 9 10
   13.2000
  - 8.6205
 ──────────
   4.5795
```

58.
```
   8 11 9 9 9 10
   92.0000
  -19.2909
 ──────────
   72.7091
```

59.
```
   6 9 10 10
   7.010
  -2.325
 ────────
   4.685
```

60.
```
   7 9 16 10
   8.070
  -5.392
 ────────
   2.678
```

61.
```
   35.70 million
 -20.93 million
 ───────────────
   14.77 million
```

62.
```
   6.20 billion
 -4.95 billion
 ──────────────
   1.25 billion
```

63.
```
   19.0 thousand
 -10.4 thousand
 ───────────────
   8.6 thousand
```

64.
```
   5.0 trillion
 -2.3 trillion
 ──────────────
   2.7 trillion
```

65.
```
   23.45
   18.25
   36.90
 +12.75
 ───────
 $91.35
```

66.
```
   67.50
   67.50
   67.50
 + 67.50
 ───────
 $270.00
```

67.
```
   5.42
   3.64
 + 4.96
 ───────
 $14.02
```

68.
```
 $78.80
```

69.
```
   52.40
 + 52.40
 ────────
 $104.80
```

70.
```
   3.49
   8.22
 + 2.75
 ───────
 $14.46
```

71.
```
   23.45
   67.50
   5.42
 + 52.40
 ────────
 $148.77
```

72.
```
   18.25
   67.50
 + 3.49
 ───────
 $89.24
```

73.
```
   36.90
   67.50
 + 3.64
 ───────
 $108.04
```

74.
```
   67.50
   78.80
 + 8.22
 ───────
 $154.52
```

75.
```
   12.75
   4.96
   52.40
 + 2.75
 ───────
 $72.86
```

76.
```
   91.35        148.77
  270.00         89.24
   14.02        108.04
   78.80        154.52
  104.80      + 72.86
 + 14.46       ────────
 ────────      $573.43
 $573.43
```

77.	27.63 19.48 31.94 + 8.25 $87.30	78.	72.25 72.25 72.25 + 72.25 $289.00	79. 4.17 8.27 + 6.42 $18.86 80. $63.40

81.   28.45
       5.50
      +28.45
      $62.40

82.   6.50
      + 4.82
      $11.32

83.   27.63
      72.25
       4.17
      + 28.45
      $132.50

84.   19.48
      72.25
      + 6.50
      $98.23

85.   72.25
       8.27
      63.40
      + 5.50
      $149.42

86.   31.94
      72.25
      + 4.82
      $109.01

87.   8.25
       6.42
      +28.45
      43.12

88.   87.30
     289.00   132.50
      18.86   98.23
      63.40   149.42
      62.40   109.01
      + 11.32   + 43.12
     $532.28 $532.28

89.   17.25
      23.48
      19.60
      27.35
      + 31.85
      $119.53

90.   87.50
      87.50
      87.50
      87.50
      + 87.50
      $437.50

91.   5.82
       4.67
      + 6.89
      $17.38

92.   84.90
      + 76.25
      $161.15

93. $78.80

94.   5.50
      + 6.45
      $11.95

95.   17.25
      87.50
       5.82
      + 78.80
      $189.37

96.   23.48
      87.50
      84.90
      + 5.50
      $201.38

97.   19.60
      87.50
       4.67
      + 6.45
      $118.22

98.   27.35
      87.50
      + 76.25
      $191.10

99.   31.85
      87.50
      + 6.89
      $126.24

100. 119.53
      437.50   189.37
       17.38   201.38
      161.15   118.22
       78.80   191.10
      + 11.95   +126.24
      $826.31 $826.31

Section 3.2, pages 89–92

1.   Given place value
      |
      7.359
      |
          5=5
      7.4

2.   Given place value
      |
      6.405
       |
          0 is less than 5.
      6.4

3.   Given place value
      |
      89.19204
          |
           9 is greater than 5.
      89.2

4.   Given place value
      |
      480.325
          |
             5=5
      480.33

5.   Given place value
      |
      670.974
          |
           4 is less than 5.
      670.97

6.   Given place value
      |
      22.68259
         |
          2 is less than 5.
      22.68

7.   Given place value
```
       |
  1.03925
       |
       2 is less than 5.
  1.039
```

8.   Given place value
```
       |
  7.072854
       |
       8 is greater than 5.
  7.073
```

9.   Given place value
```
       |
  8.6273402
       |
       7 is greater than 5.
  8.63
```

10.   Given place value
```
       |
  36.41859
       |
       8 is greater than 5.
  36.42
```

11.   Given place value
```
       |
  1946.395
       |
       5=5
  1946.40
```

12.   Given place value
```
       |
  728.5963
       |
       6 is greater than 5.
  728.60
```

13.
```
    7.7
   x0.9
   ────
   6.93
```

14.
```
    0.67
  x 0.9
  ─────
  0.603
```

15.
```
     2.5
   x 5.4
   ─────
     100
     125
   ─────
   13.50
```

16.
```
    0.83
   x 5.2
   ─────
     166
     415
   ─────
   4.316
```

17.
```
    1.47
  x 0.09
  ──────
  0.1323
```

18.
```
     6.75
  x 0.007
  ───────
  0.04725
```

19.
```
    0.86
  x 0.07
  ──────
  0.0602
```

20.
```
    0.49
  x 0.16
  ──────
     294
      49
  ──────
  0.0784
```

21.
```
    5.41
  x 0.7
  ─────
  3.787
```

22.
```
    8.62
  x    4
  ─────
  34.48
```

23.
```
     2.19
   x 9.2
   ──────
     438
    1971
   ──────
   20.148
```

24.
```
    0.478
  x 0.37
  ───────
    3346
    1434
  ───────
  0.17686
```

25.
```
    0.0173
  x    0.89
  ─────────
      1557
      1384
  ─────────
  0.015397
```

26.
```
    2.437
  x   6.1
  ────────
     2437
    14622
  ────────
  14.8657
```

27.
```
    94.73
  x  0.57
  ────────
    66311
    47365
  ────────
  53.9961
```

28.
```
    8.005
  x 0.067
  ─────────
    56035
    48030
  ─────────
  0.536335
```

29.
```
    1.25
  x 5.6
  ─────
   750
   625
  ─────
  7.000
```

30.
```
    89.23
  x 0.62
  ───────
   17846
   53538
  ───────
  55.3226
```

31.   0.039 x 100 = 3.9

32.   3.57 x 10,000 = 35,700

33.   8.52 x 10 = 85.2

34.   6.8 x 1000 = 6800

35.   64.93 x 100 = 6493

36.   4.625 x 1000 = 4625

37.
```
            6.32 ≈ 6.3
      8.8.)55.6.20
           -52 8
           ─────
            2 8 2
           -2 6 4
           ──────
             1 80
            -1 76
            ─────
                4
```

38.
```
            4.70 ≈ 4.7
      5.4.)25.4.30
           -21 6
           ─────
            3 8 3
           -3 7 8
           ──────
              50
             -0
             ───
              50
```

39.
```
            0.57 ≈ 0.6
      9.5.)5.4.27
           -4 7 5
           ──────
            6 77
           -6 65
           ──────
              12
```

40.
```
            1.31 ≈ 1.3
      _____
1.4. | 1.8.37
         -1 4
         ____
           4 3
          -4 2
          ____
             17
            -14
            ____
              3
```

41.
```
            2.52 ≈ 2.5
      _____
7.3. | 18.4.00
         -14 6
         _____
           3 80
          -3 65
          _____
           1 50
          -1 46
          _____
              4
```

42.
```
            6.53 ≈ 6.5
      _____
8.1. | 52.9.00
         -48 6
         _____
           4 3 0
          -4 0 5
          _____
            2 50
           -2 43
           _____
               7
```

43.
```
            1.07 ≈ 1.1
      _____
0.17. | 0.18.30
         - 17
         ____
           1 3
          - 0
          ___
           1 30
          -1 19
          _____
             11
```

44.
```
            0.81 ≈ 0.8
      _____
0.47. | 0.38.11
         - 37 6
         _____
             51
            -47
            ___
              4
```

45.
```
            0.83 ≈ 0.8
      _____
0.65. | 0.54.20
         - 52 0
         _____
            2 20
           -1 95
           _____
             25
```

46.
```
            130.64 ≈ 130.6
      _____
0.053. | 6.924.00
          -53
          ___
           162
          -159
          ____
            34
           - 0
           ___
            340
           -318
           ____
            220
           -212
           ____
              8
```

47. 8137 + 1000 = 8.137 ≈ 8.1

48. 357.92 + 10 = 35.792 ≈ 35.8

49.
```
           0.301 ≈ 0.30
      _____
16 | 4.817
     -4 8
     ____
       01
      - 0
      ___
       17
      -16
      ___
        1
```

50.
```
           0.808 ≈ 0.81
      _____
8 | 6.467
    -6 4
    ____
      06
     - 0
     ___
      67
     -64
     ___
       3
```

51.
```
             0.078 ≈ 0.08
       _____
0.53. | 0.04.180
          - 3 71
          _____
            470
           -424
           ____
             46
```

52.
```
              0.089 ≈ 0.09
0.72. 0.06.470
       - 5 76
         710
        -648
          62
```

53.
```
          18.75
0.48. 9.00.00
     - 4 8
       4 20
      -3 84
        36 0
       -33 6
         2 40
        -2 40
           0
```

54.
```
              12.727 ≈ 12.73
0.55. 7.00.000
       - 5 5
         1 50
        -1 10
          40 0
         -38 5
           1 50
          -1 10
            400
           -385
             15
```

55.
```
          42.40
0.45. 19.08.00
     -18 0
       1 08
       - 90
         18 0
        -18 0
           0
```

56.
```
          22.70
0.96. 21.79.20
     -19 2
       2 59
      - 1 92
         67 2
        -67 2
           0
```

57.
```
          40.70
0.95. 38.66.50
     -38 0
        66
       - 0
         66 5
        -66 5
           0
```

58. 42.67 ÷ 10 = 4.267
≈ 4.27

59. 82,547 ÷ 1000 = 82.547
≈ 82.55

60. 23.627 ÷ 100 = 0.23627
≈ 0.24

61.
```
    0.625
8 5.000
```

62.
```
    0.5833 ≈ 0.583
12 7.0000
```

63.
```
    0.6666 ≈ 0.667
3 2.0000
```

64.
```
    0.8333 ≈ 0.833
6 5.0000
```

65.
```
    0.1666 ≈ 0.167
6 1.0000
```

66.
```
    0.875
8 7.000
```

67.
```
    0.4166 ≈ 0.417
12 5.0000
```

68.
```
    0.5625 ≈ 0.563
16 9.0000
```

69. $2\frac{3}{1000} = \frac{2003}{1000}$
```
        2.003
1000 2003.000
```

70. $3\frac{5}{10} = \frac{35}{10}$
```
     3.500
10 35.000
```

71.
```
    0.375
8 3.000
```

72.
```
    0.6875 ≈ 0.688
16 11.0000
```

73. $0.8 = \frac{8}{10} = \frac{4}{5}$

74. $0.4 = \frac{4}{10} = \frac{2}{5}$

75. $0.32 = \frac{32}{100} = \frac{8}{25}$

76. $0.48 = \frac{48}{100} = \frac{12}{25}$

77. $0.125 = \frac{125}{1000} = \frac{1}{8}$

78. $0.485 = \frac{485}{1000} = \frac{97}{200}$

79. $1.25 = 1\frac{25}{100} = 1\frac{1}{4}$

80. $3.75 = 3\frac{75}{100} = 3\frac{3}{4}$

81. $0.045 = \frac{45}{1000} = \frac{9}{200}$

82. $0.085 = \frac{85}{1000} = \frac{17}{200}$

83. $0.33\frac{1}{3} = \frac{33\frac{1}{3}}{100} = 33\frac{1}{3} \div 100 = \frac{100}{3} \times \frac{1}{100} = \frac{1}{3}$ 84. $0.66\frac{2}{3} = \frac{66\frac{2}{3}}{100} = 66\frac{2}{3} \div 100 = \frac{200}{3} \times \frac{1}{100} = \frac{2}{3}$

85. $150 \times 3.49 = \$523.50$ 86. $250 \times 0.85 = \$212.50$ 87. $75 \times 0.99 = \$74.25$

88. $125 \times 0.49 = \$61.25$ 89. $523.50 + 212.50 + 74.25 + 61.25 = \$871.50$

90. $150 \times 1.99 = \$298.50$ 91. $225 \times 2.09 = \$470.25$ 92. $175 \times 2.29 = \$400.75$

93. $55 \times 2.49 = \$136.95$ 94. $298.50 + 470.25 + 400.75 + 136.95 = \$1306.45$

95. $100 \times 29.99 = \$2999.00$ 96. $100 \times 12.99 = \$1299.00$ 97. $25 \times 14.95 = \$373.75$

98. $10 \times 129.95 = \$1299.50$ 99. $5 \times 15.95 = \$79.75$

100. $2999.00 + 1299.00 + 373.75 + 1299.50 + 79.75 = \$6051.00$

Section 3.3, pages 97–98

1. $42 \text{ cm} = 420 \text{ mm}$ 2. $420 \text{ g} = 0.420 \text{ kg}$ 3. $4200 \text{ ml} = 4.200 \text{ L}$

4. $81 \text{ mm} = 8.1 \text{ cm}$ 5. $127 \text{ mg} = 0.127 \text{ g}$ 6. $3.42 \text{ L} = 3420 \text{ ml}$

7. $6804 \text{ m} = 6.804 \text{ km}$ 8. $4.2 \text{ kg} = 4200 \text{ g}$ 9. $423 \text{ mm} = 42.3 \text{ cm}$

10. $2.109 \text{ km} = 2109 \text{ m}$ 11. $0.45 \text{ g} = 450 \text{ mg}$ 12. $642 \text{ m} = 0.642 \text{ km}$

13. $432 \text{ cm} = 4.32 \text{ m}$ 14. $1856 \text{ g} = 1.856 \text{ kg}$ 15. $1.37 \text{ kg} = 1370 \text{ g}$

16. $42,350 \text{ g} = 42.350 \text{ kg}$ 17. $0.88 \text{ m} = 88 \text{ cm}$ 18. $4057 \text{ mg} = 4.057 \text{ g}$

19. $0.0456 \text{ g} = 45.6 \text{ mg}$ 20. $2.3 \text{ kg} = 2300 \text{ g}$ 21. $4.62 \text{ kl} = 4620 \text{ L}$

22. $1423 \text{ L} = 1.423 \text{ kl}$ 23. $2.5 \text{ km} = 2500 \text{ m}$ 24. $3750 \text{ m} = 3.750 \text{ km}$

25. $0.037 \text{ L} = 37 \text{ ml}$ 26. $0.035 \text{ kl} = 35 \text{ L}$

27. Strategy
To find the freight charges, multiply
the charge per kilogram ($.05) by the
number of kilograms (27,500).

Solution
$\$.05 \times 27,500 = \$1375$

The freight charges are $1375.

28. Strategy
To find the freight charges, multiply
the charge per kilogram ($.03) by the
number of kilograms (10,000).

Solution
$\$.03 \times 10,000 = \$300$

The freight charges are $300.

29. Strategy
    To find the freight charges:
    • Find the weight of each catalogue
      in kilograms.
    • Multiply the weight in kilograms of
      one catalogue by the number of
      catalogues (1,000,000).
    • Multiply the cost per kilogram
      ($.25) by the total number of
      kilograms.

    Solution
    748 g = 0.748 kg
    0.748 x 1,000,000 = 748,000
    $.25 x 748,000 = $187,000

    The freight charges are $187,000.

30. Strategy
    To find the freight charges:
    • Find the weight of each book in
      kilograms.
    • Multiply the weight in kilograms of
      one catalogue by the number of
      books (1000).
    • Multiply the cost per kilogram
      ($.35) by the total number of
      kilograms.

    Solution
    862 g = 0.862 kg
    0.862 x 1000 = 862
    $.35 x 862 = $301.70

    The freight charges are $301.70.

31. Strategy
    To find the fright charges:
    • Find the total weight by multiply-
      ing the weight of each range (75.5
      kg) by the number of ranges (12).
    • Multiply the charge per kilogram
      ($1.20) by the total weight.

    Solution
    12 x 75.5 = 906
    $1.20 x 906 = $1087.20

    The freight charges are $1087.20.

32. Strategy
    To find the fright charges:
    • Find the total weight by multiply-
      ing the weight of each television
      (36.5 kg) by the number of
      televisions (25). Round the product
      up to the nearest whole number.
    • Multiply the charge per kilogram
      ($.80) by the total weight.

    Solution
    25 x 36.5 = 912.5 ≈ 913
    $.80 x 913 = $730.40

    The freight charges are $730.40.

33. Strategy
    To find the total weight:
    • Multiply to find the weight for the
      3 cars each weighing 1258.5 kg.
    • Multiply to find the weight of the
      5 cars each weighing 1476.5 kg.
    • Add the two products.

    Solution
    3 x 1258.5 = 3775.5
    5 x 1476.5 = 7382.5
    3775.5 + 7382.5 = 11,158

    The total weight is 11,158 kg.

34. Strategy
    To find the total weight:
    • Multiply to find the weight of the
      5 dressers each weighing 26.75 kg.
    • Multiply to find the weight of the
      6 night tables each weighing 14.5
      kg.
    • Add the two products.

    Solution
    5 x 26.75 = 133.75
    6 x 14.5 = 87
    133.75 + 87 = 220.75

    The total weight is 220.75 kg.

35. Strategy
    To find the freight charge:
    • Divide the weight by 100 kg. Round
      the quotient up to the nearest
      whole number.
    • Multiply the number of 100 kg
      transported by the charge per 100
      kg ($15).

    Solution
    347.8 ÷ 100 = 3.478 ≈ 4
    $15 x 4 = $60

    The freight charge is $60.

36. Strategy
    To find the freight charge:
    • Divide the weight by 100 kg. Round
      the quotient up to the nearest
      whole number.
    • Multiply the number of 100 kg
      transported by the charge per 100
      kg ($18).

    Solution
    692.4 ÷ 100 = 6.924 ≈ 7
    $18 x 7 = $126

    The freight charge is $126.

37. Strategy
    To find the freight charge:
    • Find the total weight by multiply-
      ing the number of items (250) by
      the weight of each item (68.5 kg).
    • Divide the total weight by 100 kg.
      Round the quotient up to the
      nearest whole number.
    • Multiply the number of 100 kg
      transported by the charge per 100
      kg ($12).

    Solution
    250 x 68.5 = 17,125
    17,125 ÷ 100 = 171.25 ≈ 172
    $12 x 172 = $2064

    The freight charge is $2064.

38. Strategy
    To find the freight charge:
    • Find the total weight by multiply-
      ing the number of items (375) by
      the weight of each item (22.8 kg).
    • Divide the total weight by 100 kg.
      Round the quotient up to the
      nearest whole number.
    • Multiply the number of 100 kg
      transported by the charge per 100
      kg ($9).

    Solution
    375 x 22.8 = 8550
    8550 ÷ 100 = 85.5 ≈ 86
    $9 x 86 = $774

    The freight charge is $774.

39. Strategy
    To find the freight charge:
    • Find the total weight of the tires
      by multiplying the number of tires
      (100) by the weight of each tire
      (9.1 kg).
    • Find the total weight transported
      by adding the weight of the auto
      parts (908 kg) to the weight of the
      tires.
    • Divide the total weight by 100 kg.
      Round the quotient up to the
      nearest whole number.
    • Multiply the number of 100 kg
      transported by the charge per 100
      kg ($7.50).

    Solution
    100 x 9.1 = 910
    910 + 908 = 1818
    1818 ÷ 100 = 18.18 ≈ 19
    $7.50 x 19 = $142.50

    The freight charge is $142.50.

40. Strategy
    To find the freight charge:
    • Find the total weight of the
      girders by multiplying the number
      of girders (50) by the weight of
      each girder (136.5 kg).
    • Find the total weight transported
      by adding the weight of the iron
      angles (1750 kg) to the weight of
      the girders.
    • Divide the total weight by 100 kg.
      Round the quotient up to the
      nearest whole number.
    • Multiply the number of 100 kg
      transported by the charge per 100
      kg ($8.50).

    Solution
    50 x 136.5 = 6825
    6825 + 1750 = 8575
    8575 ÷ 100 = 85.75 ≈ 86
    $8.50 x 86 = $731

    The freight charge is $731.

Business Case Study

1. Original Cost Estimate:

Raw materials	$4000
Wages: 10 workers x 5 days x 8 hours per day x 12.50 per hour	5000
Shipping: 8 hundred kilograms x 13.50 per one hundred kilograms	108
	$9108

   The original cost estimate was $9108.

2. Number of hours required to complete the job: 10 hours x 5 days x 8 hours per day = 400 hours

   400 hours ÷ 4 weekdays (Thursday, Friday, Monday, Tuesday) = 100 hours per day

   100 hours per day ÷ 10 workers = 10 hours per day per worker

   Each of the 10 workers must work 10 - 8 = 2 hours of overtime on each of the 4 weekdays.

   10 workers x 2 hours of overtime x 4 days = 80 hours of overtime.

   A total of 80 hours of overtime will be required of the employees.

3. Yes, it is possible to avoid having the employees work on the weekend. As shown in the answer to Question 2 above, each worker could work 2 hours of overtime on each of the 4 weekdays.

4. Revised Cost Estimate:

Raw materials	$4000
Wages: 10 workers x 4 days x 8 hours per day x 12.50 per hour	4000
10 workers x 4 days x 2 hours of overtime per day x 18.75 per hour	1500
Shipping: 2 x original shipping cost of 108	216
	$9716

   The cost estimate for production and delivery of goods by October 10 is $9716.

5. Answers will vary. For example:

   The company is undoubtedly interested in preserving a good relationship with a current customer or establishing a good relationship with a potential customer. Either situation leads to a decision to accept the order. However, perhaps accepting the order would require that the company stop production on a job currently in progress. If postponing completion of a job in progress will not jeopardize meeting the delivery date on that job, this is not an issue; if postponing the completion of a job in progress will jeopardize meeting the delivery date, then this needs to be taken into account.

Review/Test, pages 103–104

1. forty-five and three hundred two ten-thousandths

2. 209.07086

3. 11.8 million = 11,800,000

4.
   ```
     2 1 2   1 1
     270.93
      97.
       1.976
   +  88.675
   ─────────
     458.581
   ```

5.
   ```
     2 16  9 9 12 9 10
     37.00300
   -  9.23674
   ──────────
     27.76626
   ```

6.
   ```
     10.2  million
   +  3.75 million
   ──────────────
     13.95 million
   ```

7.   Given place value

    |

0.07395

      |

    9 is greater than 5

0.07395 rounded to the
nearest thousandth is
0.074.

8.
$$
\begin{array}{r}
0.369 \\
\times\ 6.7 \\
\hline
2583 \\
2\ 214\ \ \\
\hline
2.4723
\end{array}
$$

9.   58.9 x 1000 = 58,900

10.
$$
\begin{array}{r}
1.7810 \approx 1.781
\end{array}
$$

0.037. |0.065.9000

    - 37

    289

  -259

    300

  -296

     40

    -37

     30

    - 0

11.   61,924 + 10,000 = 6.1924

12.
$$
\begin{array}{r}
0.8 \\
5\overline{\smash)4.0}
\end{array}
$$

13. $0.875 = \frac{875}{1000} = \frac{7}{8}$

14. $6.4 = 6\frac{4}{10} = 6\frac{2}{5}$

15.   730 g = 0.730 kg

16.   820 cm = 8.20 m

17.   Strategy
To find the freight charges:
- Find the total weight by multiplying the number of items (250) by the weight of
each item (16.5 kg).
- Divide the total weight by 100 kg, since the charge is based on the number of 100
kg shipped. Round the quotient up to the nearest whole number.
- Multiply the number of 100 kg transported by the charge per 100 kg ($6.50).

Solution
250 x 16.5 = 4125
4125 + 100 = 41.25 ≈ 42
6.50 x 42 = 273

The freight charges are $273.

18.   12.78 + 9.42 + 10.56 = $32.76

19. $0

20.   3.47 + 4.63 = $8.10

21. $0

22.   4.75 + 3.50 = $8.25

23.   2.85 + 3.16 = $6.01

24.   12.78 + 2.85 = $15.63

25.   9.42 + 3.47 + 4.75 = $17.64

26. $0

27.   4.63 + 3.16 = $7.79

28.   10.56 + 3.50 = $14.06

29.   32.76 + 0 + 8.10 + 0 + 8.25 + 6.01 = $55.12
15.63 + 17.64 + 0 + 7.79 + 14.06 = $55.12

30.   15(29.99) = $449.85

31.   25(9.99) = $249.75

32.   10(49.99) = $499.90

33.   449.85 + 249.75 + 499.90 = $1199.50

CHAPTER 4
Banking

Section 4.1, pages 115–116

1.

<table>
<tr><td colspan="2">East Phoenix Rental Equipment
3011 N. W. Ventura Street
Phoenix, Arizona 85280</td><td>No. 2847</td></tr>
</table>

East Phoenix Rental Equipment
3011 N. W. Ventura Street
Phoenix, Arizona 85280

No. 2847

January 24 19 _95_ 8 – 461 / 1052

PAY TO THE
ORDER OF _Perox Corporation_ $ _145 90/100_

One hundred forty-five and 90/100 ————— DOLLARS

Meyers National Bank
11 N. W. Nova Street
Phoenix, Arizona 85212

Memo _____   _Gloria B. Masters_

|:1052||0461|:5008 2847

2.

DEPOSIT TICKET

East Phoenix
Rental Equipment

DATE _Jan, 25_ 19 _95_

MEYERS NATIONAL BANK
11 N. W. Nova Street
Phoenix, Arizona 85215

CURRENCY		275	00
COIN			
C H E C K S	62-420	398	75
	53-7159	63	50
TOTAL		737	25

BE SURE
EACH ITEM
IS PROPERLY
ENDORSED

|:1052||0461|:5008 287||ᵐ

ITEMS CREDITED SUBJECT TO VERIFICATION AND DEPOSIT AGREEMENT OF THIS BANK.

3. Strategy
    To calculate the balance carried
    forward:
    • Add the deposit to the balance
      brought forward.
    • Subtract the amount of the check
      written.

    Solution
    ```
      1126.20
    + 250.00
    ─────────
      1376.20
    - 193.87
    ─────────
      1182.33
    ```

    The balance carried forward is
    $1182.33.

4. Strategy
    To calculate the balance carried
    forward:
    • Add the deposits to the balance
      brought forward.
    • Subtract the amount of the check
      written.

    Solution
    ```
      2189.52
        351.06      2735.85
    + 195.27      - 327.46
    ─────────      ─────────
      2735.85        2408.39
    ```

    The balance carried forward is
    $2408.39.

5. $247.63

6.  ```
      892.46
    -247.63
    ─────────
    $644.83
    ```

7. $550.00

8.  ```
      644.83
    -550.00
    ─────────
     $94.83
    ```

9. $678.49

10. ```
       94.83
    +678.49
    ─────────
    $773.32
    ```

11. $289.57

12. ```
      1247.63
    - 289.57
    ─────────
    $958.06
    ```

13. $461.06

14. ```
       958.06
    +461.06
    ─────────
    $1419.12
    ```

15. $43.92

16. ```
      1419.12
    -   43.92
    ─────────
    $1375.20
    ```

17. $75.00

18. ```
      1375.20
    -   75.00
    ─────────
    $1300.20
    ```

19. Strategy
    To find the checkbook balance:
    • Subtract the amount of the
      withdrawal and the amount of the
      previous balance.
    • Add the amount of the deposit.

    Solution
    ```
      3476.85
    - 250.00
    ─────────
      3226.85
    - 848.37
    ─────────
      2378.48
    +1048.53
    ─────────
      3427.01
    ```

    The checkbook balance is $3427.01.

20. Strategy
    To find the checkbook balance:
    • Subtract the amount of the purchase
      from the previous balance.
    • Add the amount of each deposit.

    Solution
    ```
      1894.32
    - 187.46
    ─────────
      1706.86
       162.42
    + 259.83
    ─────────
      2129.11
    ```

    The checkbook balance is $2129.11.
    ```

Section 4.2, pages 121–122

1.		2.		3.		4.	
	$387.42		$465.91		$609.84		$1357.84
	+ 47.60		+131.85		+225.39		114.63
	$435.02		$597.76		$835.23		84.97
	-128.97		-276.50		-311.47		+ 286.59
	$306.05		$321.26		$523.76		$1844.03
	- 1.75		- 3.25		+ 2.28		- 526.92
	$304.30		$318.01		$526.04		$1317.11
							+ 5.11
							$1322.22

5.		6.		7.		8.	
	$2943.24		$ 976.83		$3854.32		$2068.41
	387.45		47.92		347.91		378.29
	476.02		502.66		1087.62		550.00
	+ 92.18		+ 275.83		+ 567.53		264.06
	$3898.89		$1803.24		$5857.38		+ 143.75
	- 642.93		- 284.27		-1243.86		$3404.51
	$3255.96		$1518.97		$4613.52		- 575.50
	- 5.50		- 319.60		- 319.60		$2829.01
	$3250.46		$1199.37		$4293.92		- 380.95
			- 3.00		+ 14.46		$2448.06
			$1196.37		$4308.38		- 2.50
							$2445.56

9. List the correct checkbook balance: $2328.03

10. Add the checks outstanding and any additions to the balance:
                                                              Check No. **898** $ 386.25

11.   Check No. **899** $ 192.14

12.   Subtotal: $2906.42

13. Subtract deposits in transit and any bank charges: $ 408.25

14.   Subtotal: $2498.17

15. $ 4.75

16.   Balance $2493.42

Business Case Study

1. Number of checks written per year:
    7 checks monthly (rent, telephone, electricity, car payment,
      newspaper advertisements, 2 credit cards) x 12 months
      = 84 checks per year   84 checks
    2 checks every three months (auto insurance, health insurance)
      x 4 times per year = 8 checks per year   8 checks
    4 checks annually (car registration, dues, trade journal
      subscription, accountant's fee)   4 checks
                                                                    96 checks

    Annual cost of present checking account:
      $3 monthly service fee x 12 months: $36.00
      $.10 per check x 96 checks: 9.60
                                                                    $45.60

Your present business checking account is costing $45.60 per year.

Annual cost of checking account at the other bank:
No fees will be paid for checks written, as in no month are
more than 20 checks drawn on the account.

$5 monthly service fee x 4 months the balance is below $500:	$20
$.50 ATM charge x 2 times a month x 12 months:	12
	$32

An account at the bank that approved your loan will cost $32 per year.

$45.60 - $32 = $13.60

The difference in cost between the two banks is $13.60 per year.

2. Answers will vary. For example:
   The bank that approved your loan has the lower annual cost.
   The bank at which you presently have an account is more convenient, as it is five
   miles closer in distance.
   We might assume that the two banks are equally safe, as they are both members of
   FDIC.
   We might assume that you find the treatment of customers superior at the bank that
   approved your loan, since they approved your loan and the bank at which you
   presently have an account did not approve your loan.
   The bank that approved your loan appears to have a wider range of services, as they
   offer automatic drafting, automatic funds transfer, and use of an ATM.

Review/Test, pages 125–126

1.

East Phoenix Rental Equipment 3011 N. W. Ventura Street Phoenix, Arizona 85280		No. 2936
	February 8 19 *95*	8 – 461 1052
PAY TO THE ORDER OF *White River Company*	$ *342 97/100*	
Three hundred forty-two and 97/100		DOLLARS
Meyers National Bank 11 N. W. Nova Street Phoenix, Arizona 85212		
Memo _____	*Gloria B. Masters*	
⑈1052⑈0461⑈5008 2936		

2.

```
East Phoenix
Rental Equipment


DATE  Feb. 10 19 95

MEYERS NATIONAL BANK
11 N. W. Nova Street
Phoenix, Arizona 85215

|:1052||0461|:5008 287||ⁿ
ITEMS CREDITED SUBJECT TO VERIFICATION AND DEPOSIT AGREEMENT OF THIS BANK.
```

DEPOSIT TICKET

CURRENCY	150	00
COIN		
62-111	247	50
66-72	199	98
TOTAL	597	48

BE SURE
EACH ITEM
IS PROPERLY
ENDORSED

3. Strategy
To calculate the balance carried
forward:
• Add the deposit to the balance
brought forward.
• Subtract the amount of the check
written.

Solution
```
   847.25
 + 268.47
 ────────
  1115.72
 - 319.62
 ────────
   796.10
```

The balance carried forward is
$796.10.

4. Strategy
To calculate the balance carried
forward:
• Add the deposit to the balance
brought forward.
• Subtract the amount of the check
written.

Solution
```
  1680.55
   297.48      2140.12
 + 162.09    - 493.27
 ────────    ────────
  2140.12     1646.85
```

The balance carried forward is
$1646.85.

5. Strategy
To find the checkbook balance:
• Add the amount of the deposit to
the previous balance.
• Subtract the amount of the purchase
and the amount of the check.

Solution
```
$1267.84
+ 392.50
─────────
$1660.34
- 124.33
─────────
$1536.01
- 872.15
─────────
$ 663.86
```

The checkbook balance is $663.86.

6. Strategy
To find the checkbook balance:
• Subtract the amount of the purchase
from the previous balance.
• Add the amount of each deposit.

Solution
```
$618.43
- 93.48
────────
$524.95
 277.90
+175.00
────────
$977.85
```

The checkbook balance is $977.85.

7. $351.08

8. ```
   $ 947.62
   + 351.08
   ────────
   $1298.70
   ```

9. $593.47

10. ```
   $1298.70
   - 593.47
   ────────
   $ 705.23
   ```

11. $260.89

12. $705.23
     +260.89
     ────────
     $966.12

13. $150.00

14. $966.12
     −150.00
     ────────
     $816.12

15. $1286.43
       239.70
        91.87
     + 306.45
     ─────────
     $1924.45
     − 481.93
     ─────────
     $1442.52
     − 162.58
     ─────────
     $1279.94
     −   4.00
     ─────────
     $1275.94

16. $1945.36
       432.38
       647.92
        35.25
     + 183.44
     ─────────
     $3244.35
     − 549.27
     ─────────
     $2695.08
     − 392.64
     ─────────
     $2302.44
     +   7.29
     ─────────
     $2309.73

CHAPTER 5
Equations

Section 5.1, pages 135–136

1.
$$x + 2.3 = 7.8$$
$$5.5 + 2.3 \mid 7.8$$
$$7.8 = 7.8$$

Yes, 5.5 is a solution of the equation $x + 2.3 = 7.8$.

2.
$$12.2 - y = 2.6$$
$$12.2 - 9.6 \mid 2.6$$
$$2.6 = 2.6$$

Yes, 9.6 is a solution of the equation $12.2 - y = 2.6$.

3.
$$3n = 7.4$$
$$3(2.4) \mid 7.4$$
$$7.2 \neq 7.4$$

No, 2.4 is not a solution of the equation $3n = 7.4$.

4.
$$15.5 = 2.5V$$
$$15.5 \mid 2.5(6.1)$$
$$15.5 \neq 15.25$$

No, 6.1 is not a solution of the equation $15.5 = 2.5V$.

5.
$$15 = \frac{3}{4}T$$
$$15 \mid \frac{3}{4}(20)$$
$$15 = 15$$

Yes, 20 is a solution of the equation $15 = \frac{3}{4}T$.

6.
$$25P = 10$$
$$25\left(\frac{2}{5}\right) \mid 10$$
$$10 = 10$$

Yes, $\frac{2}{5}$ is a solution of the equation $25P = 10$.

7.
$$d + 5 = 7$$
$$d + 5 - 5 = 7 - 5$$
$$d = 2$$

The solution is 2.

8.
$$y + 3 = 9$$
$$y + 3 - 3 = 9 - 3$$
$$y = 6$$

The solution is 6.

9.
$$b - 4 = 11$$
$$b - 4 + 4 = 11 + 4$$
$$b = 15$$

The solution is 15.

10.
$$z - 6 = 10$$
$$z - 6 + 6 = 10 + 6$$
$$z = 16$$

The solution is 16.

11.
$$2 + A = 8$$
$$2 - 2 + A = 8 - 2$$
$$A = 6$$

The solution is 6.

12.
$$5 + L = 12$$
$$5 - 5 + L = 12 - 5$$
$$L = 7$$

The solution is 7.

13.
$$10 = 4 + c$$
$$10 - 4 = 4 - 4 + c$$
$$6 = c$$

The solution is 6.

14.
$$12 = 3 + w$$
$$12 - 3 = 3 - 3 + w$$
$$9 = w$$

The solution is 9.

15.
$$5 = m - 3$$
$$5 + 3 = m - 3 + 3$$
$$8 = m$$

The solution is 8.

16. $7 = n - 2$
$7 + 2 = n - 2 + 2$
$9 = n$

The solution is 9.

17. $5R = 15$
$\frac{5R}{5} = \frac{15}{5}$
$R = 3$

The solution is 3.

18. $4T = 28$
$\frac{4T}{4} = \frac{28}{4}$
$T = 7$

The solution is 7.

19. $20 = 4D$
$\frac{20}{4} = \frac{4D}{4}$
$5 = D$

The solution is 5.

20. $18 = 2S$
$\frac{18}{2} = \frac{2S}{2}$
$9 = S$

The solution is 9.

21. $N = 3.9 + 8.72$
$N = 12.62$

The solution is 12.62.

22. $M = 261.5 - 77.9$
$M = 183.6$

The solution is 183.6.

23. $a = 49.6 - 25.7$
$a = 23.9$

The solution is 23.9.

24. $f = 0.342 + 0.164$
$f = 0.506$

The solution is 0.506.

25. $F + 1.7 = 5.4$
$F + 1.7 - 1.7 = 5.4 - 1.7$
$F = 3.7$

The solution is 3.7.

26. $V + 3.6 = 9.2$
$V + 3.6 - 3.6 = 9.2 - 3.6$
$V = 5.6$

The solution is 5.6.

27. $P - 8.1 = 4.3$
$P - 8.1 + 8.1 = 4.3 + 8.1$
$P = 12.4$

The solution is 12.4.

28. $r - 2.7 = 3.6$
$r - 2.7 + 2.7 = 3.6 + 2.7$
$r = 6.3$

The solution is 6.3.

29. $\frac{5}{8} = s + \frac{1}{8}$
$\frac{5}{8} - \frac{1}{8} = s + \frac{1}{8} - \frac{1}{8}$
$\frac{4}{8} = s$
$\frac{1}{2} = s$

The solution is $\frac{1}{2}$.

30. $\frac{5}{6} = x + \frac{1}{6}$
$\frac{5}{6} - \frac{1}{6} = x + \frac{1}{6} - \frac{1}{6}$
$\frac{4}{6} = x$
$\frac{2}{3} = x$

The solution is $\frac{2}{3}$.

31. $6.4t = 128$
$\frac{6.4t}{6.4} = \frac{128}{6.4}$
$t = 20$

The solution is 20.

32. $2.7v = 3.24$
$\frac{2.7v}{2.7} = \frac{3.24}{2.7}$
$v = 1.2$

The solution is 1.2.

33. $54 = 0.15W$
$\frac{54}{0.15} = \frac{0.15W}{0.15}$
$360 = W$

The solution is 360.

34. $36 = 0.75C$
$\frac{36}{0.75} = \frac{0.75C}{0.75}$
$48 = C$

The solution is 48.

35. $3486 = 2910 + P$
$3486 - 2910 = 2910 - 2910 + P$
$576 = P$

The solution is 576.

36. $12,475 = 8602 + B$
$12,475 - 8602 = 8602 - 8602 + B$
$3873 = B$

The solution is 3873.

37. $62.58 = G - 47.30$
$62.58 + 47.30 = G - 47.30 + 47.30$
$109.88 = G$

The solution is 109.88.

38.
$$902.74 = H - 381.66$$
$$902.74 + 381.66 = H - 381.66 + 381.66$$
$$1284.40 = H$$

The solution is 1284.40.

39.
$$88 = d(0.55)$$
$$\frac{88}{0.55} = \frac{d(0.55)}{0.55}$$
$$160 = d$$

The solution is 160.

40.
$$75 = b(1.2)$$
$$\frac{75}{1.2} = \frac{b(1.2)}{1.2}$$
$$62.5 = b$$

The solution is 62.5.

41.
$$A(3.6) = 90$$
$$\frac{A(3.6)}{3.6} = \frac{90}{3.6}$$
$$A = 25$$

The solution is 25.

42.
$$L(4.2) = 63$$
$$\frac{L(4.2)}{4.2} = \frac{63}{4.2}$$
$$L = 15$$

The solution is 15.

43.
$$874.35 = R + 362.19$$
$$874.35 - 362.19 = R + 362.19 - 362.19$$
$$512.16 = R$$

The solution is 512.16.

44.
$$620.47 = T + 493.55$$
$$620.47 - 493.55 = T + 493.55 - 493.55$$
$$126.92 = T$$

The solution is 126.92.

Section 5.2, pages 139–140

1. Strategy
   To find the monthly payment:
   - Replace the variables A and N in the formula by the given values ($A = 864$, $N = 12$).
   - Solve the equation for P.

   Solution
   $$A = P \cdot N$$
   $$864 = P \cdot 12$$
   $$\frac{864}{12} = \frac{P \cdot 12}{12}$$
   $$72 = P$$

   The monthly payment is $72.

2. Strategy
   To find the monthly payment:
   - Replace the variables A and N in the formula by the given values ($A = 3000$, $N = 8$).
   - Solve the equation for P.

   Solution
   $$A = P \cdot N$$
   $$3000 = P \cdot 8$$
   $$\frac{3000}{8} = \frac{P \cdot 8}{8}$$
   $$375 = P$$

   The monthly payment is $375.

3. Strategy
   To find the number of monthly payments in which the debt is repaid:
   - Replace the variables A and P in the formula by the given values ($A = 5400$, $P = 180$).
   - Solve the equation for N.

   Solution
   $$A = P \cdot N$$
   $$5400 = 180 \cdot N$$
   $$\frac{5400}{180} = \frac{180 \cdot N}{180}$$
   $$30 = N$$

   The debt is repaid in 30 payments.

4. Strategy
   To find the number of months in which the debt is repaid:
   - Replace the variables A and P in the formula by the given values ($A = 4500$, $P = 375$).
   - Solve the equation for N.

   Solution
   $$A = P \cdot N$$
   $$4500 = 375 \cdot N$$
   $$\frac{4500}{375} = \frac{375 \cdot N}{375}$$
   $$12 = N$$

   The debt is repaid in 12 months.

5. Strategy
    To find the increase in value:
    - Replace the variables *A* and *P* in the formula by the given values ($A = 3000$, $P = 1800$).
    - Solve the equation for *I*.

    Solution
    $$A = P + I$$
    $$3000 = 1800 + I$$
    $$3000 - 1800 = 1800 - 1800 + I$$
    $$1200 = I$$

    The increase in value of the investment is $1200.

6. Strategy
    To find the increase in value:
    - Replace the variables *A* and *P* in the formula by the given values ($A = 5700$, $P = 4900$).
    - Solve the equation for *I*.

    Solution
    $$A = P + I$$
    $$5700 = 4900 + I$$
    $$5700 - 4900 = 4900 - 4900 + I$$
    $$800 = I$$

    The increase in value of the investment is $800.

7. Strategy
    To find the amount of the original investment:
    - Replace the variables *A* and *I* in the formula by the given values ($A = 17,000$, $I = 3500$).
    - Solve the equation for *P*.

    Solution
    $$A = P + I$$
    $$17,000 = P + 3500$$
    $$17,000 - 3500 = P + 3500 - 3500$$
    $$13,500 = P$$

    The original investment was $13,500.

8. Strategy
    To find the amount of the original investment:
    - Replace the variables *A* and *I* in the formula by the given values ($A = 23,000$, $I = 2500$).
    - Solve the equation for *P*.

    Solution
    $$A = P + I$$
    $$23,000 = P + 2500$$
    $$23,000 - 2500 = P + 2500 - 2500$$
    $$20,500 = P$$

    The original investment was $20,500.

9. Strategy
    To find the equity:
    - Replace the variables *V* and *L* in the formula by the given values ($V = 125,000$, $L = 67,853.25$).
    - Solve the formula for *E*.

    Solution
    $$E = V - L$$
    $$E = 125,000 - 67,853.25$$
    $$E = 57,146.75$$

    The equity is $57,146.75.

10. Strategy
    To find the equity:
    - Replace the variables *V* and *L* in the formula by the given values ($V = 240,000$, $L = 142,976.80$).
    - Solve the formula for *E*.

    Solution
    $$E = V - L$$
    $$E = 240,000 - 142,976.80$$
    $$E = 97,023.20$$

    The equity is $97,023.20.

11. Strategy
    To find the loan amount:
    • Replace the variables E and V in
      the formula by the given values
      ($E = 28,500$, $V = 167,000$).
    • Solve the formula for L.

    Solution
    $$E = V - L$$
    $$28,500 = 167,000 - L$$
    $$28,500 + L = 167,000 - L + L$$
    $$28,500 + L = 167,000$$
    $$28,500 - 28,500 + L = 167,000 - 28,500$$
    $$L = 138,500$$

    The loan amount is $138,500.

12. Strategy
    To find the loan amount:
    • Replace the variables E and V in
      the formula by the given values
      ($E = 36,500$, $V = 98,000$).
    • Solve the formula for L.

    Solution
    $$E = V - L$$
    $$36,500 = 98,000 - L$$
    $$36,500 + L = 98,000 - L + L$$
    $$36,500 + L = 98,000$$
    $$36,500 - 36,500 + L = 98,000 - 36,500$$
    $$L = 61,500$$

    The loan amount is $61,500.

13. Strategy
    To find the selling price:
    • Replace the variables M and D in
      the formula by the given values
      ($M = 130,500$, $D = 14,500$).
    • Solve the formula for S.

    Solution
    $$M = S - D$$
    $$130,500 = S - 14,500$$
    $$130,500 + 14,500 = S - 14,500 + 14,500$$
    $$145,000 = S$$

    The selling price was $145,000.

14. Strategy
    To find the selling price:
    • Replace the variables M and D in
      the formula by the given values
      ($M = 94,400$, $D = 23,600$).
    • Solve the formula for S.

    Solution
    $$M = S - D$$
    $$94,400 = S - 23,600$$
    $$94,400 + 23,600 = S - 23,600 + 23,600$$
    $$118,000 = S$$

    The selling price was $118,000.

15. Strategy
    To find the rate per line:
    • Replace the variables C and N in
      the formula by the given values
      ($C = 340.80$, $N = 480$).
    • Solve the formula for R.

    Solution
    $$C = N \cdot R$$
    $$340.80 = 480 \cdot R$$
    $$\frac{348.80}{480} = \frac{480 \cdot R}{480}$$
    $$0.71 = R$$

    The rate per line is $.71.

16. Strategy
    To find the rate per line:
    • Replace the variables C and N in
      the formula by the given values
      ($C = 95.20$, $N = 140$).
    • Solve the formula for R.

    Solution
    $$C = N \cdot R$$
    $$95.20 = 140 \cdot R$$
    $$\frac{95.20}{140} = \frac{140 \cdot R}{140}$$
    $$0.68 = R$$

    The rate per line is $.68.

17. Strategy
     To find the cost:
     • Replace the variables w, t, and k
       in the formula by the given values
       (w = 1800, t = 5, k = 0.006).
     • Solve the formula for c.

     Solution
     $c = \frac{1}{1000} wtk$
     $c = \frac{1}{1000} (1800)(5)(0.06)$
     $c = 1.8(5)(0.06) = 9(0.06) = 0.54$

     The cost is $.54.

18. Strategy
     To find the cost:
     • Replace the variables w, t, and k
       in the formula by the given values
       (w = 200, t = 3, k = 0.10).
     • Solve the formula for c.

     Solution
     $c = \frac{1}{1000} wtk$
     $c = \frac{1}{1000} (200)(3)(0.10)$
     $c = 0.2(3)(0.10) = 0.6(0.10) = 0.06$

     The cost is $.06.

19. Strategy
     To find the cost per kilowatt-hour:
     • Replace the variables c, w, and t
       in the formula by the given values
       (c = 0.08, w = 250, t = 4).
     • Solve the formula for k.

     Solution
     $c = \frac{1}{1000} wtk$
     $0.08 = \frac{1}{1000} (250)(4)k$
     $0.08 = 0.250(4)k$
     $0.08 = 1k$
     $0.08 = k$

     The cost per kilowatt-hour is $.08.

20. Strategy
     To find the cost per kilowatt-hour:
     • Replace the variables c, w, and t
       in the formula by the given values
       (c = 0.28, w = 2000, t = 2).
     • Solve the formula for k.

     Solution
     $c = \frac{1}{1000} wtk$
     $0.28 = \frac{1}{1000} (2000)(2)k$
     $0.28 = 2(2)k$
     $0.28 = 4k$
     $\frac{0.28}{4} = \frac{4k}{4}$
     $0.07 = k$

     The cost per kilowatt-hour is $.07.

Section 5.3, pages 143–144

1. Strategy
    To express the amount of peanuts in
    terms of the amount of cashews:
    • Assign a variable to the amount of
      cashews.
    • Express the amount of peanuts in
      terms of the assigned variable.

    Solution
    Amount of cashews: c
    The amount of peanuts is 3
    times the amount of cashews: $3c$

2. Strategy
    To express the dividend paid in terms
    of the price of the stock:
    • Assign a variable to the price of
      the stock.
    • Express the dividend paid in terms
      of the assigned variable.

    Solution
    Price of the stock: p
    The dividend paid is one-twentieth
    the price of the stock: $\frac{1}{20}p$

3. Strategy
   To express the amount of mocha java beans in terms of the amount of espresso beans:
   • Assign a variable to the amount of espresso beans.
   • Express the amount of mocha java beans in terms of the assigned variable.

   Solution
   Amount of espresso beans: e
   The amount of mocha java beans is 35 pounds more than the amount of the espresso beans: $e + 35$

4. Strategy
   To express the number served on Thursday in terms of the number served on Friday:
   • Assign a variable to the number served on Friday.
   • Express the number served on Thursday in terms of the assigned variable.

   Solution
   Number of customers served on Friday: F
   The number of customers served on Thursday was 145 less than were served on Friday: $F - 145$

5. Strategy
   To express the number of hours the store is open on Sunday in terms of the number of hours it is open on Saturday:
   • Assign a variable to the number of hours the store is open on Saturday.
   • Express the number of hours the store is open on Sunday in terms of the assigned variable.

   Solution
   Number of hours it is open on Saturday: N
   The number of hours it is open on Sunday is 4 less than the number it is open on Saturday: $N - 4$

6. Strategy
   To express the number of Nikes ordered in a women's size 7 in terms of the number ordered in a women's size 11:
   • Assign a variable to the number ordered in a women's size 11.
   • Express the number ordered in a women's size 7 in terms of the assigned variable.

   Solution
   Number ordered in a women's size 11: N
   The number ordered in a women's size 7 is 8 times the number ordered in a size 11: $8N$

7. Strategy
   To express the amount the customer spent this month in terms of the amount spent last month:
   • Assign a variable to the amount spent last month.
   • Express the amount spent this month in terms of the assigned variable.

   Solution
   Amount spent last month: A
   The amount spent this month is 18.75 more than the amount spent last month: $A + 18.75$

8. Strategy
   To express the number of requests during the weekend in terms of the number of requests during the weekdays:
   • Assign a variable to the number of requests during the weekdays.
   • Express the number of requests during the weekend in terms of the assigned variable.

   Solution
   Number of requests during the weekdays: R
   The number of requests during the weekend was 16 more than the number during the weekdays: $R + 16$

9. **Strategy**
   To express the Consumer Price Index for energy in 1990 in terms of the Consumer Price Index for energy in 1970:
   - Assign a variable to the index in 1970.
   - Express the index in 1990 in terms of the assigned variable.

   Solution
   Consumer Price Index for energy in 1970: I
   The index in 1990 was 4 times the index in 1970: $4I$

11. **Strategy**
    To find the number of bytes that can be stored on a low-density disk:
    - Assign a variable to the number that can be stored on a low-density disk.
    - Write two expressions for the same value.
    - Write and solve an equation.

    Solution
    Number of bytes that can be stored on a low-density disk: L

    | 1,400,000 | is | five times as much as can be stored on a low-density disk. |

    $$1{,}400{,}000 = 5L$$
    $$\frac{1{,}400{,}000}{5} = \frac{5L}{5}$$
    $$280{,}000 = L$$

    280,000 bytes can be stored on a low-density disk.

10. **Strategy**
    To express the number of pixels displayed horizontally in terms of the number displayed vertically:
    - Assign a variable to the number displayed vertically.
    - Express the number displayed horizontally in terms of the assigned variable.

    Solution
    The number of pixels displayed vertically: P
    The number of pixels displayed horizontally is 170 more than the number displayed vertically: $P + 170$

12. **Strategy**
    To find the length of the screen:
    - Assign a variable to the length of the screen.
    - Write two expressions for the same value.
    - Write and solve an equation.

    Solution
    The length of the screen: L

    | 15 | is | 0.75 times the length of the screen. |

    $$15 = 0.75L$$
    $$\frac{15}{0.75} = \frac{0.75L}{0.75}$$
    $$20 = L$$

    The length of the computer monitor screen is 20 inches.

13. Strategy
    To find the per capita personal income in 1980:
    • Assign a variable to the per capita personal income in 1980.
    • Write two expressions for the same value.
    • Write and solve an equation.

    Solution
    The per capita personal income in 1980: I

18,696	is	8786 more than the per capita personal income in 1980.

    $$18,696 = I + 8786$$
    $$18,696 - 8786 = I + 8786 - 8786$$
    $$9910 = I$$

    The per capita personal income in 1980 was $9910.

14. Strategy
    To find the median income in 1980:
    • Assign a variable to the median family income in 1980.
    • Write two expressions for the same value.
    • Write and solve an equation.

    Solution
    The median family income in 1980: M

33,956	is	12,933 more than the median family income in 1980.

    $$33,956 = M + 12,933$$
    $$33,956 - 12,933 = M + 12,933 - 12,933$$
    $$21,023 = M$$

    The median family income in 1980 was $21,023.

15. Strategy
    To find the average amount spent on nondurable goods by a U.S. consumer in 1990:
    • Assign a variable to the amount spent on nondurable goods in 1990.
    • Write two expressions for the same value.
    • Write and solve an equation.

    Solution
    Amount spent on nondurable goods in 1990: A

1910	is	2838 less than the amount spent on nondurable goods in 1990.

    $$1910 = A - 2838$$
    $$1910 + 2838 = A - 2838 + 2838$$
    $$4748 = A$$

    The average amount spent on nondurable goods by a U.S. consumer in 1990 was $4748.

16. Strategy
    To find the number of housing starts in the United States in 1990:
    • Assign a variable to the number of housing starts in 1990.
    • Write two expressions for the same value.
    • Write and solve an equation.

    Solution
    Number of housing starts in 1990: H

1,014,000	is	179,000 less housing starts than in 1990.

    $$1,014,000 = H - 179,000$$
    $$1,014,000 + 179,000 = H - 179,000 + 179,000$$
    $$1,193,000 = H$$

    The number of housing starts in the United States in 1990 was 1,193,000.

17. Strategy
    To find the number of passenger cars
    made in the United States and sold in
    foreign countries in 1990:
    • Assign a variable to the number of
      cars made in the United States and
      sold in foreign countries.
    • Write two expressions for the same
      value.
    • Write and solve an equation.

    Solution
    The number of cars made in the United
    States and sold in foreign countries
    in 1990: N

5,502,000	is	10 times the number made in the U.S. and sold in foreign countries.

    $$5,502,000 = 10N$$
    $$\frac{5,502,000}{10} = \frac{10N}{10}$$
    $$550,200 = N$$

    550,200 passenger cars were made in
    the United States and sold in foreign
    countries in 1990.

18. Strategy
    To find the circulation of *Family
    Circle:*
    • Assign a variable to the
      circulation of *Family Circle.*
    • Write two expressions for the same
      value.
    • Write and solve an equation.

    Solution
    The circulation of *Family Circle: C*

15,000,000	is	3 times the circulation of *Family Circle.*

    $$15,000,000 = 3C$$
    $$\frac{15,000,000}{3} = \frac{3C}{3}$$
    $$5,000,000 = C$$

    The circulation of *Family Circle* is
    5,000,000.

19. Strategy
    To find PepsiCo's total sales in 1991:
    • Assign a variable to PepsiCo's
      total sales.
    • Write two expressions for the same
      value.
    • Write and solve an equation.

    Solution
    PepsiCo's total sales: P

11,571.6 million	is	8199.6 million less than PepsiCo's total sales.

    $$11,571.6 = P - 8199.6$$
    $$11,571.6 + 8199.6 = P - 8199.6 + 8199.6$$
    $$19,771.2 = P$$

    PepsiCo's total sales in 1991 were
    $19,771.2 million.

20. Strategy
    To find the operating revenues of
    Federal Express in 1991:
    • Assign a variable to the operating
      revenues of Federal Express.
    • Write two expressions for the same
      value.
    • Write and solve an equation.

    Solution
    The operating revenues of Federal
    Express: F

15,047.4 million	is	7359.1 million more than the operating revenues of Federal Express.

    $$15,047.4 = F + 7359.1$$
    $$15,047.4 - 7359.1 = F + 7359.1 - 7359.1$$
    $$7688.3 = F$$

    The operating revenues of Federal
    Express in 1991 were $7688.3 million.

Business Case Study

1. Use the formula $B = \dfrac{F}{S-V}$, since F, S, and V are known and B is being determined.

   $B = \dfrac{F}{S-V} = \dfrac{24,000}{230-80} = \dfrac{24,000}{150} = 160$

   When the selling price of a chair is $230, the break-even point is 160 chairs.
   Total sales = number of chairs sold x selling price per chair = 160 x 230 = 36,800
   The total sales would be $36,800.

2. Use the formula $S = \dfrac{F+BV}{B}$, since F, B, and V are known and S is being determined.

   $S = \dfrac{F+BV}{B} = \dfrac{24,000 + (120)(80)}{120} = \dfrac{24,000 + 9600}{120} = \dfrac{33,600}{120} = 280$

   When the break-even point is 120 chairs, the selling price is $280 per chair.

3. $B = \dfrac{F}{S-V} = \dfrac{24,000}{250-80} = \dfrac{24,000}{170} \approx 141$ chairs

   At a selling price of $250 per chair, the break-even point is about 141 chairs.
   Since 141 is greater than 130, the company did not reach the break-even point and
   the company lost money.

Review/Test, pages 147–148

1. $\dfrac{d + 3.92 = 8.62}{4.7 + 3.92 \mid 8.62}$
   $\qquad\qquad 8.62 = 8.62$

   Yes, 4.7 is a solution
   of the equation
   $d + 3.92 = 8.62$.

2. $\dfrac{10.9 = 4.7t}{10.9 \mid 4.7(2.3)}$
   $\quad 10.9 \neq 10.81$

   No, 2.3 is a not a
   solution of the
   equation $10.9 = 4.7t$.

3. $M = 247.50 - 184.75$
   $M = 62.75$

   The solution is 62.75.

4. $F - 18 = 32$
   $F - 18 + 18 = 32 + 18$
   $\qquad\quad F = 50$

   The solution is 50.

5. $0.90R = 18$
   $\dfrac{0.90R}{0.90} = \dfrac{18}{0.90}$
   $\quad R = 20$

   The solution is 20.

6. $4.9 + C = 8.7$
   $4.9 - 4.9 + C = 8.7 - 4.9$
   $\qquad\qquad C = 3.8$

   The solution is 3.8.

7. $11.2 = 6.3 + b$
   $11.2 - 6.3 = 6.3 - 6.3 + b$
   $\quad 4.9 = b$

8. $48 = 0.75S$
   $\dfrac{48}{0.75} = \dfrac{0.75S}{0.75}$
   $\quad 64 = S$

   The solution is 64.

9. $2.46 = P - 8.19$
   $2.46 + 8.19 = P - 8.19 + 8.19$
   $\quad 10.65 = P$

   The solution is 10.65.

10. $1.36 = N + 0.59$
    $1.36 - 0.59 = N + 0.59 - 0.59$
    $\qquad 0.77 = N$

    The solution is 0.77.

11.
$$\frac{3}{8} + n = \frac{5}{8}$$
$$\frac{3}{8} - \frac{3}{8} + n = \frac{5}{8} - \frac{3}{8}$$
$$n = \frac{2}{8}$$
$$n = \frac{1}{4}$$

The solution is $\frac{1}{4}$.

12.
$$72 = B(0.45)$$
$$\frac{72}{0.45} = \frac{B(0.45)}{0.45}$$
$$160 = B$$

The solution is 160.

13. **Strategy**
To find the number of months in which the debt will be paid off:
• Replace the variables A and P in the formula by the given values ($A = 2760$, $P = 345$).
• Solve the equation for N.

Solution
$$A = P \cdot N$$
$$2760 = 345 \cdot N$$
$$\frac{2760}{345} = \frac{345 \cdot N}{345}$$
$$8 = N$$

The debt will be paid off in 8 months.

14. **Strategy**
To find the increase in value of the investment:
• Replace the variables A and P in the formula by the given values ($A = 2800$, $P = 2150$).
• Solve the equation for I.

Solution
$$A = P + I$$
$$2800 = 2150 + I$$
$$2800 - 2150 = 2150 - 2150 + I$$
$$650 = I$$

The increase in value of the investment is $650.

15. **Strategy**
To find the selling price:
• Replace the variables M and D in the formula by the given values ($M = 75,600$, $D = 18,900$).
• Solve the formula for S.

Solution
$$M = S - D$$
$$75,600 = S - 18,900$$
$$75,600 + 18,900 = S - 18,900 + 18,900$$
$$94,500 = S$$

The selling price was $94,500.

16. **Strategy**
To find the cost per kilowatt-hour:
• Replace the variables c, w, and t in the formula by the given values ($c = 0.81$, $w = 1800$, $t = 5$).
• Solve the formula for k.

Solution
$$c = \frac{1}{1000} wtk$$
$$0.81 = \frac{1}{1000}(1800)(5)k$$
$$0.81 = 1.8(5)k$$
$$0.81 = 9k$$
$$\frac{0.81}{9} = \frac{9k}{9}$$
$$0.09 = k$$

The cost per kilowatt-hour is $.09.

58 *Chapter 5*

17. To express the circulation of the Sunday edition in terms of the circulation of the weekday morning edition:
    • Assign a variable to the circulation of the weekday morning edition.
    • Express the circulation of the Sunday edition in terms of the assigned variable.

    Solution
    Circulation of the weekday morning edition: C

    The circulation of the Sunday edition is 570,000 more than the circulation of the weekday morning edition:
    $C + 570,000$

19. Strategy
    To find the per capita property tax in 1980:
    • Assign a variable to the per capita property tax in 1980.
    • Write two expressions for the same value.
    • Write and solve an equation.

    Solution
    The per capita property tax in 1980: T

626	is	324 more than the per capita property tax in 1980.

    $$626 = T + 324$$
    $$626 - 324 = T + 324 - 324$$
    $$302 = T$$

    The per capita property tax in 1980 was $302.

18. Strategy
    To express the amount of freight carried by railroads in terms of the amount of freight carried by air carriers:
    • Assign a variable to the amount of freight carried by air carriers.
    • Express the amount of freight carried by railroads in terms of the assigned variable.

    Solution
    Amount of freight carried by air carriers: F

    The amount of freight carried by railroads is 10 times the amount carried by air carriers: $10F$

20. Strategy
    To find J.C. Penney's total sales in 1991:
    • Assign a variable to J.C. Penney's total sales in 1991.
    • Write two expressions for the same value.
    • Write and solve an equation.

    Solution
    J.C. Penney's total sales in 1991: S

34,969 million	is	twice J.C. Penney's total sales.

    $$34,969 = 2S$$
    $$\frac{34,969}{2} = \frac{2S}{2}$$
    $$17,484.5 = S$$

    J.C. Penney's total sales in 1991 were approximately $17,484.5 million.

CHAPTER 6
Percent and Business Applications

Section 6.1, pages 153–154

1. $25\% = 25\left(\frac{1}{100}\right) = \frac{25}{100} = \frac{1}{4}$
   $25\% = 25(0.01) = 0.25$

2. $40\% = 40\left(\frac{1}{100}\right) = \frac{40}{100} = \frac{2}{5}$
   $40\% = 40(0.01) = 0.4$

3. $130\% = 130\left(\frac{1}{100}\right) = \frac{130}{100} = 1\frac{3}{10}$
   $130\% = 130(0.01) = 1.3$

4. $150\% = 150\left(\frac{1}{100}\right) = \frac{150}{100} = 1\frac{1}{2}$
   $150\% = 150(0.01) = 1.5$

5. $100\% = 100\left(\frac{1}{100}\right) = \frac{100}{100} = 1$
   $100\% = 100(0.01) = 1.0$

6. $425\% = 425\left(\frac{1}{100}\right) = \frac{425}{100} = 4\frac{1}{4}$
   $425\% = 425(0.01) = 4.25$

7. $70\% = 70\left(\frac{1}{100}\right) = \frac{70}{100} = \frac{7}{10}$
   $70\% = 70(0.01) = 0.7$

8. $55\% = 55\left(\frac{1}{100}\right) = \frac{55}{100} = \frac{11}{20}$
   $55\% = 55(0.01) = 0.55$

9. $45\% = 45\left(\frac{1}{100}\right) = \frac{45}{100} = \frac{9}{20}$
   $45\% = 45(0.01) = 0.45$

10. $90\% = 90\left(\frac{1}{100}\right) = \frac{90}{100} = \frac{9}{10}$
    $90\% = 90(0.01) = 0.9$

11. $64\% = 64\left(\frac{1}{100}\right) = \frac{64}{100} = \frac{16}{25}$
    $64\% = 64(0.01) = 0.64$

12. $32\% = 32\left(\frac{1}{100}\right) = \frac{32}{100} = \frac{8}{25}$
    $32\% = 32(0.01) = 0.32$

13. $8\% = 8\left(\frac{1}{100}\right) = \frac{8}{100} = \frac{2}{25}$
    $8\% = 8(0.01) = 0.08$

14. $6\% = 6\left(\frac{1}{100}\right) = \frac{6}{100} = \frac{3}{50}$
    $6\% = 6(0.01) = 0.06$

15. $1\% = 1\left(\frac{1}{100}\right) = \frac{1}{100}$
    $1\% = 1(0.01) = 0.01$

16. $66\frac{2}{3}\% = 66\frac{2}{3}\left(\frac{1}{100}\right) = \frac{200}{3}\left(\frac{1}{100}\right) = \frac{2}{3}$

17. $12\frac{1}{2}\% = 12\frac{1}{2}\left(\frac{1}{100}\right) = \frac{25}{2}\left(\frac{1}{100}\right) = \frac{1}{8}$

18. $3\frac{1}{8}\% = 3\frac{1}{8}\left(\frac{1}{100}\right) = \frac{25}{8}\left(\frac{1}{100}\right) = \frac{1}{32}$

19. $11\frac{1}{9}\% = 11\frac{1}{9}\left(\frac{1}{100}\right) = \frac{100}{9}\left(\frac{1}{100}\right) = \frac{1}{9}$

20. $37\frac{1}{2}\% = 37\frac{1}{2}\left(\frac{1}{100}\right) = \frac{75}{2}\left(\frac{1}{100}\right) = \frac{3}{8}$

21. $6.5\% = 6.5(0.01) = 0.065$

22. $8.25\% = 8.25(0.01) = 0.0825$

23. $12.3\% = 12.3(0.01) = 0.123$

24. $80.4\% = 80.4(0.01) = 0.804$

25. $2\% = 2(0.01) = 0.02$

26. $0.16 = 0.16(100\%) = 16\%$

27. $0.73 = 0.73(100\%) = 73\%$

28. $0.59 = 0.59(100\%) = 59\%$

29. $0.82 = 0.82(100\%) = 82\%$

30. $0.05 = 0.05(100\%) = 5\%$

31. $0.01 = 0.01(100\%) = 1\%$

32. $0.7 = 0.7(100\%) = 70\%$

33. $0.9 = 0.9(100\%) = 90\%$

34. $0.2 = 0.2(100\%) = 20\%$

35. $0.8 = 0.8(100\%) = 80\%$

36. $1.24 = 1.24(100\%) = 124\%$

37. $1.37 = 1.37(100\%) = 137\%$

38. $1.1 = 1.1(100\%) = 110\%$

39. $0.004 = 0.004(100\%) = 0.4\%$

40. $0.006 = 0.006(100\%) = 0.6\%$

41. $\dfrac{37}{100} = \dfrac{37}{100}(100\%) = \dfrac{3700}{100}\% = 37\%$

42. $\dfrac{1}{3} = \dfrac{1}{3}(100\%) = \dfrac{100}{3}\% \approx 33.3\%$

43. $\dfrac{2}{5} = \dfrac{2}{5}(100\%) = \dfrac{200}{5}\% = 40\%$

44. $\dfrac{5}{8} = \dfrac{5}{8}(100\%) = \dfrac{500}{8}\% = 62.5\%$

45. $\dfrac{1}{6} = \dfrac{1}{6}(100\%) = \dfrac{100}{6}\% \approx 16.7\%$

46. $\dfrac{1}{3} = \dfrac{1}{3}(100\%) = \dfrac{100}{3}\% = 33\dfrac{1}{3}\%$

47. $\dfrac{1}{12} = \dfrac{1}{12}(100\%) = \dfrac{100}{12}\% = 8\dfrac{1}{3}\%$

48. $\dfrac{2}{9} = \dfrac{2}{9}(100\%) = \dfrac{200}{9}\% = 22\dfrac{2}{9}\%$

49. $1\dfrac{2}{3} = 1\dfrac{2}{3}(100\%) = \dfrac{5}{3}(100\%) = \dfrac{500}{3}\% = 166\dfrac{2}{3}\%$

50. $\dfrac{1}{8} = \dfrac{1}{8}(100\%) = \dfrac{100}{8}\% = 12\dfrac{1}{2}\%$

Section 6.2, pages 159–160

1.
$$P = B \times R$$
$$12 = 50 \cdot R$$
$$\dfrac{12}{50} = \dfrac{50 \cdot R}{50}$$
$$0.24 = R$$
$$24\% = R$$

12 is 24% of 50.

2.
$$P = B \times R$$
$$50 = 125 \cdot R$$
$$\dfrac{50}{125} = \dfrac{125 \cdot R}{125}$$
$$0.4 = R$$
$$40\% = R$$

40% of 125 is 50.

3.
$$P = B \times R$$
$$P = 40(0.18)$$
$$P = 7.2$$

18% of 40 is 7.2.

4.
$$P = B \times R$$
$$P = 60(0.25)$$
$$P = 15$$

25% of 60 is 15.

5.
$$P = B \times R$$
$$48 = B(0.12)$$
$$\dfrac{48}{0.12} = \dfrac{B(0.12)}{0.12}$$
$$400 = B$$

12% of 400 is 48.

6.
$$P = B \times R$$
$$9 = B(0.45)$$
$$\dfrac{9}{0.45} = \dfrac{B(0.45)}{0.45}$$
$$20 = B$$

45% of 20 is 9.

7.
$$P = B \times R$$
$$P = 27\left(\dfrac{1}{3}\right)$$
$$P = 9$$

$33\dfrac{1}{3}\%$ of 27 is 9.

8.
$$P = B \times R$$
$$P = 30\left(\dfrac{1}{6}\right)$$
$$P = 5$$

$16\dfrac{2}{3}\%$ of 30 is 5.

9.
$$P = B \times R$$
$$3 = 12 \cdot R$$
$$\dfrac{3}{12} = \dfrac{12 \cdot R}{12}$$
$$0.25 = R$$
$$25\% = R$$

25% of 12 is 3.

10. $P = B \times R$
$10 = 15 \cdot R$
$\frac{10}{15} = \frac{15 \cdot R}{15}$
$\frac{2}{3} = R$

$66\frac{2}{3}\% = R$

10 is $66\frac{2}{3}\%$ of 15.

11. $P = B \times R$
$3 = B(0.60)$
$\frac{3}{0.60} = \frac{B(0.60)}{0.60}$
$5 = B$

60% of 5 is 3.

12. $P = B \times R$
$6 = B(0.75)$
$\frac{6}{0.75} = \frac{B(0.75)}{0.75}$
$8 = B$

75% of 8 is 6.

13. $P = B \times R$
$37 = 148 \cdot R$
$\frac{37}{148} = \frac{148 \cdot R}{148}$
$0.25 = R$
$25\% = R$

37 is 25% of 148.

14. $P = B \times R$
$33 = 150 \cdot R$
$\frac{33}{150} = \frac{150 \cdot R}{150}$
$0.22 = R$
$22\% = R$

22% of 150 is 33.

15. $P = B \times R$
$82 = B(0.205)$
$\frac{82}{0.205} = \frac{B(0.205)}{0.205}$
$400 = B$

82 is 20.5% of 400.

16. $P = B \times R$
$21 = B(0.024)$
$\frac{21}{0.024} = \frac{B(0.024)}{0.024}$
$875 = B$

2.4% of 875 is 21.

17. $P = B \times R$
$P = 200(0.065)$
$P = 13$

6.5% of 200 is 13.

18. $P = B \times R$
$12 = 6 \cdot R$
$\frac{12}{6} = \frac{6 \cdot R}{6}$
$2 = R$
$200\% = R$

12 is 200% of 6.

19. $P = B \times R$
$P = 18(2.50)$
$P = 45$

250% of 18 is 45.

20. $P = B \times R$
$33 = B(2.20)$
$\frac{33}{2.20} = \frac{B(2.20)}{2.20}$
$15 = B$

33 is 220% of 15.

21. $P = B \times R$
$40 = B(1.60)$
$\frac{40}{1.60} = \frac{B(1.60)}{1.60}$
$25 = B$

160% of 25 is 40.

22. $P = B \times R$
$43 = 344 \cdot R$
$\frac{43}{344} = \frac{344 \cdot R}{344}$
$0.125 = R$
$12.5\% = R$

12.5% of 344 is 43.

23. $P = B \times R$
$P = 50(0.154)$
$P = 7.7$

15.4% of 50 is 7.7.

24. $P = B \times R$
$P = 46(0.185)$
$P = 8.51$

18.5% of 46 is 8.51.

25. $P = B \times R$
$3 = B(0.015)$
$\frac{3}{0.015} = \frac{B(0.015)}{0.015}$
$200 = B$

3 is 1.5% of 200.

26. $P = B \times R$
$3 = B(0.0075)$
$\frac{3}{0.0075} = \frac{B(0.0075)}{0.0075}$
$400 = B$

0.75% of 400 is 3.

27. Strategy
    To find the number of crates damaged, solve the basic percent equation for part (base = 560, rate = 0.05).

    Solution
    $P = B \times R$
    $ = 560(0.05)$
    $ = 28$

    During shipping, 28 crates were damaged.

28. Strategy
    To find the increase in the employee's hourly wage, solve the basic percent equation for part (base = 12.50, rate = 0.06).

    Solution
    $P = B \times R$
    $ = 12.50(0.06)$
    $ = 0.75$

    The increase in the employee's hourly wage is $.75.

29. Strategy
    To find the amount spent for newspaper advertising, solve the basic percent equation for part (base = 35,000, rate = 0.15).

    Solution
    $P = B \times R$
    $ = 35,000(0.15)$
    $ = 5250$

    The company spent $5250 for newspaper advertising.

30. Strategy
    To find the percent, solve the basic percent equation for rate (part = 50, base = 1250).

    Solution
    $P = B \times R$
    $50 = 1250 \cdot R$
    $\dfrac{50}{1250} = \dfrac{1250 \cdot R}{1250}$
    $0.04 = R$
    $4\% = R$

    4% of the vegetables inspected were spoiled.

31. Strategy
    To find the percent, solve the basic percent equation for rate (part = 15, base = 250).

    Solution
    $P = B \times R$
    $15 = 250 \cdot R$
    $\dfrac{15}{250} = \dfrac{250 \cdot R}{250}$
    $0.06 = R$
    $6\% = R$

    6% of the nylon ropes tested did not meet the standards.

32. Strategy
    To find the percent, solve the basic percent equation for rate (part = 7, base = 200).

    Solution
    $P = B \times R$
    $7 = 200 \cdot R$
    $\dfrac{7}{200} = \dfrac{200 \cdot R}{200}$
    $0.035 = R$
    $3.5\% = R$

    3.5% of the people tested liked the product.

33. Strategy
    To find the increase, solve the basic percent equation for part (base = 50, rate = 0.08).

    Solution
    $P = B \times R$
    $P = 50 \times 0.08$
    $P = 4$

    The increase in the market price is $4.

34. Strategy
    To find the number of words typed, solve the basic percent equation for base (part = 3, rate = 0.02).

    Solution
    $P = B \times R$
    $3 = B(0.02)$
    $\dfrac{3}{0.02} = \dfrac{B(0.02)}{0.02}$
    $150 = B$

    The total number of words typed was 150.

35. Strategy
    To find the price at the competitor's
    store, solve the basic percent
    equation for base (part = 109.25,
    rate = 1.15).

    Solution
    $$P = B \times R$$
    $$109.25 = B(1.15)$$
    $$\frac{109.25}{1.15} = \frac{B(1.15)}{1.15}$$
    $$95 = B$$

    The price at the competitor's store
    was $95.

36. Strategy
    To find the number of employees
    needed:
    • Find the number of additional
      employees needed by solving the
      basic percent equation for part
      (base = 125, rate = 0.20).
    • Add the number employed to the
      number of additional employees
      needed.

    Solution
    $$P = B \times R$$
    $$= 125(0.20)$$
    $$= 25$$
    $$125 + 25 = 150$$

    For the holiday season, 150 employees
    are needed.

37. Strategy
    To find the manager's monthly salary
    next year:
    • Find the increase in salary by
      solving the basic percent equation
      for part (base = 4500,
      rate = 0.05).
    • Add the increase in salary to this
      year's salary.

    Solution
    $$P = B \times R$$
    $$P = 4500 \times 0.05$$
    $$P = 225$$
    $$4500 + 225 = 4725$$

    The manager's monthly salary next year
    will be $4725.

Section 6.3, pages 165–166

1. Strategy
   To find the percent increase, solve
   the basic percent equation for rate.

   Solution
   $$P = B \times R$$
   $$500 = 2500 \cdot R$$
   $$0.2 = R$$
   $$20\% = R$$

   The percent increase is 20%.

2. Strategy
   To find the percent increase, solve
   the basic percent equation for rate.

   Solution
   $$P = B \times R$$
   $$1.50 = 30 \cdot R$$
   $$0.05 = R$$
   $$5\% = R$$

   The percent increase is 5%.

3. Strategy
   To find the percent increase:
   • Find the amount of increase.
   • Solve the basic percent equation
     for rate.

   Solution
   275 − 250 = 25

   $P = B \times R$
   $25 = 250 \cdot R$
   $0.1 = R$
   $10\% = R$

   The percent increase is 10%.

4. Strategy
   To find the percent increase:
   • Find the amount of increase.
   • Solve the basic percent equation
     for rate.

   Solution
   42 − 36 = 6

   $P = B \times R$
   $6 = 36 \cdot R$
   $\frac{1}{6} = R$
   $16\frac{2}{3}\% = R$

   The percent increase is $16\frac{2}{3}$%.

5. Strategy
   To find the amount of increase, solve
   the basic percent equation for part.

   Solution
   $P = B \times R$
   $P = 2000(0.15)$
   $P = 300$

   The amount of increase is 300 radios.

6. Strategy
   To find how much larger the home is
   now, solve the basic percent equation
   for part.

   Solution
   $P = B \times R$
   $P = 1250(0.20)$
   $P = 250$

   The home is now larger by 250 square
   feet.

7. Strategy
   • To find the amount of increase,
     solve the basic percent equation
     for part.
   • To find the weekly wage after the
     wage increase, add the amount of
     increase to the present wage.

   Solution
   $P = B \times R$
   $P = 256(0.085)$
   $P = 21.76$

   The amount of increase is $21.76.

   256 + 21.76 = 277.76

   The weekly wage after the wage
   increase is $277.76.

8. Strategy
   To find next year's salary:
   • Find the amount of increase in the
     salary by solving the basic percent
     equation for part.
   • Add the amount of increase to this
     year's salary.

   Solution
   $P = B \times R$
   $P = 32,000(0.11)$
   $P = 3520$

   32,000 + 3520 = 35,520

   The salary will be $35,520 next year.

9. Strategy
   To find the percent increase:
   • Find the amount of increase.
   • Solve the basic percent equation
     for rate.

   Solution
   525 − 500 = 25

   $$P = B \times R$$
   $$25 = 500 \cdot R$$
   $$0.05 = R$$
   $$5\% = R$$

   The percent increase is 5%.

10. Strategy
    To find the number of units that will
    be produced each month:
    • Find the amount of increase by
      solving the basic percent equation
      for part.
    • Add the amount of increase to the
      present production level.

    Solution
    $$P = B \times R$$
    $$P = 5000(0.065)$$
    $$P = 325$$

    5000 + 325 = 5325

    5325 units will be produced each
    month.

11. Strategy
    To find the percent decrease:
    • Find the amount of decrease.
    • Solve the basic percent equation
      for rate.

    Solution
    35,000 − 28,000 = 7000

    $$P = B \times R$$
    $$7000 = 35,000 \cdot R$$
    $$0.2 = R$$
    $$20\% = R$$

    The percent decrease is 20%.

12. Strategy
    To find the percent decrease:
    • Find the amount of decrease.
    • Solve the basic percent equation
      for rate.

    Solution
    2500 − 2300 = 200

    $$P = B \times R$$
    $$200 = 2500 \cdot R$$
    $$0.08 = R$$
    $$8\% = R$$

    The percent decrease is 8%.

13. Strategy
    To find the percent decrease, solve
    the basic percent equation for rate.

    Solution
    $$P = B \times R$$
    $$300 = 1250 \cdot R$$
    $$0.24 = R$$
    $$24\% = R$$

    The percent decrease is 24%.

14. Strategy
    To find the percent decrease, solve
    the basic percent equation for rate.

    Solution
    $$P = B \times R$$
    $$80 = 400 \cdot R$$
    $$0.2 = R$$
    $$20\% = R$$

    The percent decrease is 20%.

15. Strategy
    To find the decrease in the number of
    employees, solve the basic percent
    equation for part.

    Solution
    $P = B \times R$
    $P = 1200(0.45)$
    $P = 540$

    The decrease is 540 employees.

16. Strategy
    To find the percent decrease:
    • Find the amount of decrease.
    • Solve the basic percent equation
      for rate.

    Solution
    $8 - 5 = 3$

    $P = B \times R$
    $3 = 8 \cdot R$
    $0.375 = R$
    $37.5\% = R$

    The percent decrease is 37.5%.

17. Strategy
    To find the percent decrease:
    • Find the amount of decrease.
    • Solve the basic percent equation
      for rate.

    Solution
    $20 - 8 = 12$

    $P = B \times R$
    $12 = 20 \cdot R$
    $0.6 = R$
    $60\% = R$

    The percent decrease is 60%.

18. Strategy
    To find this year's profit:
    • Find the amount of decrease by
      solving the basic percent equation
      for part.
    • Subtract the amount of decrease
      from last year's profit.

    Solution
    $P = B \times R$
    $P = 250,000(0.8)$
    $P = 20,000$

    $250,000 - 20,000 = 230,000$

    The profit this year is $230,000.

19. Strategy
    To find the amount of the monthly
    bill:
    • Find the amount of decrease by
      solving the basic percent equation
      for part.
    • Subtract the amount of decrease
      from the previous monthly bill.

    Solution
    $P = B \times R$
    $P = 76(0.20)$
    $P = 15.20$

    $76 - 15.20 = 60.80$

    The monthly gasoline bill is $60.80.

20. Strategy
    To find the percent decrease:
    • Find the amount of decrease.
    • Solve the basic percent equation
      for rate.

    Solution
    $3.5 - 2.8 = 0.7$

    $P = B \times R$
    $0.7 = 3.5 \cdot R$
    $0.2 = R$
    $20\% = R$

    The percent decrease is 20%.

Section 6.4, pages 173–176

1. Strategy
   To find the amounts received by each of the partners:
   - Add the numbers in the ratio.
   - Form fractions by placing each number in the ratio over the sum of the numbers.
   - Multiply each fraction by last year's profit ($140,000).

   Solution

   $4 + 3 = 7$ $\quad \frac{4}{7}, \frac{3}{7}$

   $\frac{4}{7}(140,000) = 80,000$

   $\frac{3}{7}(140,000) = 60,000$

   The amounts received were $80,000 and $60,000.

2. Strategy
   To find the amounts received by the two partners:
   - Add the numbers in the ratio.
   - Form fractions by placing each number in the ratio over the sum of the numbers.
   - Multiply each fraction by last year's profit ($180,000).

   Solution

   $5 + 3 = 8$ $\quad \frac{5}{8}, \frac{3}{8}$

   $\frac{5}{8}(180,000) = 112,500$

   $\frac{3}{8}(180,000) = 67,500$

   The amounts received were $112,500 and $67,500.

3. Strategy
   To find the amounts received by the three partners:
   - Add the numbers in the ratio.
   - Form fractions by placing each number in the ratio over the sum of the numbers.
   - Multiply each fraction by last year's profit ($180,000).

   Solution

   $3 + 2 + 1 = 6$ $\quad \frac{3}{6}, \frac{2}{6}, \frac{1}{6}$

   $\frac{3}{6}(180,000) = 90,000$

   $\frac{2}{6}(180,000) = 60,000$

   $\frac{1}{6}(180,000) = 30,000$

   The amounts received were $90,000, $60,000, and $30,000.

4. Strategy
   To find the amounts received by the three partners:
   - Add the numbers in the ratio.
   - Form fractions by placing each number in the ratio over the sum of the numbers.
   - Multiply each fraction by last year's profit ($150,000).

   Solution

   $7 + 5 + 3 = 15$ $\quad \frac{7}{15}, \frac{5}{15}, \frac{3}{15}$

   $\frac{7}{15}(150,000) = 70,000$

   $\frac{5}{15}(150,000) = 50,000$

   $\frac{3}{15}(150,000) = 30,000$

   The amounts received were $70,000, $50,000, and $30,000.

5. Strategy
   To find the amounts allocated, multiply each department's percent of the cost by the cost.

   Solution
   Department A: 0.30(35,000) = 10,500
   Department B: 0.70(35,000) = 24,500

   Department A is allocated $10,500.
   Department B is allocated $24,500.

6. Strategy
   To find the amounts allocated, multiply each department's percent of the cost by the cost.

   Solution
   Department A: 0.25(25,000) = 6,250
   Department B: 0.75(25,000) = 18,750

   Department A is allocated $6,250.
   Department B is allocated $18,750.

7. Strategy
   To find the amounts allocated,
   multiply each division's percent of
   the expense by the expense.

   Solution
   0.20(1200) = 240
   0.35(1200) = 420
   0.45(1200) = 540

   The amounts allocated are $240, $420,
   and $540.

8. Strategy
   To find the amounts allocated,
   multiply each department's percent of
   the expense by the expense.

   Solution
   0.25(220,000) = 55,000
   0.35(220,000) = 77,000
   0.40(220,000) = 88,000

   The amounts allocated are $55,000,
   $77,000, and $88,000.

9. Strategy
   To find the percents, solve the basic
   percent equation for rate.

   Solution
   $$P = B \times R \qquad\qquad P = B \times R$$
   $$3400 = 8500 \cdot R \qquad 5100 = 8500 \cdot R$$
   $$0.4 = R \qquad\qquad 0.6 = R$$
   $$40\% = R \qquad\qquad 60\% = R$$

   40% is allocated to Department A.
   60% is allocated to Department B.

10. Strategy
    To find the percents, solve the basic
    percent equation for rate.

    Solution
    $$P = B \times R \qquad\qquad P = B \times R$$
    $$1694 = 4840 \cdot R \qquad 3146 = 4840 \cdot R$$
    $$0.35 = R \qquad\qquad 0.65 = R$$
    $$35\% = R \qquad\qquad 65\% = R$$

    35% is allocated to Department A.
    65% is allocated to Department B.

11. Strategy
    To find the amounts to be received:
    • Add the two investments.
    • Form fractions by placing each
      investment over the sum of the
      investments.
    • Multiply each fraction by the
      year's profits ($84,000).

    Solution
    $20,000 + 15,000 = 35,000 \quad \dfrac{20,000}{35,000}, \dfrac{15,000}{35,000}$

    $\dfrac{20,000}{35,000}(84,000) = 48,000$

    $\dfrac{15,000}{35,000}(84,000) = 36,000$

    The amounts to be received are $48,000
    and $36,000.

12. Strategy
    To find the amounts to be received:
    • Add the two investments.
    • Form fractions by placing each
      investment over the sum of the
      investments.
    • Multiply each fraction by the
      year's profits ($78,000).

    Solution
    $35,000 + 25,000 = 60,000 \quad \dfrac{35,000}{60,000}, \dfrac{25,000}{60,000}$

    $\dfrac{35,000}{60,000}(78,000) = 45,500$

    $\dfrac{25,000}{60,000}(78,000) = 32,500$

    The amounts to be received are $45,500
    and $32,500.

13. Strategy
    To find the amounts allocated:
    • Find the percent allocated by
      solving the basic percent equation
      for rate.
    • Multiply each department's percent
      of the expense by the expense.

    Solution
    $$P = B \times R$$
    $$20{,}000 = 50{,}000 \cdot R$$
    $$0.4 = R$$
    $$40\% = R$$

    $$P = B \times R$$
    $$30{,}000 = 50{,}000 \cdot R$$
    $$0.6 = R$$
    $$60\% = R$$

    $$0.40(32{,}000) = 12{,}800$$
    $$0.60(32{,}000) = 19{,}200$$

    Department A is allocated $12,800.
    Department B is allocated $19,200.

14. Strategy
    To find the amounts allocated:
    • Find the percent allocated by
      solving the basic percent equation
      for rate.
    • Multiply each department's percent
      of the expense by the expense.

    Solution
    $$P = B \times R$$
    $$14{,}000 = 35{,}000 \cdot R$$
    $$0.4 = R$$
    $$40\% = R$$

    $$P = B \times R$$
    $$21{,}000 = 35{,}000 \cdot R$$
    $$0.6 = R$$
    $$60\% = R$$

    $$0.40(24{,}000) = 9{,}600$$
    $$0.60(24{,}000) = 14{,}400$$

    Department A is allocated $9600.
    Department B is allocated $14,400.

15. $$\frac{x}{4} = \frac{6}{8}$$
    $$x \cdot 8 = 4 \cdot 6$$
    $$8x = 24$$
    $$x = 3$$

    The solution is 3.

16. $$\frac{x}{7} = \frac{9}{21}$$
    $$x \cdot 21 = 7 \cdot 9$$
    $$21x = 63$$
    $$x = 3$$

    The solution is 3.

17. $$\frac{12}{18} = \frac{x}{9}$$
    $$12 \cdot 9 = 18 \cdot x$$
    $$108 = 18x$$
    $$6 = x$$

    The solution is 6.

18. $$\frac{7}{21} = \frac{35}{x}$$
    $$7 \cdot x = 21 \cdot 35$$
    $$7x = 735$$
    $$x = 105$$

    The solution is 105.

19. $$\frac{6}{n} = \frac{24}{36}$$
    $$6 \cdot 36 = n \cdot 24$$
    $$216 = 24n$$
    $$9 = n$$

    The solution is 9.

20. $$\frac{3}{n} = \frac{15}{10}$$
    $$3 \cdot 10 = n \cdot 15$$
    $$30 = 15n$$
    $$2 = n$$

    The solution is 2.

21. $$\frac{9}{4} = \frac{18}{n}$$
    $$9 \cdot n = 4 \cdot 18$$
    $$9n = 72$$
    $$n = 8$$

    The solution is 8.

22. $$\frac{7}{15} = \frac{21}{n}$$
    $$7 \cdot n = 15 \cdot 21$$
    $$7n = 315$$
    $$n = 45$$

    The solution is 45.

23. $$\frac{x}{12} = \frac{5}{6}$$
    $$x \cdot 6 = 12 \cdot 5$$
    $$6x = 60$$
    $$x = 10$$

    The solution is 10.

24. $$\frac{3}{5} = \frac{x}{10}$$
    $$3 \cdot 10 = 5 \cdot x$$
    $$30 = 5x$$
    $$6 = x$$

    The solution is 6.

25. $$\frac{18}{x} = \frac{9}{5}$$
    $$18 \cdot 5 = x \cdot 9$$
    $$90 = 9x$$
    $$10 = x$$

    The solution is 10.

26. $$\frac{n}{11} = \frac{32}{4}$$
    $$n \cdot 4 = 11 \cdot 32$$
    $$4n = 352$$
    $$n = 88$$

    The solution is 88.

27.
$$\frac{3}{n} = \frac{5}{2}$$
$$3 \cdot 2 = n \cdot 5$$
$$6 = 5n$$
$$1.2 = n$$

The solution is 1.2.

28.
$$\frac{2}{5} = \frac{n}{4}$$
$$2 \cdot 4 = 5 \cdot n$$
$$8 = 5n$$
$$1.6 = n$$

The solution is 1.6.

29.
$$\frac{n}{6} = \frac{2}{15}$$
$$n \cdot 15 = 6 \cdot 2$$
$$15n = 12$$
$$n = 0.8$$

The solution is 0.8.

30.
$$\frac{10}{3} = \frac{5}{x}$$
$$10 \cdot x = 3 \cdot 5$$
$$10x = 15$$
$$x = 1.5$$

The solution is 1.5.

31. Strategy
To find the amount of the rebate,
write and solve a proportion
(rate = 7%, base = 22,500).

Solution
$$\frac{7}{100} = \frac{P}{22,500}$$
$$7(22,500) = 100 \cdot P$$
$$157,500 = 100P$$
$$1575 = P$$

The rebate would be $1575.

32. Strategy
To find the percent, write and solve a
proportion (part = 3, base = 250).

Solution
$$\frac{R}{100} = \frac{3}{250}$$
$$R \cdot 250 = 100 \cdot 3$$
$$250R = 300$$
$$R = 1.2$$

1.2% of the slabs tested did not meet
safety requirements.

33. Strategy
To find the original price, write and
solve a proportion (rate = 55%,
part = 825).

Solution
$$\frac{55}{100} = \frac{825}{B}$$
$$55 \cdot B = 100 \cdot 825$$
$$55B = 82,500$$
$$B = 1500$$

The original price was $1500.

34. Strategy
To find the percent, write and solve a
proportion (part = 1,350,000,
base = 450,000).

Solution
$$\frac{R}{100} = \frac{1,350,000}{450,000}$$
$$R \cdot 450,000 = 1,350,000 \cdot 100$$
$$450,000R = 135,000,000$$
$$R = 300$$

The 1993 sales are 300% of the 1983
sales.

35. Strategy
To find the percent decrease:
• Find the amount of decrease.
• Write and solve a proportion.

Solution
$$450 - 360 = 90$$

$$\frac{R}{100} = \frac{90}{450}$$
$$R \cdot 450 = 100 \cdot 90$$
$$450R = 9000$$
$$R = 20$$

The percent decrease in price was 20%.

36. Strategy
To find the cost, write and solve a
proportion.

Solution
$$\frac{6.87}{1000} = \frac{C}{15,000}$$
$$6.87 \cdot 15,000 = 1000 \cdot C$$
$$103,050 = 1000C$$
$$103.05 = C$$

The cost for $15,000 of insurance
coverage is $103.05.

37. Strategy
    To find the monthly payment, write and
    solve a proportion.

    Solution
    $$\frac{10.84}{1000} = \frac{P}{5000}$$
    $$10.84 \cdot 5000 = 1000 \cdot P$$
    $$54,200 = 1000P$$
    $$54.2 = P$$

    The monthly payment for a $5000 loan
    is $54.20.

38. Strategy
    To find the number of defective blend-
    ers, write and solve a proportion.

    Solution
    $$\frac{2}{100} = \frac{N}{500}$$
    $$2 \cdot 500 = 100 \cdot N$$
    $$1000 = 100N$$
    $$10 = N$$

    In a shipment of 500 blenders, 10
    would be defective.

39. Strategy
    To find the number of steering
    defects, write and solve a proportion.

    Solution
    $$\frac{38}{1000} = \frac{N}{25,000}$$
    $$38 \cdot 25,000 = 1000 \cdot N$$
    $$950,000 = 1000N$$
    $$950 = N$$

    In 25,000 cars, 950 steering defects
    would be found.

40. Strategy
    To find the salary, write and solve a
    proportion.

    Solution
    $$\frac{5}{4} = \frac{S}{18,000}$$
    $$5 \cdot 18,000 = 4 \cdot S$$
    $$90,000 = 4S$$
    $$22,500 = S$$

    The midmanagement salary is $22,500.

41. Strategy
    To find the number of hours, write and
    solve a proportion.

    Solution
    $$\frac{2}{3} = \frac{200}{N}$$
    $$2 \cdot N = 3 \cdot 200$$
    $$2N = 600$$
    $$N = 300$$

    The computer was used for administra-
    tion for 300 hours.

42. Strategy
    To find the amount received, write and
    solve a proportion.

    Solution
    $$\frac{7}{5} = \frac{28,000}{n}$$
    $$7 \cdot n = 5 \cdot 28,000$$
    $$7n = 140,000$$
    $$n = 20,000$$

    The other partner receives $20,000.

43. Strategy
    To find the amount received, write and
    solve a proportion.

    Solution
    $$\frac{4}{3} = \frac{n}{24,000}$$
    $$4 \cdot 24,000 = 3 \cdot n$$
    $$96,000 = 3n$$
    $$32,000 = n$$

    The other partner receives $32,000.

44. Strategy
    To find the amount to be invested,
    write and solve a proportion.

    Solution
    $$\frac{6000}{500} = \frac{n}{800}$$
    $$6000 \cdot 800 = 500 \cdot n$$
    $$4,800,000 = 500n$$
    $$9600 = n$$

    $9600 must be invested to earn $800
    each year.

45. Strategy
To find the number of pounds, write and solve a proportion.

Solution
$$\frac{50}{130} = \frac{n}{156}$$
$$50 \cdot 156 = 130 \cdot n$$
$$7800 = 130n$$
$$60 = n$$

To serve 156 people, 60 pounds of vegetables are needed.

47. Strategy
To find the number of acres, write and solve a proportion.

Solution
$$\frac{5600}{160} = \frac{8120}{n}$$
$$5600 \cdot n = 160 \cdot 8120$$
$$5600n = 1{,}299{,}200$$
$$n = 232$$

To harvest 8120 bushels of wheat, 232 acres are needed.

49. Strategy
To find the number that did not favor the new program:
• Find the number that favored the new program by writing and solving a proportion (rate = 57%; base = 1500).
• Subtract the number that favored the new program from the number of employees.

Solution
$$\frac{57}{100} = \frac{P}{1500}$$
$$57 \cdot 1500 = 100 \cdot P$$
$$85{,}500 = 100P$$
$$855 = P$$

$$1500 - 855 = 645$$

645 employees did not favor the new program.

46. Strategy
To find the number of liters, write and solve a proportion.

Solution
$$\frac{12}{40} = \frac{n}{60}$$
$$12 \cdot 60 = 40 \cdot n$$
$$720 = 40n$$
$$18 = n$$

To serve 60 people, 18 liters of fruit punch are needed.

48. Strategy
To find the number that were not defective:
• Find the number that were defective by writing and solving a proportion (rate = 1.2%, base = 2500).
• Subtract the number that were defective from the number inspected.

Solution
$$\frac{1.2}{100} = \frac{P}{2500}$$
$$1.2 \cdot 2500 = 100 \cdot P$$
$$3000 = 100P$$
$$30 = P$$

$$2500 - 30 = 2470$$

2470 phones were not defective.

50. Strategy
To find the total number produced, write and solve a proportion (rate = 0.1%, part = 545).

Solution
$$\frac{0.1}{100} = \frac{545}{n}$$
$$0.1 \cdot n = 100 \cdot 545$$
$$0.1n = 54{,}500$$
$$n = 545{,}000$$

545,000 diodes were produced in that week.

Business Case Study

1. $12,475 + $13,225 + $20,490 + $39,330 + $47,595 = $133,115
    The total of the current base salaries is $133,115.

2. 6% of $133,115 = 0.06($133,115) = $7986.90
    The maximum amount of money you can give in salary increases for next year is $7986.90.

3. $133,115 + $7986.90 = $141,101.90
    The largest possible total of the annual salaries for the five sales representatives next year is $141,101.90.

4. Answers will vary. Students might reward largest total sales, largest increase in sales, seniority, or junior sales representatives' base annual salaries. A sample schedule is shown below.

	% Increase in Base Annual Salary	New Base Annual Salary	Increase in Base Annual Salary
A. McNeil ($408,688 increase in sales; Expenses only 1.1% of total sales)	9%	$13,597.75	$1122.75
G. Seymour ($25,383 increase in sales)	4%	$13,754.00	$529.00
M. Stevens ($182,450 decrease in sales; Expenses 2.8% of total sales)	2%	$20,899.80	$409.80
B. Peters ($1320 increase in sales)	4%	$40,903.20	$1573.20
S. Masters (largest total sales)	9%	$51,878.55	$4283.55
			$7918.30

5. Answers will vary. For example:
    Did any of the representatives have a personal problem during the year, such as a serious illness or a death in the family? What percent increase in salary did each of the representatives receive last year? Do any of the representatives have an easier or more difficult sales territory than the others?

6. Answers will vary. For example:
    Consider giving, overall, less than a 6% increase. Include in each representative's performance review either praise or criticism with respect to the percent of total sales that were expenses.

Review/Test, pages 181–182

1. $75\% = 75 \left(\frac{1}{100}\right) = \frac{75}{100} = \frac{3}{4}$

    $75\% = 75(0.01) = 0.75$

2. $66\frac{2}{3}\% = \frac{2}{3}$

3. $0.08 = 0.08(100\%) = 8\%$

4. $\frac{3}{5} = \frac{3}{5}(100\%) = \frac{300}{5}\% = 60\%$

5. $\frac{7}{9} = \frac{7}{9}(100\%) = \frac{700}{9}\% \approx 77.8\%$

6. $P = B \times R$
$P = 550 \times 0.16$
$P = 88$

16% of 550 is 88.

7. $P = B \times R$
$20 = 16 \cdot R$
$\frac{20}{16} = \frac{16 \cdot R}{16}$
$1.25 = R$
$125\% = R$

20 is 125% of 16.

8. $P = B \times R$
$12 = B(0.15)$
$\frac{12}{0.15} = \frac{B(0.15)}{0.15}$
$80 = B$

12 is 15% of 80.

9. $\frac{n}{16} = \frac{9}{4}$
$n \cdot 4 = 16 \cdot 9$
$4n = 144$
$n = 36$

The solution is 36.

10. $\frac{16}{3} = \frac{8}{n}$
$16 \cdot n = 3 \cdot 8$
$16n = 24$
$n = 1.5$

The solution is 1.5.

11. **Strategy**
To find the increase in the hourly wage, solve the basic percent equation for part (base = 9.50, rate = 8%).

Solution
$P = B \times R$
$P = 9.50(0.08)$
$P = 0.76$

The increase is \$.76 per hour.

12. **Strategy**
To find Delta Air Lines' operating revenues for 1991, solve the basic percent equation for the base (part = 7500, rate = 0.82).

Solution
$P = B \times R$
$7500 = 0.82R$
$\frac{7500}{0.82} = \frac{0.82R}{0.82}$
$9146 \approx R$

Delta Air Lines' operating revenues in 1991 were approximately \$9146 million.

13. **Strategy**
To find the percent:
• Solve the basic percent equation for rate ($P = 9$, $B = 300$).
To find the number of people who do *not* like the product, subtract the rate from 100%.

Solution
$P = B \times R$
$9 = 300 \cdot R$
$\frac{9}{300} = \frac{300 \cdot R}{300}$
$0.03 = R$
$3\% = R$

3% of the people liked the product.

$100\% - 3\% = 97\%$

97% of the people surveyed did not like the product.

14. **Strategy**
To find the percent increase:
• Find the amount of increase.
• Solve the basic percent equation for rate.

Solution
Amount of increase
$= 8.10 - 7.50 = 0.60$

$P = B \times R$
$0.60 = 7.50 \cdot R$
$\frac{0.60}{7.50} = \frac{7.50 \cdot R}{7.50}$
$0.08 = R$
$8\% = R$

The percent increase is 8%.

15. Strategy
    To find next year's salary:
    • Solve the basic percent equation
      for part to find the amount of
      increase in salary.
    • Add the amount of increase to the
      present wage.

    Solution
    $P = B \times R$
    $ = 18,000(0.09)$
    $ = 1620$

    $18,000 + 1620 = 19,620$

    The reporter's salary will be $19,620
    next year.

16. Strategy
    To find next year's budget:
    • Solve the basic percent equation
      for part to find the amount of
      decrease in the budget.
    • Subtract the amount of decrease
      from this year's budget.

    Solution
    $P = B \times R$
    $ = 25,000(0.02)$
    $ = 500$

    $25,000 - 500 = 24,500$

    Next year the advertising budget will
    be $24,500.

17. Strategy
    To find the amounts allocated,
    multiply each division's percent of
    the expense by the expense.

    Solution
    $0.50(1275) = 637.50$
    $0.30(1275) = 382.50$
    $0.20(1275) = 255$

    The amounts allocated to the three
    divisions are $637.50, $382.50, and
    $255.

18. Strategy
    To find the amounts received:
    • Add the numbers in the ratio.
    • Form fractions by placing each
      number in the ratio over the sum of
      the numbers.
    • Multiply each fraction by the
      profits.

    Solution
    $3 + 2 + 1 = 6 \qquad \frac{3}{6}, \frac{2}{6}, \frac{1}{6}$

    $\frac{3}{6}(144,000) = 72,000$

    $\frac{2}{6}(144,000) = 48,000$

    $\frac{1}{6}(144,000 = 24,000$

    The attorneys received $72,000,
    $48,000, and $24,000.

19. Strategy
    To find the percent, write and solve a
    proportion

    Solution
    $\frac{rate}{100} = \frac{part}{base}$
    $\frac{R}{100} = \frac{150,000}{120,000}$
    $R(120,000) = 100(150,000)$
    $ R = 125$

    The second year's sales are 125% of
    the first year's sales.

20. Strategy
    To find the amount that must be
    invested, write and solve a proportion
    using x to represent the amount of
    money.

    Solution
    $\frac{720}{9000} = \frac{1800}{x}$
    $720 \cdot x = 9000 \cdot 1800$
    $720x = 16,200,000$
    $x = 22,500$

    $22,500 must be invested each year.

CHAPTER 7
Purchasing

Section 7.1, pages 193-196

1. Strategy
   To find the discount, multiply the
   discount rate (30%) by the list price
   (5000).
   To find the net price, subtract the
   discount from the list price.

   Solution
   Discount = list price x discount rate
          = 5000(0.30)
          = 1500

   The discount is $1500.

   Net price = list price - discount
          = 5000 - 1500
          = 3500

   The net price is $3500.

2. Strategy
   To find the discount, multiply the
   discount rate (60%) by the list price
   (1500).
   To find the net price, subtract the
   discount from the list price.

   Solution
   Discount = list price x discount rate
          = 1500(0.60)
          = 900

   The discount is $900.

   Net price = list price - discount
          = 1500 - 900
          = 600

   The net price is $600.

3. (a) 100% - 45% = 55%
   (b) 55% = 0.55

4. (a) 100% - 34% = 66%
   (b) 66% = 0.66

5. Strategy
   To find the complement of the discount
   rate, subtract the discount rate from
   100%.
   To find the net price, multiply the
   list price by the complement of the
   discount rate.

   Solution
   100% - 25% = 75%

   The complement of the discount rate is
   75%.

   Net price = 315(0.75) = 236.25

   The net price is $236.25.

6. Strategy
   To find the complement of the discount
   rate, subtract the discount rate from
   100%.
   To find the net price, multiply the
   list price by the complement of the
   discount rate.

   Solution
   100% - 35% = 65%

   The complement of the discount rate is
   65%.

   Net price = 8200(0.65) = 5330

   The net price is $5330.

7. Strategy
    To find the discount, multiply the
    discount rate (45%) by the list price
    (2200).
    To find the net price, subtract the
    discount from the list price.

    Solution
    Discount = list price x discount rate
             = 2200(0.45)
             = 990

    The discount is $990.

    Net price = list price - discount
              = 2200 - 990
              = 1210

    The net price is $1210.

8. Strategy
    To find the discount, multiply the
    discount rate (40%) by the list price
    (7500).
    To find the net price, subtract the
    discount from the list price.

    Solution
    Discount = list price x discount rate
             = 7500(0.40)
             = 3000

    The discount is $3000.

    Net price = list price - discount
              = 7500 - 3000
              = 4500

    The net price is $4500.

9. Strategy
    To find the net price:
    - Find the list price of 500
      answering machines by multiplying
      the list price of one answering
      machine ($80) by 500.
    - Multiply the list price of 500
      answering machines by the
      complement of the discount rate
      (100% - 25% = 75%).

    Solution
    List price for 500 answering machines
    = 80 x 500 = 40,000

    Net price = 40,000(0.75) = 30,000

    The net price is $30,000.

10. Strategy
    To find the net price:
    - Find the list price of 1000 CD
      players by multiplying the list
      price of one CD player ($120) by
      1000.
    - Multiply the list price of 1000 CD
      players by the complement of the
      discount rate (100% - 40% = 60%).

    Solution
    List price for 1000 CD players
    = 120 x 1000 = 120,000

    Net price = 120,000(0.60) = 72,000

    The net price is $72,000.

11. Strategy
    To find the net price:
    - Find the list price of 250
      telephones by multiplying the list
      price of one telephone ($90) by
      250.
    - Multiply the list price of 250
      telephones by the complement of the
      discount rate (100% - 20% = 80%).

    Solution
    List price for 250 telephones
    = 90 x 250 = 22,500

    Net price = 22,500(0.80) = 18,000

    The net price is $18,000.

12. Strategy
    To find the net price:
    - Find the list price of 100
      camcorders by multiplying the list
      price of one ($800) by 100.
    - Multiply the list price of 100
      camcorders by the complement of the
      discount rate (100% - 30% = 70%).

    Solution
    List price for 100 camcorders
    = 800 x 100 = 80,000

    Net price = 80,000(0.70) = 56,000

    The net price is $56,000.

13. Strategy
    To determine which is the better buy:
    - Calculate the net price of each item by multiplying the list price by the complement of the discount rate.
    - Compare the net prices of the two items.

    Solution
    Net price = 40(0.65) = 26
    Net price = 30(0.80) = 24
    24 is less than 26.

    The calculator with a list price of $30 and a discount rate of 20% is the better buy.

14. Strategy
    To determine which is the better buy:
    - Calculate the net price of each item by multiplying the list price by the complement of the discount rate.
    - Compare the net prices of the two items.

    Solution
    Net price = 60(0.80) = 48
    Net price = 55(0.75) = 41.25
    41.25 is less than 48.

    The speaker phone with a list price of $55 and a discount rate of 25% is the better buy.

15. Strategy
    To find the list price, divide the net price ($300) by the complement of the trade discount rate
    (100% - 25% = 75%).

    Solution
    List price = $\frac{300}{0.75}$ = 400

    The list price is $400.

16. Strategy
    To find the list price, divide the net price ($227.50) by the complement of the trade discount rate
    (100% - 35% = 65%).

    Solution
    List price = $\frac{227.50}{0.65}$ = 350

    The list price is $350.

17. Strategy
    To find the list price, divide the net price ($570) by the complement of the trade discount rate
    (100% - 40% = 60%).

    Solution
    List price = $\frac{570}{0.60}$ = 950

    The list price is $950.

18. Strategy
    To find the list price, divide the net price ($105) by the complement of the trade discount rate
    (100% - 30% = 70%).

    Solution
    List price = $\frac{105}{0.70}$ = 150

    The list price is $150.

19. Strategy
    To find the discount, multiply the
    list price by the first discount rate
    to find the first discount, subtract
    the first discount from the list price
    to find the first net price, multiply
    the first net price by the second
    discount rate to find the second
    discount, and add the first and second
    discounts.

    To find the net price, subtract the
    second discount from the first net
    price.

    Solution
    First discount = 2200(.30) = 660
    First net price = 2200 - 660 = 1540
    Second discount = 1540(.10) = 154
    Sum of the discounts = 660 + 154 = 814

    The discount is $814.

    Net price = 1540 - 154 = 1386

    The net price is $1386.

20. Strategy
    To find the discount, multiply the
    list price by the first discount rate
    to find the first discount, subtract
    the first discount from the list price
    to find the first net price, multiply
    the first net price by the second
    discount rate to find the second
    discount, and add the first and second
    discounts.

    To find the net price, subtract the
    second discount from the first net
    price.

    Solution
    First discount = 200(0.25) = 50
    First net price = 200 - 50 = 150
    Second discount = 150(0.05) = 7.50
    Sum of the discounts = 50 + 7.50
                         = 57.50

    The discount is $57.50.

    Net price = 150 - 7.50 = 142.50

    The net price is $142.50.

21. Strategy
    To find the amount of the second trade
    discount:
    • Multiply the list price by the
      first discount rate to find the
      first discount.
    • Subtract the first discount from
      the list price to find the first
      net price.
    • Multiply the first net price by the
      second discount rate.

    Solution
    First discount = 1200(0.25) = 300
    First net price = 1200 - 300 = 900
    Second discount = 900(0.10) = 90

    The amount of the second trade
    discount is $90.

22. Strategy
    To find the amount of the second trade
    discount:
    • Multiply the list price by the
      first discount rate to find the
      first discount.
    • Subtract the first discount from
      the list price to find the first
      net price.
    • Multiply the first net price by the
      second discount rate.

    Solution
    First discount = 4200(.30) = 1260
    First net price = 4200 - 1260 = 2940
    Second discount = 2940(0.10) = 294

    The amount of the second trade
    discount is $294.

23. Strategy
    To find the decimal equivalent,
    calculate the product of the
    complements of the discount rates.

    Solution
    (0.70)(0.90)(0.95) = 0.5985

    The decimal equivalent is 0.5985.

24. Strategy
    To find the decimal equivalent,
    calculate the product of the
    complements of the discount rates.

    Solution
    (0.60)(0.80)(0.90) = 0.432

    The decimal equivalent is 0.432.

25. Strategy
    To find the net price, multiply the
    list price by the product of the
    complements of the discount rates.

    Solution
    Net price = 22,000 x (0.70)(0.85)
              = 22,000 x 0.595
              = 13,090

    The net price is $13,090.

26. Strategy
    To find the net price, multiply the
    list price by the product of the
    complements of the discount rates.

    Solution
    Net price = 7000 x (0.75)(0.90)
              = 7000 x 0.675
              = 4725

    The net price is $4725.

27. Strategy
    To find the net price, multiply the
    list price by the product of the
    complements of the discount rates.

    Solution
    Net price = 920 x (0.75)(0.85)
              = 920 x 0.6375
              = 586.5

    The net price is $586.50.

28. Strategy
    To find the net price, multiply the
    list price by the product of the
    complements of the discount rates.

    Solution
    Net price = 240 x (0.80)(0.90)
              = 240 x 0.72
              = 172.8

    The net price is $172.80.

29. Strategy
    To find the net price, multiply the
    list price by the product of the
    complements of the discount rates.

    Solution
    Net price = 225 x (0.60)(0.80)(0.90)
              = 225 x 0.432
              = 97.20

    The net price is $97.20.

30. Strategy
    To find the net price, multiply the
    list price by the product of the
    complements of the discount rates.

    Solution
    Net price = 290 x (0.70)(0.80)(0.90)
              = 290 x 0.504
              = 146.16

    The net price is $146.16.

31. Strategy
    To find the net price, multiply the
    list price by the product of the
    complements of the discount rates.

    Solution
    Net price = 9000 x (0.80)(0.90)(0.95)
              = 9000 x 0.684
              = 6156

    The net price is $6156.

32. Strategy
    To find the net price, multiply the
    list price by the product of the
    complements of the discount rates.

    Solution
    Net price = 14,000 x (0.60)(0.80)(0.90)
              = 14,000 x 0.605525
              = 8478.75

    The net price is $8478.75.

33. Strategy
    To find the net price, multiply the
    list price by the product of the
    complements of the discount rates.

    Solution
    Net price = 75,000 x (0.75)(0.80)(0.90)
              = 75,000 x 0.54
              = 40,500

    The net price is $40,500.

34. Strategy
    To find the net price, multiply the
    list price by the product of the
    complements of the discount rates.

    Solution
    Net price = 30,000 x (0.80)(0.88)(0.92)
              = 30,000 x 0.64768
              = 19,430.4

    The net price is $19,430.40.

35. Strategy
    To find the single discount
    equivalent, subtract the product of
    the complements of the discount rates
    from 1.00. Express the answer as a
    percent and as a decimal.

    Solution
    $1.00 - (0.60)(0.90)(0.95)$
    $= 1.00 - 0.513 = 0.487$

    The single discount equivalent is
    (a) 48.7% or (b) 0.487.

36. Strategy
    To find the single discount
    equivalent, subtract the product of
    the complements of the discount rates
    from 1.00. Express the answer as a
    percent and as a decimal.

    Solution
    $1.00 - (0.70)(0.80)(0.90)$
    $= 1.00 - 0.504 = 0.496$

    The single discount equivalent is
    (a) 49.6% or (b) 0.496.

37. Strategy
    To find the discount:
    • Find the single discount
      equivalent.
    • Multiply the list price by the
      single discount equivalent.

    Solution
    $1.00 - (0.70)(0.95) = 1.00 - 0.665$
    $= 0.335$
    Discount $= 4000(0.335) = 1340$

    The discount is $1340.

38. Strategy
    To find the discount:
    • Find the single discount
      equivalent.
    • Multiply the list price by the
      single discount equivalent.

    Solution
    $1.00 - (0.60)(0.85) = 1.00 - 0.51$
    $= 0.49$
    Discount $= 6000(0.49) = 2940$

    The discount is $2940.

39. Strategy
    To find the discount:
    • Find the single discount
      equivalent.
    • Multiply the list price by the
      single discount equivalent.

    Solution
    $1.00 - (0.70)(0.90)(0.95)$
    $= 1.00 - 0.5985 = 0.4015$
    Discount $= 10,000(0.4015) = 4015$

    The discount is $4015.

40. Strategy
    To find the discount, multiply the
    list price by the single discount
    equivalent.
    To find the net price, subtract the
    discount from the list price.

    Solution
    $1.00 - (0.85)(0.90)(0.95)$
    $= 1.00 - 0.72675 = 0.27325$
    Discount $= 2250(0.27325) \approx 614.81$

    The discount is $614.81.

    Net price $= 2250 - 614.81 = 1635.19$

    The net price is $1635.19.

41. Strategy
     To find the discount, multiply the
     list price by the single discount
     equivalent.
     To find the net price, subtract the
     discount from the list price.

     Solution
     1.00 - (0.80)(0.90)(0.95)
       = 1.00 - 0.684 = 0.316
     Discount = 3200(0.316) = 1011.2

     The discount is $1011.20.

     Net price = 3200 - 1011.20 = 2188.8

     The net price is $2188.80.

42. Strategy
     To find the discount, multiply the
     list price by the single discount
     equivalent.
     To find the net price, subtract the
     discount from the list price.

     Solution
     1.00 - (0.80)(0.88)(0.95)
       = 1.00 - 0.6688 = 0.3312
     Discount = 5500(0.3312) = 1821.6

     The discount is $1821.60.

     Net price = 5500 - 1821.60 = 3678.4

     The net price is $3678.40.

43. Strategy
     To find the discount, multiply the
     list price by the single discount
     equivalent.
     To find the net price, subtract the
     discount from the list price.

     Solution
     1.00 - (0.75)(0.88)(0.95)
       = 1.00 - 0.627 = 0.373
     Discount = 3000(0.373) = 1119

     The discount is $1119.

     Net price = 3000 - 1119 = 1881

     The net price is $1881.

44. Strategy
     To find the discount:
     • Find the total list price by
       multiplying the list price by the
       number of items purchased.
     • Find the single discount equivalent
       of the series discount.
     • Multiply the total list price by
       the single discount equivalent.

     Solution
     Total list price = 345 x 15 = 5175
     1.00 - (0.80)(0.90)(0.95)
       = 1.00 - 0.684 = 0.316
     Discount = 5175(0.316) = 1635.3

     The discount is $1635.30.

45. Strategy
     To find the discount:
     • Find the total list price by
       multiplying the list price by the
       number of items purchased.
     • Find the single discount equivalent
       of the series discount.
     • Multiply the total list price by
       the single discount equivalent.

     Solution
     Total list price = 460 x 20 = 9200
     1.00 - (0.85)(0.90)(0.95)
       = 1.00 - 0.72675 = 0.27325
     Discount = 9200(0.27325) = 2513.9

     The discount is $2513.90.

46. Strategy
     To find the discount, multiply the
     total list price by the single
     discount equivalent.
     To find the net price, subtract the
     discount from the total list price.

     Solution
     Total list price = 240 x 50 = 12,000
     1.00 - (0.75)(0.85)(0.95)
       = 1.00 - 0.605625 = 0.394375
     Discount = 12,000(0.394375) = 4732.50

     The discount is $4732.50.

     Net price = 12,000 - 4732.50 = 7267.50

     The net price is $7267.50.

47. Strategy
    To determine which is the better buy:
    • Find the single discount equivalent
      of a 30/20/5 series discount.
    • Find the single discount equivalent
      of a 40/10/5 series discount.
    • Compare the two single discount
      equivalents.

    Solution
    1.00 − (0.70)(0.80)(0.95)
      = 1.00 − 0.532 = 0.468 = 46.8%
    1.00 − (0.60)(0.90)(0.95)
      = 1.00 − 0.513 = 0.487 = 48.7%

    48.7% is greater than 46.8%.

    The better buy is the 40/10/5 series
    discount.

48. Strategy
    To determine which is the better buy:
    • Find the single discount equivalent
      of a 25/15/10 series discount.
    • Find the single discount equivalent
      of a 30/15/5 series discount.
    • Compare the two single discount
      equivalents.

    Solution
    1.00 − (0.75)(0.85)(0.90)
      = 1.00 − 0.57375 = 0.42625 = 42.625%
    1.00 − (0.70)(0.85)(0.95)
      = 1.00 − 0.56525 = 0.43475 = 43.475%

    43.475% is greater than 42.625%.

    The better buy is the 30/15/5 series
    discount.

49. Strategy
    To determine which is the better buy:
    • Find the net price for each
      computer by multiplying the list
      price by the complements of the
      discount rates.
    • Compare the two net prices.

    Solution
    Net price = 2450 x (0.70)(0.90)(0.95)
              = 2450 x 0.5985
              ≈ 1466.33
    Net price = 2000 x (0.75)(0.90)
              = 2000 x 0.675
              = 1350

    1350 is less than 1466.33.

    The better buy is the $2000 computer
    system with a series discount of
    25/10.

50. Strategy
    To determine which is the better buy:
    • Find the net price for each washer-
      dryer by multiplying the list price
      by the complements of the discount
      rates.
    • Compare the two net prices.

    Solution
    Net price = 720 x (0.70)(0.80)(0.95)
              = 720 x 0.532
              = 383.04
    Net price = 850 x (0.60)(0.80)
              = 850 x 0.48
              = 408

    383.04 is less than 408.

    The better buy is the $720 washer-
    dryer with a series discount of
    30/20/5.

Section 7.2, pages 203–206

1. Strategy
   To find the discount, multiply the net
   price by the cash discount rate of 4%.

   Solution
   4500(0.04) = 180

   The discount is $180.

2. Strategy
   To find the discount, multiply the net
   price by the cash discount rate of 3%.

   Solution
   1750(0.03) = 52.5

   The discount is $52.50.

3. Strategy
    To find the amount due, multiply the
    net price by the complement of the
    discount rate of 5%.

    Solution
    755(0.95) = 717.25

    The amount due is $717.25.

4. Strategy
    To find the amount due, multiply the
    net price by the complement of the
    discount rate of 4%.

    Solution
    680(0.96) = 652.8

    The amount due is $652.80.

5. Strategy
    To find the discount, multiply the net
    price by the cash discount rate of 3%.
    To find the amount due, subtract the
    discount from the net price.

    Solution
    3000(0.03) = 90

    The discount is $90.

    3000 - 90 = 2910

    The amount due is $2910.

6. Strategy
    To find the discount, multiply the net
    price by the cash discount rate of 4%.
    To find the amount due, subtract the
    discount from the net price.

    Solution
    1860(0.04) = 74.4

    The discount is $74.40.

    1860 - 74.40 = 1785.60

    The amount due is $1785.60.

7. Strategy
    To find the amount due, multiply the
    net price by the complement of the
    discount rate of 4%.

    Solution
    5200(0.96) = 4992

    The amount due is $4992.

8. Strategy
    To find the amount due, multiply the
    net price by the complement of the
    discount rate of 3%.

    Solution
    2150(0.97) = 2085.5

    The amount due is $2085.50.

9. Strategy
    To find the last date the discount may
    be taken, find the date 10 days from
    July 28.
    To find the due date of the invoice,
    find the date 30 days after the end of
    the month.
    To find the amount due if the discount
    is earned, multiply the net price by
    the complement of the cash discount
    rate of 5%.

    Solution
    10 days from July 28 is August 7.
    The last date the discount may be
    taken is August 7.
    30 days after the end of the month is
    August 30.
    The due date of the invoice is
    August 30.
    Amount due = 11,420(0.95) = 10,849

    The amount due if the discount is
    earned is $10,849.

10. Strategy
    To find the last date the discount may
    be taken, find the date 10 days from
    July 12.
    To find the due date of the invoice,
    find the date 30 days after the end of
    the month.
    To find the amount due if the discount
    is earned, multiply the net price by
    the complement of the cash discount
    rate of 3%.

    Solution
    10 days from July 12 is July 22.
    The last date the discount may be
    taken is July 22.
    30 days after the end of the month is
    August 30.
    The due date of the invoice is
    August 30.
    Amount due = 2150(0.97) = 2085.5

    The amount due if the discount is
    earned is $2085.50.

11. Strategy
    To find the last date the discount may
    be taken, find the date 10 days from
    May 27.
    To find the due date of the invoice,
    find the date 30 days from May 27.
    To find the amount due if the discount
    is earned, multiply the net price by
    the complement of the cash discount
    rate of 2%.

    Solution
    There are 4 days from May 27 to
    May 31.
    10 days from May 27 is June 6.
    The last date the discount may be
    taken is June 6.
    30 days after May 27 is June 26.
    The due date of the invoice is
    June 26.
    Amount due = 2245(0.98) = 2200.1

    The amount due if the discount is
    earned is $2200.10.

12. Strategy
    To find the last date the discount may
    be taken, find the date 10 days from
    March 24.
    To find the due date of the invoice,
    find the date 30 days from March 24.
    To find the amount due if the discount
    is earned, multiply the net price by
    the complement of the cash discount
    rate of 4%.

    Solution
    There are 7 days from March 24 to
    March 31.
    10 days from March 24 is April 3.
    The last date the discount may be
    taken is April 3.
    30 days after March 24 is April 23.
    The due date of the invoice is
    April 23.
    Amount due = 866(0.96) = 831.36

    The amount due if the discount is
    earned is $831.36.

13. 48.20 x 20 = $964.00   14. 6.70 x 50 = $335.00   15. 106.75 x 25 = $2668.75

16. 23.40 x 24 = $561.60   17. 5.80 x 48 = $278.40

18. Total list price = 964.00 + 335.00 + 2668.75 + 561.60 + 278.40
                     = $4807.75

19. Series discount = 4807.75[1.00 - (0.80)(0.95)]
                    = 4807.75(1.00 - 0.76)
                    = 4807.75(0.24) = $1153.86

20. Net price = list price - discount   21. Cash discount = 3653.89(0.05) ≈ $182.69
              = 4807.75 - 1153.86
              = $3653.89

22. Total amount paid = net price - cash discount
                      = 3653.89 - 182.69
                      = $3471.20

23. 914.50 x 5 = $4572.50   24. 74.60 x 3 = $223.80

25. 108.40 x 3 = $325.20   26. 9.25 x 64 = $592.00

27. 419.25 x 12 = $5031.00

28. Total list price = 4572.50 + 223.80 + 325.20 + 592.00 + 5031.00
                     = $10,744.50

29. Trade discount = 10,744.50[1.00 - (0.85)(0.90)] = 10,744.50(1.00 - 0.765)
                   = 10,744.50(0.235) ≈ $2524.96

30. Net price = list price - discount   31. Cash discount = 8219.54(0.03)
              = 10,744.50 - 2524.96   ≈ $246.59
              = $8219.54

32. Total amount paid = net price - cash discount
                        = 8219.54 - 246.96
                        = $7972.95

33. 174.50 x 24 = $4188.00   34. 32.25 x 36 = $1161.00   35. 11.30 x 36 = $406.80

36. 39.70 x 30 = $1191.00   37. 88.40 x 12 = $1060.80

38. Total list price = 4188.00 + 1161.00 + 406.80 + 1191.00 + 1060.80
                      = $8007.60

39. Trade discount = 8007.60[1.00-(0.80)(0.90)] = 8007.60(1.00 - 0.72)
                    = 8007.60(0.28) ≈ 2242.13

40. Net price = list price - discount   41. Cash discount = 5765.47(0.04)
              = 8007.60 - 2242.13   ≈ $230.62
              = $5765.47

42. Total amount paid = net price - cash discount
                       = 5765.47 - 230.62
                       = $5534.85

43. Strategy
     To find the amount credited to the
     bill, solve the basic percent equation
     for the base.
     The rate is the complement of the cash
     discount rate.

     Solution
         part = base x rate
      payment = amount credited x rate
         3000 = amount credited x 0.96
       $\frac{3000}{0.96}$ = amount credited
         3125 = amount credited

     The amount credited to the bill is
     $3125.

44. Strategy
     To find the amount credited to the
     bill, solve the basic percent equation
     for the base.
     The rate is the complement of the cash
     discount rate.

     Solution
         part = base x rate
      payment = amount credited x rate
          800 = amount credited x 0.98
       $\frac{800}{0.98}$ = amount credited
       816.33 ≈ amount credited

     The amount credited to the bill is
     $816.33.

45. Strategy
     To find the amount credited to the
     bill, solve the basic percent equation
     for the base.
     The rate is the complement of the cash
     discount rate.

     Solution
         part = base x rate
      payment = amount credited x rate
         1000 = amount credited x 0.95
       $\frac{1000}{0.95}$ = amount credited
      1052.63 ≈ amount credited

     The amount credited to the bill is
     $1052.63.

46. Strategy
     To find the amount credited to the
     bill, solve the basic percent equation
     for the base.
     The rate is the complement of the cash
     discount rate.

     Solution
         part = base x rate
      payment = amount credited x rate
          500 = amount credited x 0.97
       $\frac{500}{0.97}$ = amount credited
       515.46 ≈ amount credited

     The amount credited to the bill is
     $515.46.

47. Strategy
    To find the amount remaining to be
    paid:
    • Find the amount credited for the
      first payment.
    • Subtract the amount credited from
      the amount of the invoice.

    Solution
    $$part = base \times rate$$
    $$payment = amount\ credited \times rate$$
    $$20,000 = amount\ credited \times 0.96$$
    $$\frac{20,000}{0.96} = amount\ credited$$
    $$20,833.33 \approx amount\ credited$$

    $$32,000 - 20,833.33 = 11,166.67$$

    The amount remaining to be paid is
    $11,166.67.

48. Strategy
    To find the amount remaining to be
    paid:
    • Find the amount credited for the
      first payment.
    • Subtract the amount credited from
      the amount of the invoice.

    Solution
    $$part = base \times rate$$
    $$payment = amount\ credited \times rate$$
    $$10,000 = amount\ credited \times 0.98$$
    $$\frac{10,000}{0.98} = amount\ credited$$
    $$10,204.08 \approx amount\ credited$$

    $$18,500 - 10,204.08 = 8295.92$$

    The amount remaining to be paid is
    $8295.92.

49. Strategy
    To find the total amount paid:
    • Find the amount credited for the
      first payment.
    • Find the amount due by subtracting
      the amount credited from the amount
      of the invoice.
    • Add the first payment to the amount
      due.

    Solution
    $$part = base \times rate$$
    $$payment = amount\ credited \times rate$$
    $$2000 = amount\ credited \times 0.96$$
    $$\frac{2000}{0.96} = amount\ credited$$
    $$2083.33 \approx amount\ credited$$

    $$3000 - 2083.33 = 916.67$$
    $$2000 + 916.67 = 2916.67$$

    The total amount paid is $2916.67.

50. Strategy
    To find the total amount paid:
    • Find the amount credited for the
      first payment.
    • Find the amount due by subtracting
      the amount credited from the amount
      of the invoice.
    • Add the first payment to the amount
      due.

    Solution
    $$part = base \times rate$$
    $$payment = amount\ credited \times rate$$
    $$1000 = amount\ credited \times 0.97$$
    $$\frac{1000}{0.97} = amount\ credited$$
    $$1030.93 \approx amount\ credited$$

    $$1400 - 1030.93 = 369.07$$
    $$1000 + 369.07 = 1369.07$$

    The total amount paid is $1369.07.

Business Case Study

1.

Quantity	Catalogue Number	Description	Unit Price	Amount
47	BP-8033	Bumper Pad	25.00	1175
25	HC-3729	Maple Highchair	55.00	1375
19	MP-5216	Mesh Playpen	60.00	1140
15	PC-2473	Porta-crib	90.00	1350
20	RG-7904	Restraining Gate	20.00	400
48	US-4651	Umbrella Stroller	50.00	2400

Total List Price	7840
Trade Discount	1881.60
Net Price	5958.40
Transportation	175.00
Cash Discount	119.17
Total Amount Paid	6014.23

2.

Quantity	Catalogue Number	Description	Unit Price	Amount
47	BP-8033	Bumper Pad	25.00	1175
25	HC-3729	Maple Highchair	55.00	1375
19	MP-5216	Mesh Playpen	60.00	1140
15	PC-2473	Porta-crib	90.00	1350
20	RG-7904	Restraining Gate	20.00	400
48	US-4651	Umbrella Stroller	50.00	2400

Total List Price	7840
Trade Discount	1881.60
Net Price	5958.40
Transportation	175.00
Cash Discount	59.58
Total Amount Paid	6073.82

3.

Quantity	Catalogue Number	Description	Unit Price	Amount
47	BP-8033	Bumper Pad	25.00	1175
25	HC-3729	Maple Highchair	55.00	1375
19	MP-5216	Mesh Playpen	60.00	1140
15	PC-2473	Porta-crib	90.00	1350
20	RG-7904	Restraining Gate	20.00	400
48	US-4651	Umbrella Stroller	50.00	2400

Total List Price	7840
Trade Discount	1881.60
Net Price	5958.40
Transportation	175.00
Cash Discount	--
Total Amount Paid	6133.40

4. The invoice must be paid 30 days after October 24.
   Thirty days after October 24 is November 23.

5.   Part = base x rate
    Payment = amount credited x rate
        4000 = amount credited x 0.98
        $\frac{4000}{0.98}$ = amount credited
    4081.63 ≈ amount credited

    5958.40 - 4081.63 = 1876.77
    1876.77 + 175 (transportation charges)
      = 2051.77

    \$2051.77 remains to be paid after
    November 1.

        Part = base x rate
    Payment = amount credited x rate
        2000 = amount credited x 0.99
        $\frac{2000}{0.99}$ = amount credited
    2020.20 ≈ amount credited

    2051.77 - 2020.20 = 31.57

    \$31.57 remains to be paid by the date
    30 days from the date of invoice.

7. 2 hours x \$8.50 per hour = \$17.00
    $\frac{1}{6}$ hour x \$9.60 per hour = \$1.60
    $\frac{1}{4}$ hour x \$9.20 per hour = \$2.30
    \$17.00 + \$1.60 + \$2.30 = \$20.90

    The cost to the company in wages for
    the receipt of the damaged goods was
    \$20.90.

6. Total number of items shipped
      = 50 + 25 + 20 + 15 + 20 + 50 = 170
    Total number of defective items
      = 3 + 1 + 2 = 6

      Part = base x rate
        6 = 170 x rate
      $\frac{6}{170}$ = rate
    0.035 ≈ rate

    Approximately 3.5% of the items
    shipped by the Concord Company were
    defective. This is three and a half
    times, or 2.5% more than, the percent
    of damaged goods received from the
    Lexington Company.

8. Answers will vary. For example:
    Those goods will not be in stock in
    the store. Consequently, sales could
    be lost. If customers do not find the
    goods they want to purchase in the
    store, customers could be lost as
    well.

9.

Quantity	Catalogue Number	Description	Unit Price	Amount
50	BP-8033	Bumper Pad	25.00	1250
25	HC-3729	Maple Highchair	55.00	1375
20	MP-5216	Mesh Playpen	60.00	1200
15	PC-2473	Porta-crib	90.00	1350
20	RG-7904	Restraining Gate	20.00	400
50	US-4651	Umbrella Stroller	50.00	2500

	Amount
Total List Price	8075
Trade Discount	1554.44
Net Price	6520.56
Transportation	175.00
Cash Discount	65.21
Total Amount Paid	6630.35

\$6630.35 would be due the Lexington Company.

Quantity	Catalogue Number	Description	Unit Price	Amount
50	BP-8033	Bumper Pad	25.00	1250
25	HC-3729	Maple Highchair	55.00	1375
20	MP-5216	Mesh Playpen	60.00	1200
15	PC-2473	Porta-crib	90.00	1350
20	RG-7904	Restraining Gate	20.00	400
50	US-4651	Umbrella Stroller	50.00	2500

Total List Price	8075
Trade Discount	1938
Net Price	6137
Transportation	175.00
Cash Discount	122.74
Total Amount Paid	6189.26

$6189.26 would be due the Concord Company if there were no damaged goods and the bill was paid by November 1.

$6630.35 - $6189.26 = $441.09
The amount due the Lexington Company would be $441.09 more than the amount due the Concord Company.

$441.09 is greater than $20.90.
The difference is greater than the additional cost to the company for employee wages related to the receipt of damaged goods.

10. Answers will vary. For example, the following might be considered:
The cost of merchandise ordered from the Concord Company is lower. If the company generally takes advantage of the fifteen-day cash discount period, the savings are even greater, as the Lexington Company does not offer a fifteen-day cash discount period. Even if transportation charges from the Lexington Company were $0, the Concord Company invoice is still lower. If transportation charges from the Lexington Company are greater than they are from the Concord Company, the difference in price would be that much greater than it is at present.

Review/Test, pages 211–212

1. (a) 100% - 40% = 60%   (b) 60% = 0.60

2. Strategy
To find the discount, multiply the discount rate (30%) by the list price (6200).
To find the net price, subtract the discount from the list price.

Solution
Discount = list price x discount
        = 6200(0.30)
        = 1860

The discount is $1860.

Net price = list price - discount
         = 6200 - 1860
         = 4340

The net price is $4340.

3. Strategy
To find the net price:
• Find the list price of 100 roof racks by multiplying the list price of one rack ($150) by 100.
• Multiply the list price of 100 roof racks by the complement of the discount rate (100% - 25% = 75%).

Solution
List price for 100 racks
 = 150 x 100 = 15,000

Net price = 15,000(0.75) = 11,250

The net price is $11,250.

4. Strategy
   To determine which is the better buy:
   • Calculate the net price of each
     item by multiplying the list price
     by the complement of the discount
     rate.
   • Compare the net prices of the two
     items.

   Solution
   Net price = 700(0.65) = 455
   Net price = 600(0.80) = 480

   455 is less than 480.

   The tool set with a list price of $700
   and a discount rate of 35% is the
   better buy.

5. Strategy
   To find the list price, divide the net
   price ($59.50) by the complement of
   the trade discount rate
   (100% - 15% = 85%).

   Solution
   List price = $\frac{59.50}{0.85}$ = 70

   The list price is $70.

6. Strategy
   To find the discount, multiply the
   list price by the first discount rate
   to find the first discount, subtract
   the first discount from the list price
   to find the first net price, multiply
   the first net price by the second
   discount rate to find the second
   discount, and add the first and second
   discounts.
   To find the net price, subtract the
   second discount from the first net
   price.

   Solution
   First discount = 950(0.20) = 190
   First net price = 950 - 190 = 760
   Second discount = 760(0.10) = 76
   Sum of the discounts = 190 + 76 = 266

   The discount is $266.

   Net price = 760 - 76 = 684

   The net price is $684.

7. Strategy
   To find the net price, multiply the
   list price by the product of the
   complements of the discount rates.

   Solution
   Net price = 9400 x (0.70)(0.90)
             = 9400 x (0.63) = 5922

   The net price is $5922.

8. Strategy
    To find the net price, multiply the
    list price by the product of the
    complements of the discount rates.

    Solution
    Net price = 3600 x (0.75)(0.85)
             = 3600 x (0.6375) = 2295

    The net price is $2295.

9. Strategy
    To find the amount of the second trade
    discount:
    • Multiply the list price by the
      first discount rate to find the
      first discount.
    • Subtract the first discount from
      the list price to find the first
      net price.
    • Multiply the first net price by the
      second discount rate.

    Solution
    First discount = 170(0.20) = 34
    First net price = 170 - 34 = 136
    Second discount = 136(0.10) = 13.60

    The amount of the second trade
    discount is $13.60.

10. Strategy
    To find the net price, multiply the
    list price by the product of the
    complements of the discount rates.

    Solution
    Net price = 420 x (0.80)(0.085)(0.95)
             = 420 x (0.646) = 271.32

    The net price is $271.32.

11. Strategy
    To find the single discount
    equivalent, subtract the product of
    the complements of the discount rates
    from 1.00. Express the answer as a
    percent and as a decimal.

    Solution
    1.00 - (0.65)(0.85)(0.95)
     = 1.00 - 0.524875 = 0.475125

    The single discount equivalent is
    (a) 47.5125% or (b) 0.475125.

12. Strategy:
    To find the discount:
    • Find the single discount
      equivalent.
    • Multiply the list price by the
      single discount equivalent.

    Solution
    1.00 - (0.75)(0.90)
     = 1.00 - 0.675 = 0.325
    Discount = 5500(0.325) = 1787.50

    The discount is $1787.50.

13. Strategy
    To find the discount:
    • Find the total list price by
      multiplying the list price by the
      number of items purchased.
    • Determine if the discount is
      earned.
    • Find the single discount equivalent
      of the series discount.
    • Multiply the total list price by
      the single discount equivalent.

    Solution
    Total list price = 25 x 75 = 1875
    The order is for over $1500.
    The discount is earned.
    1.00 - (0.75)(0.90)(0.95)
     = 1.00 - 0.64125 = 0.35875
    Discount = 1875(0.35875) ≈ 672.66

    The discount is $672.66.

14. Strategy
    To determine which is the better buy:
    • Find the single discount equivalent
      of a 35/15/10 series discount.
    • Find the single discount equivalent
      of a 30/20/10 series discount.
    • Compare the two single discount
      equivalents.

    Solution
    $1.00 - (0.65)(0.85)(0.90)$
    $= 1.00 - 0.49725 = 0.50275 = 50.275\%$
    $1.00 - (0.70)(0.80)(0.90)$
    $= 1.00 - 0.504 = 0.496 = 49.6\%$
    50.275% is greater than 49.6%.

    The better buy is the 35/15/10 series
    discount.

15. Strategy
    To find the discount, multiply the net
    price by the discount rate.

    Solution
    $4800(0.02) = 96$

    The discount is $96.

16. Strategy
    To find the amount due, multiply the
    net price by the complement of the
    discount rate of 3%.

    Solution
    $2350(0.97) = 2279.50$

    The amount due is $2279.50.

17. Strategy
    To find the cash discount, multiply
    the net price by the cash discount
    rate of 4%.
    To find the amount due, subtract the
    discount from the net price.

    Solution
    $1500(0.04) = 60$

    The cash discount is $60.

    $1500 - 60 = 1440$

    The amount due is $1440.

18. To find the last date the discount may
    be taken, find the date 10 days from
    August 24.
    To find the due date of the invoice,
    find the date 30 days from August 31.
    To find the amount due if the discount
    is earned, multiply the net price by
    the complement of the cash discount
    rate of 2%.

    Solution
    There are 7 days from August 24 to
    August 31.
    The last date the discount may be
    taken is September 3.
    30 days after August 31 is
    September 30.
    The due date of the invoice is
    September 30.
    Amount due $= 16,280(0.98) = 15,954.40$

    The amount due if the discount is
    earned is $15,954.40.

19. Strategy
    To find the total amount paid:
    • Find the amount credited for the
      first payment.
    • Find the amount due by subtracting
      the amount credited from the amount
      of the invoice.
    • Add the first payment to the amount
      due.

    Solution
    part = base x rate
    payment = amount credited x rate
    5000 = amount credited x 0.96
    $\frac{5000}{0.96}$ = amount credited
    $5208.33 \approx$ amount credited

    $8240 - 5208.33 = 3031.67$
    $5000 + 3031.67 = 8031.67$

    The total amount paid is $8031.67.

20. Strategy
     To find the total amount paid:
     • Find the amount credited for the
       first payment.
     • Find the amount due by subtracting
       the amount credited from the amount
       of the invoice.
     • Add the first payment to the amount
       due.

     Solution
           part = base x rate
     payment = amount credited x rate
         2500 = amount credited x 0.97
        $\frac{2500}{0.97}$ = amount credited
      2577.32 ≈ amount credited

      4200 - 2577.32 = 1622.68
      2500 + 1622.68 = 4122.68

     The total amount paid is $4122.68.

21. 24 x 29.90 = 717.60   22. 18 x 31.80 = 572.40   23. 30 x 13.50 = 405.00

24. 10 x 181.30 = 1813.00   25. 40 x 74.50 = 2980.00

26. Total list price = 717.60 + 572.40 + 405.00 + 1813.00 + 2980.00 = 6488.00

27. Series discount = 6488.00[1.00 - (0.80)(0.90)]
                     = 6488.00(1.00 - 0.72)
                     = 6488.00(0.28) = 1816.64

28. Net price = list price - discount   29. Cash discount = 4671.36(0.02) ≈ 93.43
               = 6488.00 - 1816.64
               = 4671.36

30. Total amount due = 4671.36 - 93.43 = 4577.93

CHAPTER 8
Pricing

Section 8.1, pages 221–224

1. Strategy
   To find the markup, solve the formula
   $M = S - C$ for M ($S = 399$, $C = 244$).

   Solution
   $M = S - C$
   $= 399 - 244$
   $= 155$

   The markup is $155.

2. Strategy
   To find the markup, solve the formula
   $M = S - C$ for M ($S = 24.95$,
   $C = 12.50$).

   Solution
   $M = S - C$
   $= 24.95 - 12.50$
   $= 12.45$

   The markup is $12.45.

3. Strategy
   To find the selling price, solve the
   formula $M = S - C$ for S ($M = 57$,
   $C = 88$).

   Solution
   $M = S - C$
   $57 = S - 88$
   $145 = S$

   The selling price is $145.

4. Strategy
   To find the selling price, solve the
   formula $M = S - C$ for S ($M = 44.50$,
   $C = 88.25$).

   Solution
   $M = S - C$
   $44.50 = S - 88.25$
   $132.75 = S$

   The selling price is $132.75.

5. Strategy
   To find the cost, solve the formula
   $M = S - C$ for C ($M = 85$, $S = 239$).

   Solution
   $M = S - C$
   $85 = 239 - C$
   $85 + C = 239 - C + C$
   $85 + C = 239$
   $C = 154$

   The cost is $154.

6. Strategy
   To find the cost, solve the formula
   $M = S - C$ for C ($M = 96$, $S = 229.90$).

   Solution
   $M = S - C$
   $96 = 229.90 - C$
   $96 + C = 229.90 - C + C$
   $96 + C = 229.90$
   $C = 133.90$

   The cost is $133.90.

7. Strategy
    To find the markup, solve the formula
    for $M = r \times C$ for M ($r = 0.30$,
    $C = 94$).

    Solution
    $M = r \times C$
    $\quad = (0.30)(94)$
    $\quad = 28.20$

    The markup is $28.20.

8. Strategy
    To find the markup, solve the formula
    $M = r \times C$ for M ($r = 0.42$, $C = 195$).

    Solution
    $M = r \times C$
    $\quad = (0.42)(195)$
    $\quad = 81.9$

    The markup is $81.90.

9. Strategy
    To find the markup, solve the formula
    $M = r \times S$ for M ($r = 0.30$, $S = 149$).

    Solution
    $M = r \times S$
    $\quad = (0.30)(149)$
    $\quad = 44.7$

    The markup is $44.70.

10. Strategy
    To find the markup, solve the formula
    $M = r \times S$ for M ($r = 0.35$, $S = 429$).

    Solution
    $M = r \times S$
    $\quad = (0.35)(429)$
    $\quad = 150.15$

    The markup is $150.15.

11. Strategy
    To find the selling price, solve the
    formula $S = (1 + r)C$ for S ($r = 0.40$,
    $C = 345$).

    Solution
    $S = (1 + r)C$
    $\quad = (1 + 0.40)(345)$
    $\quad = (1.40)(345)$
    $\quad = 483$

    The selling price is $483.

12. Strategy
    To find the selling price, solve the
    formula $S = (1 + r)C$ for S ($r = 0.60$,
    $C = 155$).

    Solution
    $S = (1 + r)C$
    $\quad = (1 + 0.60)(155)$
    $\quad = (1.60)(155)$
    $\quad = 248$

    The selling price is $248.

13. Strategy
    To find the selling price, solve the
    formula $S = (1 + r)C$ for S ($r = 0.45$,
    $C = 88$).

    Solution
    $S = (1 + r)C$
    $\quad = (1 + 0.45)88$
    $\quad = (1.45)88$
    $\quad = 127.60$

    The selling price is $127.60.

14. Strategy
    To find the selling price, solve the
    formula $S = (1 + r)C$ for S ($r = 0.25$,
    $C = 75$).

    Solution
    $S = (1 + r)C$
    $\quad = (1 + 0.25)75$
    $\quad = (1.25)75$
    $\quad = 93.75$

    The selling price is $93.75.

15. Strategy
    To find the selling price, solve the formula $C = (1 - r)S$ for S ($C = 22$, $r = 0.28$).

    Solution
    $$C = (1 - r)S$$
    $$22 = (1 - 0.28)S$$
    $$22 = 0.72S$$
    $$\frac{22}{0.72} = S$$
    $$30.56 \approx S$$

    The selling price is $30.56.

16. Strategy
    To find the selling price, solve the formula $C = (1 - r)S$ for S ($C = 172$, $r = 0.44$).

    Solution
    $$C = (1 - r)S$$
    $$172 = (1 - 0.44)S$$
    $$172 = 0.56S$$
    $$\frac{172}{0.56} = S$$
    $$307.14 \approx S$$

    The selling price is $307.14.

17. Strategy
    To find the selling price, solve the formula $C = (1 - r)S$ for S ($C = 249$, $r = 0.36$).

    Solution
    $$C = (1 - r)S$$
    $$249 = (1 - 0.36)S$$
    $$249 = 0.64S$$
    $$\frac{249}{0.64} = S$$
    $$389.06 \approx S$$

    The selling price is $389.06.

18. Strategy
    To find the selling price, solve the formula $C = (1 - r)S$ for S ($C = 107$, $r = 0.38$).

    Solution
    $$C = (1 - r)S$$
    $$107 = (1 - 0.38)S$$
    $$107 = 0.62S$$
    $$\frac{107}{0.62} = S$$
    $$172.58 \approx S$$

    The selling price is $172.58.

19. Strategy
    To find the cost, solve the formula $C = (1 - r)S$ for C ($r = 0.20$, $S = 599$).

    Solution
    $$C = (1 - r)S$$
    $$= (1 - 0.20)(599)$$
    $$= (0.80)(599)$$
    $$= 479.2$$

    The cost is $479.20.

20. Strategy
    To find the cost, solve the formula $C = (1 - r)S$ for C ($r = 0.30$, $S = 399$).

    Solution
    $$C = (1 - r)S$$
    $$= (1 - 0.30)(399)$$
    $$= (0.70)(399)$$
    $$= 279.3$$

    The cost is $279.30.

21. Strategy
    To find the cost, solve the formula $C = (1 - r)S$ for C ($S = 179$, $r = 0.24$).

    Solution
    $$C = (1 - r)S$$
    $$= (1 - 0.24)179$$
    $$= (0.76)179$$
    $$= 136.04$$

    The cost is $136.04.

22. Strategy
    To find the cost, solve the formula $C = (1 - r)S$ for C ($S = 39$, $r = 0.34$).

    Solution
    $$C = (1 - r)S$$
    $$= (1 - 0.34)39$$
    $$= (0.66)39$$
    $$= 25.74$$

    The cost is $25.74.

23. Strategy
    To find the cost, solve the formula
    $S = (1 + r)C$ for C ($S = 189$,
    $r = 0.45$).

    Solution
    $$S = (1 + r)C$$
    $$189 = (1 + 0.45)C$$
    $$189 = 1.45C$$
    $$\frac{189}{1.45} = C$$
    $$130.34 \approx C$$

    The cost is \$130.34.

24. Strategy
    To find the cost, solve the formula
    $S = (1 + r)C$ for C ($S = 399$,
    $r = 0.48$).

    Solution
    $$S = (1 + r)C$$
    $$399 = (1 + 0.48)C$$
    $$399 = 1.48C$$
    $$\frac{399}{1.48} = C$$
    $$269.59 \approx C$$

    The cost is \$269.59.

25. Strategy
    To find the cost, solve the formula
    $S = (1 + r)C$ for C ($S = 78.88$,
    $r = 0.36$).

    Solution
    $$S = (1 + r)C$$
    $$78.88 = (1 + 0.36)C$$
    $$78.88 = 1.36C$$
    $$\frac{78.88}{1.36} = C$$
    $$58 = C$$

    The cost is \$58.

26. Strategy
    To find the cost, solve the formula
    $S = (1 + r)C$ for C ($S = 69.60$,
    $r = 0.45$).

    Solution
    $$S = (1 + r)C$$
    $$69.60 = (1 + 0.45)C$$
    $$69.60 = 1.45C$$
    $$\frac{69.60}{1.45} = C$$
    $$48 = C$$

    The cost is \$48.

27. Strategy
    To find the markup rate on the cost:
    • Solve the formula $M = S - C$ for M
      ($S = 394$, $C = 280$).
    • Solve the formula $M = r \times C$ for r.

    Solution

    $M = S - C$ $M = r \times C$
    $\quad = 394 - 280$ $114 = r \times 280$
    $\quad = 114$ $\frac{114}{280} = r$
    $\qquad\qquad\qquad 0.407 \approx r$

    The markup on cost is 40.7%.

28. Strategy
    To find the markup rate on the cost:
    • Solve the formula $M = S - C$ for M
      ($S = 394$, $C = 280$).
    • Solve the formula $M = r \times C$ for r.

    Solution

    $M = S - C$ $M = r \times C$
    $\quad = 133 - 95$ $38 = r \times 95$
    $\quad = 38$ $\frac{38}{95} = r$
    $\qquad\qquad\qquad 0.4 = r$

    The markup on cost is 40%.

29. Strategy
    To find the markup rate on the selling
    price:
    • Solve the formula $M = S - C$ for M
      ($S = 390$, $C = 234$).
    • Solve the formula $M = r \times C$ for r.

    Solution

    $M = S - C$ $M = r \times S$
    $\quad = 390 - 234$ $156 = r \times 390$
    $\quad = 156$ $\frac{156}{390} = r$
    $\qquad\qquad\qquad 0.4 = r$

    The markup on the selling price is
    40%.

30. Strategy
    To find the markup rate on the selling
    price:
    • Solve the formula $M = S - C$ for M
      ($S = 292$, $C = 219$).
    • Solve the formula $M = r \times S$ for r.

    Solution

    $M = S - C$ $M = r \times S$
    $\quad = 292 - 219$ $73 = r \times 292$
    $\quad = 73$ $\frac{73}{292} = r$
    $\qquad\qquad\qquad 0.25 = r$

    The markup on the selling price is
    25%.

31. Strategy
    To find the markdown, solve the
    formula $M = R - S$ for M ($R = 89$,
    $S = 69$).

    Solution
    $M = R - S$
    $= 89 - 69$
    $= 20$

    The markdown is $20.

32. Strategy
    To find the markdown, solve the
    formula $M = R - S$ for M ($R = 599$,
    $S = 499$).

    Solution
    $M = R - S$
    $= 599 - 499$
    $= 100$

    The markdown is $100.

33. Strategy
    To find the markdown rate:
    • Solve the formula $M = R - S$ for M
      ($R = 695$, $S = 557$).
    • Solve the formula $M = r \times R$ for r.

    Solution

    $M = R - S$ $M = r \times R$
    $= 695 - 557$ $138 = r \times 695$
    $= 138$ $\frac{138}{695} = r$
        $0.199 = r$

    The markdown rate is 19.9%.

34. Strategy
    To find the markdown rate:
    • Solve the formula $M = R - S$ for M
      ($R = 380$, $S = 323$).
    • Solve the formula $M = r \times R$ for r.

    Solution

    $M = R - S$ $M = r \times R$
    $= 380 - 323$ $57 = r \times 380$
    $= 57$ $\frac{57}{380} = r$
        $0.15 = r$

    The markdown rate is 15%.

35. Strategy
    To find the markdown rate:
    • Solve the formula $M = R - S$ for M
      ($R = 390$, $S = 156$).
    • Solve the formula $M = r \times R$ for r.

    Solution

    $M = R - S$ $M = r \times R$
    $= 390 - 156$ $234 = r \times 390$
    $= .234$ $\frac{234}{390} = r$
        $0.6 = r$

    The markdown rate is 60%.

36. Strategy
    To find the markdown rate:
    • Solve the formula $M = R - S$ for M
      ($R = 215$, $S = 129$).
    • Solve the formula $M = r \times R$ for r.

    Solution

    $M = R - S$ $M = r \times R$
    $= 215 - 129$ $86 = r \times 215$
    $= 86$ $\frac{86}{215} = r$
        $0.4 = r$

    The markdown rate is 40%.

37. Strategy
    To find the markdown rate:
    • Solve the formula $M = R - S$ for M
      ($R = 95$, $S = 61.75$).
    • Solve the formula $M = r \times R$ for r.

    Solution

    $M = R - S$ $M = r \times R$
    $= 95 - 61.75$ $33.25 = r \times 95$
    $= 33.25$ $\frac{33.25}{95} = r$
        $0.35 = r$

    The markdown rate is 35%.

38. Strategy
    To find the markdown rate:
    • Solve the formula $M = R - S$ for M
      ($R = 129$, $S = 96.75$).
    • Solve the formula $M = r \times R$ for r.

    Solution

    $M = R - S$ $M = r \times R$
    $= 129 - 96.75$ $32.25 = r \times 129$
    $= 32.25$ $\frac{32.25}{129} = r$
        $0.25 = r$

    The markdown rate is 25%.

39. Strategy
    To find the sale price, solve the
    formula $S = (1 - r)R$ for S ($r = 0.30$,
    $R = 299$).

    Solution
    $S = (1 - r)R$
    $= (1 - 0.30)(299)$
    $= (0.70)(299)$
    $= 209.3$

    The sale price is $209.30.

40. Strategy
    To find the sale price, solve the
    formula $S = (1 - r)R$ for S ($r = 0.18$,
    $R = 200$).

    Solution
    $S = (1 - r)R$
    $= (1 - 0.18)(200)$
    $= (0.82)(200)$
    $= 164$

    The sale price is $164.

41. Strategy
    To find the sale price, solve the
    formula $S = (1 - r)R$ for S ($r = 0.20$,
    $R = 795$).

    Solution
    $S = (1 - r)R$
    $= (1 - 0.20)(795)$
    $= (0.80)(795)$
    $= 636$

    The sale price is $636.

42. Strategy
    To find the sale price, solve the
    formula $S = (1 - r)R$ for S ($r = 0.15$,
    $R = 232$).

    Solution
    $S = (1 - r)R$
    $= (1 - 0.15)(232)$
    $= (0.85)(232)$
    $= 197.2$

    The sale price is $197.20.

43. Strategy
    To find the sale price, solve the
    formula $S = (1 - r)R$ for S ($r = 0.25$,
    $R = 375$).

    Solution
    $S = (1 - r)R$
    $= (1 - 0.25)(375)$
    $= (0.75)(375)$
    $= 281.25$

    The sale price is $281.25.

44. Strategy
    To find the sale price, solve the
    formula $S = (1 - r)R$ for S ($r = 0.18$,
    $R = 75$).

    Solution
    $S = (1 - r)R$
    $= (1 - 0.18)(75)$
    $= (0.82)(75)$
    $= 61.5$

    The sale price is $61.50.

45. Strategy
    To find the regular price, solve the
    formula $S = (1 - r)R$ for R ($S = 124$,
    $r = 0.20$).

    Solution
    $S = (1 - r)R$
    $124 = (1 - 0.20)R$
    $124 = 0.80R$
    $\frac{124}{0.80} = R$
    $155 = R$

    The regular price is $155.

46. Strategy
    To find the regular price, solve the
    formula $S = (1 - r)R$ for R ($S = 180$,
    $r = 0.40$).

    Solution
    $S = (1 - r)R$
    $180 = (1 - 0.40)R$
    $180 = 0.60R$
    $\frac{180}{0.60} = R$
    $300 = R$

    The regular price is $300.

47. Strategy
    To find the regular price, solve the
    formula $S = (1 - r)R$ for R ($S = 78$,
    $r = 0.22$).

    Solution
    $$S = (1 - r)R$$
    $$78 = (1 - 0.22)R$$
    $$78 = 0.78R$$
    $$\frac{78}{0.78} = R$$
    $$100 = R$$

    The regular price is $100.

48. Strategy
    To find the regular price, solve the
    formula $S = (1 - r)R$ for R ($S = 49$,
    $r = 0.20$).

    Solution
    $$S = (1 - r)R$$
    $$49 = (1 - 0.20)R$$
    $$49 = 0.80R$$
    $$\frac{49}{0.80} = R$$
    $$61.25 = R$$

    The regular price is $61.25.

49. Strategy
    To find the regular price, solve the
    formula $S = (1 - r)R$ for R ($S = 45$,
    $r = 0.60$).

    Solution
    $$S = (1 - r)R$$
    $$45 = (1 - 0.60)R$$
    $$45 = 0.40R$$
    $$\frac{45}{0.40} = R$$
    $$112.5 = R$$

    The regular price is $112.50.

50. Strategy
    To find the regular price, solve the
    formula $S = (1 - r)R$ for R ($S = 120$,
    $r = 0.40$).

    Solution
    $$S = (1 - r)R$$
    $$120 = (1 - 0.40)R$$
    $$120 = 0.60R$$
    $$\frac{120}{0.60} = R$$
    $$200 = R$$

    The regular price is $200.

Section 8.2, pages 227–228

1. Strategy
   To find the total cost for the roses,
   multiply the cost per dozen times the
   number of dozen roses.
   To find the total selling price if all
   the roses are sold, solve the formula
   $S = (1 + r)C$ for S ($r = 0.45$, C is the
   total cost).

   Solution
   Total cost = unit cost per dozen
   $\qquad\qquad$ x number of dozen
   $\qquad$ = 1.20 x 10 = 12

   The total cost for the roses is $12.

   $$S = (1 + r)C$$
   $$= (1 + 0.45)12$$
   $$= (1.45)12$$
   $$= 17.40$$

   The total selling price if all the
   roses are sold is $17.40.

2. Strategy
   To find the total cost for the
   watermelon, multiply the cost per
   pound times the number of pounds.
   To find the total selling price if all
   the watermelon is sold, solve the
   formula $S = (1 + r)C$ for S ($r = 0.55$,
   C is the total cost).

   Solution
   Total cost = unit cost per pound
   $\qquad\qquad$ x number of pounds
   $\qquad$ = 0.15 x 300 = 45

   The total cost for the watermelon is
   $45.

   $$S = (1 + r)C$$
   $$= (1 + 0.55)45$$
   $$= (1.55)45$$
   $$= 69.75$$

   The total selling price if all the
   watermelon is sold is $69.75.

3. Strategy
   To find the total cost for the
   muffins:
   • Find the number of muffins
     purchased by multiplying the number
     of dozen (5) times 12.
   • Multiply the unit cost times the
     number of muffins.

   To find the total selling price if all
   the muffins are sold, solve the
   formula $S = (1 + r)C$ for S ($r = 0.60$,
   C is the total cost).

   To find the number of muffins that is
   expected to be sold, multiply the
   number of muffins purchased by
   $100\% - 5\% = 95\% = 0.95$.

   Solution
   Number of muffins purchased
    = 5 x 12 = 60
   Total cost = unit cost
                x number of units
              = 0.23 x 60 = 13.80

   The total cost for the muffins is
   $13.80.

   $S = (1 + r)C$
    $= (1 + 0.60)13.80$
    $= (1.60)13.80$
    $= 22.08$

   The total selling price if all the
   muffins are sold is $22.08.

   $0.95(60) = 57$

   57 muffins are expected to be sold.

4. Strategy
   To find the total cost of the
   carnations, multiply the unit cost
   times the number of carnations
   purchased.
   To find the total selling price if all
   the carnations are sold, solve the
   formula $S = (1 + r)C$ for S ($r = 0.50$,
   C is the total cost).

   To find the number of carnations that
   is expected to be sold, multiply the
   number of muffins purchased by
   $100\% - 4\% = 96\% = 0.96$.

   Solution
   Total cost = unit cost
                x number of units
              = 0.40 x 25 = 10

   The total cost for the carnations is
   $10.

   $S = (1 + r)C$
    $= (1 + 0.50)10$
    $= (1.50)10$
    $= 15$

   The total selling price if all the
   carnations are sold is $15.

   $0.96(25) = 24$

   24 of the carnations are expected to
   be sold.

5. Strategy
   To find the total cost of the blueberries, multiply the unit cost times the number
   of units.
   To find the total selling price if all the blueberries are sold, solve the formula
   $S = (1 + r)C$ for S ($r = 0.65$, C is the total cost).
   To find the number of quarts that are expected to be sold, use the basic percent
   equation ($B = 150$, $R = 0.94$).
   To find the price per quart, divide the total selling price by the number of quarts
   expected to be sold.

   Solution
   Total cost = unit cost x number of units = 0.80 x 150 = 120

   The total cost is $120.

   $S = (1 + r)C$
    $= (1 + 0.65)120$
    $= (1.65)120$
    $= 198$

   The total selling price if all the blueberries are sold is $198.

```
P = B x R
  = 150 x 0.94 = 141
```

141 quarts are expected to be sold.

$$\frac{\text{total selling price without spoilage}}{\text{number of quarts expected to be sold}} = \frac{198}{141} \approx 1.40$$

The retailer should charge $1.40 per quart for the blueberries.

6. Strategy
   To find the total cost of the bread, multiply the unit cost times the number of units.
   To find the total selling price if all the bread is sold, solve the formula
   $S = (1 + r)C$ for S ($r = 0.60$, C is the total cost).
   To find the number of loaves that are expected to be sold, use the basic percent equation ($B = 20$, $R = 0.90$).
   To find the price per loaf, divide the total selling price by the number of loaves expected to be sold.

   Solution
   Total cost = unit cost x number of units = 0.65 x 20 = 13

   The total cost is $13.

   ```
   S = (1 + r)C
     = (1 + 0.60)13
     = (1.60)13
     = 20.80
   ```

   The total selling price if all the bread is sold is $198.

   ```
   P = B x R
     = 20 x 0.90 = 18
   ```

   18 loaves are expected to be sold.

   $$\frac{\text{total selling price without spoilage}}{\text{number of loaves expected to be sold}} = \frac{20.80}{18} \approx 1.16$$

   The retailer should charge $1.16 for each loaf of bread.

7. Strategy
   To find the total cost of the bagels, multiply the unit cost times the number of units.
   To find the total selling price if all the bagels are sold, solve the formula
   $S = (1 + r)C$ for S ($r = 0.55$, C is the total cost).
   To find the number of bagels that are expected to be sold, use the basic percent equation ($B = 100$, $R = 100\% - 8\% = 92\% = 0.92$).
   To find the price per bagel, divide the total selling price by the number of bagels expected to be sold.

   Solution
   Total cost = unit cost x number of units = 0.15 x 100 = 15

   The total cost is $15.

   ```
   S = (1 + r)C
     = (1 + 0.55)15
     = (1.55)15
     = 23.25
   ```

The total selling price if all the bagels are sold is $23.25.

$P = B \times R$
   $= 100 \times 0.92 = 92$

92 bagels are expected to be sold.

$$\frac{\text{total selling price without spoilage}}{\text{number of bagels expected to be sold}} = \frac{23.25}{92} \approx 0.25$$

The retailer should charge $.25 for each bagel.

8. Strategy
   To find the total cost of the cantaloupe, multiply the unit cost times the number of units.
   To find the total selling price if all the cantaloupe is sold, solve the formula $S = (1 + r)C$ for S ($r = 0.45$, C is the total cost).
   To find the number of cantaloupe that are expected to be sold, use the basic percent equation ($B = 200$, $R = 100\% - 10\% = 90\% = 0.90$).
   To find the price per cantaloupe, divide the total selling price by the number of cantaloupe expected to be sold.

   Solution
   Total cost = unit cost x number of units = 0.65 x 200 = 130

   The total cost is $130.

   $S = (1 + r)C$
      $= (1 + 0.45)130$
      $= (1.45)130$
      $= 188.50$

   The total selling price if all the cantaloupe is sold is $188.50.

   $P = B \times R$
      $= 200 \times 0.90 = 180$

   180 cantaloupe are expected to be sold.

   $$\frac{\text{total selling price without spoilage}}{\text{number expected to be sold}} = \frac{188.50}{180} \approx 1.05$$

   The retailer should charge $1.05 for each cantaloupe.

9. Strategy
   To find the price per pound:
   • Find the total cost for the 300 pounds of carrots.
   • Find the total selling price if all the carrots are sold.
   • Use the basic percent equation to find the number of pounds that are expected to be sold ($B = 300$, $R = 100\% - 7\% = 93\% = 0.93$).
   • Divide the total selling price without spoilage by the number of pounds that are expected to be sold.

   Solution
   Total cost = unit cost x number of units = 0.38 x 300 = 114
   $S = (1 + r)C = (1 + 0.50)114 = (1.50)114 = 171$
   $P = B \times R = 300 \times 0.93 = 279$

   $$\frac{\text{total selling price without spoilage}}{\text{number of pounds expected to be sold}} = \frac{171}{279} \approx 0.61$$

   The price per pound should be $.61.

10. Strategy
    To find the price per head:
    • Find the total cost for the 400 heads of lettuce.
    • Find the total selling price if all the lettuce is sold.
    • Use the basic percent equation to find the number of heads that are expected to be sold ($B = 400$, $R = 100\% - 6\% = 94\% = 0.94$).
    • Divide the total selling price without spoilage by the number of heads that are expected to be sold.

    Solution
    Total cost = unit cost x number of units = 0.52 x 400 = 208
    $S = (1 + r)C = (1 + 0.65)208 = (1.65)208 = 343.20$
    $P = B \times R = 400 \times 0.94 = 376$

    $$\frac{\text{total selling price without spoilage}}{\text{number of heads expected to be sold}} = \frac{343.20}{376} \approx 0.91$$

    The price per head should be $.91.

11. Strategy
    To find the price per lily:
    • Find the total cost for the 50 lilies.
    • Find the total selling price if all the lilies are sold.
    • Use the basic percent equation to find the number of lilies that are expected to be sold ($B = 50$, $R = 100\% - 10\% = 90\% = 0.90$).
    • Divide the total selling price without spoilage by the number of lilies that are expected to be sold.

    Solution
    Total cost = unit cost x number of units = 1.10 x 50 = 55
    $S = (1 + r)C = (1 + 0.55)55 = (1.55)55 = 85.25$
    $P = B \times R = 50 \times 0.90 = 45$

    $$\frac{\text{total selling price without spoilage}}{\text{number of lilies expected to be sold}} = \frac{85.25}{45} \approx 1.89$$

    The florist should charge $1.89 per lily.

12. Strategy
    To find the price per bulky roll:
    • Find the total cost for the 150 rolls.
    • Find the total selling price if all the rolls are sold.
    • Use the basic percent equation to find the number of rolls that are expected to be sold ($B = 150$, $R = 100\% - 4\% = 96\% = 0.96$).
    • Divide the total selling price without spoilage by the number of rolls that are expected to be sold.

    Solution
    Total cost = unit cost x number of units = 0.09 x 150 = 13.50
    $S = (1 + r)C = (1 + 0.60)13.50 = (1.60)13.50 = 21.60$
    $P = B \times R = 150 \times 0.96 = 144$

    $$\frac{\text{total selling price without spoilage}}{\text{number of rolls expected to be sold}} = \frac{21.60}{144} \approx 0.15$$

    The baker should charge $.15 per bulky roll.

13. Strategy
    To find the selling price per muffin:
    • Find the total cost for the 8 dozen muffins.
    • Find the total selling price if all the muffins are sold.
    • Find the number of muffins that are expected to be sold.
    • Divide the total selling price without spoilage by the number of muffins that are expected to be sold.

    Solution
    Total cost = unit cost per dozen x number of dozen purchased = 3.80 x 8 = 30.40
    $S = (1 + r)C = (1 + 0.70)30.40 = (1.70)30.40 = 51.68$
    8 dozen muffins = 8 x 12 muffins = 96 muffins
    Expected to sell: 96 muffins – one half dozen muffins = 96 muffins – 6 muffins
    $\qquad\qquad\qquad\qquad\qquad\qquad\qquad\qquad\qquad\qquad\qquad\qquad$ = 90 muffins

    $$\frac{\text{total selling price without spoilage}}{\text{number expected to be sold}} = \frac{51.68}{90} \approx 0.57$$

    The price per muffin should be $.57.

14. Strategy
    To find the selling price per muffin:
    • Find the total cost for the 5 dozen roses.
    • Find the total selling price if all the roses are sold.
    • Find the number of roses that are expected to be sold.
    • Divide the total selling price without spoilage by the number of roses that are expected to be sold.

    Solution
    Total cost = unit cost per dozen x number of dozen = 6 x 5 = 30
    $S = (1 + r)C = (1 + 0.50)30 = (1.50)30 = 45$
    5 dozen roses = 5 x 12 roses = 60 roses
    Expected to sell: 60 roses – one half dozen roses = 60 roses – 6 roses = 54 roses

    $$\frac{\text{total selling price without spoilage}}{\text{number of roses expected to be sold}} = \frac{45}{54} \approx 0.83$$

    The price per rose should be $.83.

Business Case Study

1. Previous year: Sales: $350,000
    $\qquad\qquad\qquad$ Cost of goods sold: $227,500
    $\qquad\qquad\qquad$ Markup: $122,500

    Past year: Sales: $580,000
    $\qquad\qquad\qquad$ Cost of goods sold: $377,000
    $\qquad\qquad\qquad$ Markup: $203,000

    Extra expenses: Mail Department employee:
    $\qquad\qquad\qquad\quad$ 20 hours per week x 50 weeks x $6.50 per hour:$\qquad$ $6,500
    $\qquad\qquad\qquad$ Bookkeeping Department employee:
    $\qquad\qquad\qquad\quad$ 10 hours per week x 50 weeks x $7 per hour:$\qquad$ 3,500
    $\qquad\qquad\qquad$ Taxes, Insurance, Benefits:$\qquad$ 2,400
    $\qquad\qquad\qquad$ Shipping Charges:$\qquad$ 18,000
    $\qquad\qquad\qquad$ Packaging Materials:$\qquad$ 14,000
    $\qquad\qquad\qquad$ Cost of books neither paid nor returned:$\qquad$ 5,000
    $\qquad\quad$ Total of extra expenses:$\qquad$ $49,400

Markup from past year - markup from previous year = \$203,000 - \$122,500 = \$80,500

Increased markup - total of extra expenses = \$80,500 - \$49,400 = \$31,100

The policy is effective because the company earned \$31,100 more during the past year than was earned during the previous year when the policy was not in effect.

Review/Test, pages 233–234

1. **Strategy**
To find the markup, solve the formula $M = S - C$ for M ($S = 229$, $C = 134$).

Solution
$M = S - C$
$M = 229 - 134$
$M = 95$

The markup is \$95.

2. **Strategy**
To find the selling price, solve the formula $M = S - C$ for S ($M = 63.60$, $C = 159$).

Solution
$M = S - C$
$63.60 = S - 159$
$222.60 = S$

The selling price is \$222.60.

3. **Strategy**
To find the cost, solve the formula $M = S - C$ for C ($M = 39$, $S = 85$).

Solution
$M = S - C$
$39 = 85 - C$
$39 + C = 85 - C + C$
$39 + C = 85$
$39 - 39 + C = 85 - 39$
$C = 46$

The cost is \$46.

4. **Strategy**
To find the markup, solve the formula $M = r \times C$ for M ($r = 0.30$, $C = 59$).

Solution
$M = r \times C$
$M = 0.30 \times 59$
$M = 17.70$

The markup is \$17.70.

5. **Strategy**
To find the markup, solve the formula $M = r \times S$ for M ($r = 0.35$, $S = 180$).

Solution
$M = r \times S$
$M = 0.35 \times 180$
$M = 63$

The markup is \$63.

6. **Strategy**
To find the selling price, solve the formula $S = (1 + r)C$ for S ($r = 0.30$, $C = 55$).

Solution
$S = (1 + r)C$
$S = (1 + 0.30)55$
$S = (1.30)55$
$S = 71.50$

The selling price is \$71.50.

7. Strategy
   To find the selling price, solve the
   formula $C = (1 - r)S$ for S
   ($C = 291.20$, $r = 0.48$).

   Solution
   $$C = (1 - r)S$$
   $$291.20 = (1 - 0.48)S$$
   $$291.20 = (0.52)S$$
   $$\frac{291.20}{0.52} = S$$
   $$560 = S$$

   The selling price is $560.

8. Strategy
   To find the cost, solve the formula
   $C = (1 - r)S$ for C ($r = 0.30$,
   $S = 699$).

   Solution
   $$C = (1 - r)S$$
   $$C = (1 - 0.30)699$$
   $$C = (0.70)699$$
   $$C = 489.30$$

   The cost is $489.30.

9. Strategy
   To find the cost, solve the formula
   $S = (1 + r)C$ for C ($r = 0.45$,
   $S = 319$).

   Solution
   $$S = (1 + r)C$$
   $$319 = (1 + 0.45)C$$
   $$319 = 1.45C$$
   $$\frac{319}{1.45} = C$$
   $$220 = C$$

   The cost is $220.

10. Strategy
    To find the markup rate:
    • Solve the formula $M = S - C$ for M
      ($S = 75.92$, $C = 52$).
    • Solve the formula $M = r \times C$ for r.

    Solution
    $$M = S - C \qquad\qquad M = r \times C$$
    $$M = 75.92 - 52 \qquad 23.92 = r \times 52$$
    $$M = 23.92 \qquad\qquad \frac{23.92}{52} = r$$
    $$0.46 = r$$

    The markup rate on cost is 46%.

11. Strategy
    To find the markup rate:
    • Solve the formula $M = S - C$ for M
      ($S = 79$, $C = 52.93$).
    • Solve the formula $M = r \times S$ for r.

    Solution
    $$M = S - C \qquad\qquad M = r \times S$$
    $$M = 79 - 52.93 \qquad 26.07 = r \times 79$$
    $$M = 26.07 \qquad\qquad \frac{26.07}{79} = r$$
    $$0.33 = r$$

    The markup rate on cost is 33%.

12. Strategy
    To find the markdown, solve the
    formula $M = R - S$ for M ($R = 169$,
    $S = 129.99$).

    Solution
    $$M = R - S$$
    $$M = 169 - 129.99$$
    $$M = 39.01$$

    The markdown is $39.01.

13. Strategy
    To find the markdown rate:
    • Solve the formula $M = R - S$ for M
      ($R = 115$, $S = 92$).
    • Solve the formula $M = r \times R$ for r.

    Solution
    $$M = R - S \qquad\qquad M = r \times R$$
    $$M = 115 - 92 \qquad 23 = r \times 115$$
    $$M = 23 \qquad\qquad \frac{23}{115} = r$$
    $$0.2 = r$$

    The markdown rate is 20%.

14. Strategy
    To find the sale price, solve the
    formula $S = (1 - r)R$ for S ($r = 0.15$,
    $R = 5.80$).

    Solution
    $$S = (1 - r)R$$
    $$S = (1 - 0.15)5.80$$
    $$S = (0.85)5.80$$
    $$S = 4.93$$

    The sale price is $4.93.

15. Strategy
    To find the regular price, solve the
    formula $S = (1 - r)R$ for R
    ($S = 149.25$, $r = 0.25$).

    Solution
    $$S = (1 - r)R$$
    $$149.25 = (1 - 0.25)R$$
    $$149.25 = (0.75)R$$
    $$\frac{149.25}{0.75} = R$$
    $$199 = R$$

    The regular price is $199.

16. Strategy
    To find the price per pound for the bean sprouts:
    • Find the total cost for the 50 pounds of bean sprouts.
    • Find the total selling price if all the bean sprouts are sold.
    • Find the number of pounds that are expected to be sold.
    • Divide the total selling price without spoilage by the number of pounds that are
      expected to be sold.

    Solution
    Total cost = unit cost x number of units = 0.56 x 50 = 28
    $S = (1 + r)C = (1 + 0.50)28 = (1.50)28 = 42$
    Expected to sell: 50 pounds - 5 pounds = 45 pounds

    $$\frac{\text{total selling price without spoilage}}{\text{number of pounds expected to be sold}} = \frac{42}{45} \approx 0.93$$

    The price per pound should be $.93.

17. Strategy
    To find the price per pound for the cookies:
    • Find the total cost for the 10 pounds of cookies.
    • Find the total selling price if all the cookies are sold.
    • Use the basic percent equation to find the number of pounds that are expected to
      be sold ($B = 100$, $R = 0.92$).
    • Divide the total selling price without spoilage by the number of cookies that are
      expected to be sold.

    Solution
    Total cost = cost per pound x number of pounds = 2.15 x 100 = 215
    $S = (1 + r)C = (1 + 0.60)215 = (1.60)215 = 344$

    $P = B \times R$
    $P = 100 \times 0.92$
    $P = 92$

    $$\frac{\text{total selling price without spoilage}}{\text{number of pounds expected to be sold}} = \frac{344}{92} \approx 3.74$$

    The price per pound for the cookies should be $3.74.

18. Strategy
     To find the price per pound:
     • Find the total cost for the 200 pounds of peaches.
     • Find the total selling price if all the peaches are sold.
     • Use the basic percent equation to find the number of pounds that are expected to
       be sold ($B = 200$, $R = 100\% - 10\% = 90\% = 0.90$).
     • Divide the total selling price without spoilage by the number of pounds that are
       expected to be sold.

     Solution
     Total cost = cost per pound x number of pounds = 0.46 x 200 = 92
     $S = (1 + r)C = (1 + 0.55)92 = (1.55)92 = 142.60$

     $P = B \times R = 200 \times 0.90 = 180$

     $$\frac{\text{total selling price without spoilage}}{\text{number of pounds expected to be sold}} = \frac{142.60}{180} \approx 0.79$$

     The price per pound should be $.79.

CHAPTER 9
Payroll

Section 9.1, pages 243–246

1. Strategy
    To find the gross pay, multiply the number of hours worked by the hourly rate.

    Solution
    35(7.50) = 262.50

    The gross pay is $262.50.

2. Strategy
    To find the gross pay, multiply the number of hours worked by the hourly rate.

    Solution
    38(8.75) = 332.50

    The gross pay is $332.50.

3. Strategy
    To find the gross pay:
    • Find the regular pay.
    • Find the overtime pay.
    • Add the regular pay to the overtime pay.

    Solution
    Regular pay = 40(15.50) = 620
    Overtime pay = 15.50(1.5)(7) = 162.75
    Gross pay = 620 + 162.50 = 782.75

    The gross pay is $782.75.

4. Strategy
    To find the gross pay:
    • Find the regular pay.
    • Find the overtime pay.
    • Add the regular pay to the overtime pay.

    Solution
    Regular pay = 40(19.50) = 780
    Overtime pay = 19.50(1.5)(11) = 321.75
    Gross pay = 780 + 321.75 = 1101.75

    The gross pay is $1101.75.

5. Strategy
    To find the gross pay:
    • Find the total number of hours worked.
    • Find the regular pay.
    • Find the overtime pay.
    • Add the regular pay to the overtime pay.

    Solution
    10 + 12 + 8 + 6 + 10 + 5 = 51
    Regular pay = 40(6.50) = 260
    Overtime pay = 6.50(1.5)(11) = 107.25
    Gross pay = 260 + 107.25 = 367.25

    The gross pay is $367.25.

6. Strategy
    To find the gross pay:
    • Find the total number of hours worked.
    • Find the regular pay.
    • Find the overtime pay.
    • Add the regular pay to the overtime pay.

    Solution
    9 + 11 + 10 + 13 + 10 + 4 = 57
    Regular pay = 40(17.25) = 690
    Overtime pay = 17.25(1.5)(17) = 439.88
    Gross pay = 690 + 439.88 = 1129.88

    The gross pay is $1129.88.

7. Strategy
   To find the gross pay, divide the
   annual salary by 12.

   Solution
   62,500 ÷ 12 = 5208.33

   The monthly gross pay is $5208.33.

8. Strategy
   To find the gross pay, divide the
   annual salary by 12.

   Solution
   78,800 ÷ 12 = 6566.67

   The monthly gross pay is $6566.67.

9. Strategy
   To find the biweekly gross pay, divide
   the annual salary by 26. Round to the
   nearest cent.

   Solution
   28,400 ÷ 26 ≈ 1092.31

   The biweekly gross pay is $1092.31.

10. Strategy
    To find the biweekly gross pay, divide
    the annual salary by 26. Round to the
    nearest cent.

    Solution
    37,750 ÷ 26 ≈ 1451.92

    The biweekly gross pay is $1451.92.

11. Strategy
    To find the semimonthly gross pay,
    divide the annual pay by 24. Round to
    the nearest cent.

    Solution
    42,560 ÷ 24 ≈ 1773.33

    The semimonthly gross pay is $1773.33.

12. Strategy
    To find the semimonthly gross pay,
    divide the annual pay by 24. Round to
    the nearest cent.

    Solution
    59,200 ÷ 24 ≈ 2466.67

    The semimonthly gross pay is $2466.67.

13. Hours worked = 8(6) = 48
    Regular hours worked = 40

14. Overtime hours worked = 48 − 40 = 8

15. Regular pay = 40(7.40) = $296

16. Overtime pay = 7.40(1.5)(8) = $88.80

17. Gross earnings = 296 + 88.80 = $384.80

18. Hours worked = $4 + 6\frac{1}{2} + 7 + 5\frac{3}{4} + 4 + 4 = 31\frac{1}{4} = 31.25$
    Regular hours worked = 31.25

19. Overtime hours worked = 0

20. Regular pay = 31.25(8.20) = $256.25

21. Overtime pay = $0

22. Gross earnings = 256.25 + 0 = $256.25

23. Strategy
    To find the gross pay, multiply the
    sales by the commission rate.

    Solution
    124,500(0.03) = 3735

    The gross pay is $3735.

24. Strategy
    To find the gross pay, multiply the
    sales by the commission rate.

    Solution
    67,200(0.06) = 4032

    The gross pay is $4032.

25. Strategy
    To find the weekly pay for each
    worker:
    • Multiply the sales by the
      commission rate.
    • Add the salary and the commission.

    Solution
    (a) 15,000(0.02) = 300
        200 + 300 = 500

    The weekly pay is $500.

    (b) 22,400(0.02) = 448
        200 + 448 = 648

    The weekly pay is $648.

26. Strategy
    To find the weekly pay for each
    worker:
    • Multiply the sales by the
      commission rate.
    • Add the salary and the commission.

    Solution
    (a) 11,450(0.02) = 229
        229 + 150 = 379

    The weekly pay is $379.

    (b) 17,175(0.02) = 343.50
        150 + 343.40 = 493.50

    The weekly pay is $493.50.

27. Strategy
    To find the gross pay:
    • Multiply the hourly rate by the
      number of hours worked.
    • Multiply the sales by the
      commission rate.
    • Add the hourly rate and the
      commission.

    Solution
    5.35(36) = 192.60
    2150(0.05) = 107.50
    192.60 + 107.50 = 300.10

    The gross pay is $300.10.

28. Strategy
    To find the gross pay:
    • Multiply the hourly rate by the
      number of hours worked.
    • Multiply the sales by the
      commission rate.
    • Add the hourly rate and the
      commission.

    Solution
    7.25(32) = 232
    3250(0.03) = 97.50
    232 + 97.50 = 329.50

    The gross pay is $329.50.

29. Strategy
    (a) To find the gross monthly pay,
    find the commission on the $25,000 of
    sales.
    (b) To find the gross monthly pay:
    • Find the commission on the first
      $25,000 of sales.
    • Find the commission on the sales
      over $25,000.
    • Add the commissions.

    Solution
    (a) 25,000(0.03) = 750

    The gross monthly pay is $750.

    (b) 25,000(0.03) = 750
        74,000 - 25,000 = 49,000
        49,000(0.05) = 2450
        750 + 2450 = 3200

    The gross monthly pay is $3200.

30. Strategy
    To find the gross monthly pay for each
    worker:
    • Find the commission on the first
      $15,000 of sales.
    • Find the commission on sales over
      $15,000.
    • Add the commissions.

    Solution
    (a) 15,000(0.02) = 300
        35,500 - 15,000 = 20,500
        20,500(0.04) = 820
        300 + 820 = 1120

    The gross monthly pay is $1120.

    (b) 15,000(0.02) = 300
        48,475 - 15,000 = 33,475
        33,475(0.04) = 1339
        300 + 1339 = 1639

    The gross monthly pay is $1639.

31. Strategy
    To find the gross monthly pay for each worker:
    • Find the commission on the first $20,000 of sales.
    • Find the commission on the next $30,000 of sales.
    • Find the commission on the sales over $50,000.

    Solution
    (a) 20,000(0.025) = 500
        39,000 − 20,000 = 19,000
        19,000(0.04) = 760
        500 + 760 = 1260

    The gross monthly pay is $1260.

    (b) 20,000(0.025) = 500
        30,000(0.04) = 1200
        52,000 − 50,000 = 2000
        2000(0.06) = 120
        500 + 1200 + 120 = 1820

    The gross monthly pay is $1820.

32. Strategy
    To find the gross monthly pay for each worker:
    • Find the commission on the first $10,000 of sales.
    • Find the commission on the next $30,000 of sales.
    • Find the commission on the sales over $40,000.

    Solution
    (a) 10,000(0.015) = 150
        30,000(0.03) = 900
        42,500 − 40,000 = 2500
        2500(0.05) = 125
        150 + 900 + 125 = 1175

    The gross monthly pay is $1175.

    (b) 10,000(0.015) = 150
        30,000(0.03) = 900
        64,540 − 40,000 = 24,540
        24,540(0.05) = 1227
        150 + 900 + 1227 = 2277

    The gross monthly pay is $2277.

33. Strategy
    To find the gross pay:
    • Find the hourly wage.
    • Find the commission.
    • Add the hourly wage and the commission.

    Solution
    4.75(25) = 118.75
    4(58) = 232
    118.75 + 232 = 350.75

    The gross pay is $350.75.

34. Strategy
    To find the gross pay:
    • Find the hourly wage.
    • Find the commission.
    • Add the hourly wage and the commission.

    Solution
    4.80(36) = 172.80
    3.50(92) = 322
    172.80 + 322 = 494.80

    The gross pay is $494.80.

35. Strategy
    To find the amount due:
    • Add the pay for the first $15,000 in sales and the pay for the sales in excess of $15,000 (42,000 − 15,000 = 27,000) to find the commission.
    • Subtract the drawings from the commission.

    Solution
    15,000 x 0.02 = 300
    27,000 x 0.04 = 1080
    Commission = 300 + 1080 = 1380
    1380 − 800 = 580

    The amount due is $580.

36. Strategy
    To find the amount due:
    • Add the pay for the first $30,000 in sales and the pay for the sales in excess of $30,000 (48,000 − 30,000 = 18,000) to find the commission.
    • Subtract the drawings from the commission.

    Solution
    30,000 x 0.03 = 900
    18,000 x 0.05 = 900
    Commission = 900 + 900 = 1800
    1800 − 300 = 1500

    The amount due is $1500.

37. Strategy
    To find the wage, multiply the number
    of circuit boards completed by the
    rate per circuit board.

    Solution
    160(0.64) = 102.40

    The wage is $102.40

38. Strategy
    To find the gross pay, multiply the
    number of units completed by the rate
    per unit.

    Solution
    230(0.52) = 119.60

    The gross pay is $119.60.

39. Strategy
    To find the gross pay:
    • Find the regular pay by multiplying
      the number of units produced by the
      rate per unit.
    • Find the bonus by multiplying the
      number of units produced over 200
      (245 - 200 = 45) by the bonus per
      unit.
    • Add the regular pay and the bonus.

    Solution
    245(1.95) = 477.75
    45(0.65) = 29.25
    477.75 + 29.25 = 507

    The gross pay is $507.

40. Strategy
    To find the gross pay:
    • Find the regular pay by multiplying
      the number of units produced by the
      rate per unit.
    • Find the bonus by multiplying the
      number of units produced over 150
      (230 - 150 = 80) by the bonus per
      unit.
    • Add the regular pay and the bonus.

    Solution
    230(4.40) = 1012
    80(1.20) = 96
    1012 + 96 = 1108

    The gross pay is $1108.

41. Strategy
    To find the weekly pay for each
    worker:
    • Find the pay for the first 150
      items.
    • Find the pay for items 151-180.
    • Find the pay for the items over
      200.
    • Add the payments.

    Solution
    (a) 150(1.50) = 225
        (180 - 150)(2.00) = 30(2.00) = 60
        225 + 60 = 285

    The weekly pay is $285.

    (b) 150(1.50) = 225
        (200 - 150)(2.00) = 50(2.00) = 100
        (262 - 200)(2.50) = 62(2.50) = 155
        225 + 100 + 155 = 480

    The weekly pay is $480.

42. Strategy
    To find the weekly pay for each
    worker:
    • Find the pay for the first 80
      boxes.
    • Find the pay for boxes 81-120.
    • Find the pay for the boxes over
      120.
    • Add the payments.

    Solution
    (a) 80(4.00) = 320
        (120 - 80)(5.20) = 40(5.20) = 208
        (128 - 120)(6.40) = 8(6.40) =
        51.20
        320 + 208 + 51.20 = 579.20

    The weekly pay is $579.20.

    (b) 80(4.00) = 320
        (120 - 80)(5.20) = 40(5.20) = 208
        (143 - 120)(6.40) = 23(6.40)
                          = 147.20
        320 + 208 +147.20 = 675.20

    The weekly pay is $675.20.

116 *Chapter 9*

43. Strategy
To find the gross pay:
- Find the regular pay by multiplying the number of units produced that passed inspection (58 - 4 = 54) by the rate per unit.
- Find the bonus by multiplying the number of units produced over 45 that passed inspection (54-45=9).
- Add the regular pay and the bonus.

Solution
54(6) = 324
9(1.75) = 15.75
324 + 15.75 = 339.75

The gross pay is $339.75.

44. Strategy
To find the gross pay:
- Find the regular pay by multiplying the number of units produced that passed inspection (3200 - 100 = 3100) by the rate per unit.
- Find the bonus by multiplying the number of units produced over 45 that passed inspection (3100 - 2500 = 600).
- Add the regular pay and the bonus.

Solution
3100(0.25) = 775
600(0.10) = 60
775 + 60 = 835

The gross pay is $835.

Section 9.2, pages 259–262

1. 372.00(0.0765) ≈ 28.46
2. 864.72(0.0765) ≈ 66.15
3. 2415.55(0.0765) ≈ 184.79
4. 3015.45(0.0765) ≈ 230.68
5. 396.00(0.062) ≈ 24.55
6. 396.00(0.0145) ≈ 5.74
7. 24.55 + 5.74 = 30.29
8. 785.84(0.062) ≈ 48.72
9. 785.84(0.0145) ≈ 11.39
10. 48.72 + 11.39 = 60.11
11. 1786.55(0.062) ≈ 110.77
12. 1786.55(0.0145) ≈ 25.90
13. 110.77 + 25.90 = 136.67
14. (57,600 − 55,435.15)(0.62) = 2164.85(0.062) ≈ 134.22
15. 2843.35(0.0145) ≈ 41.23
16. 134.22 + 41.23 = 175.45

17. Social Security tax on 900 = 55.80
Social Security tax on 59.63 = 3.70
Social Security tax on 959.63 = 59.50

18. Medicare tax on 900 = 13.05
Medicare tax on 59.63 = .86
Medicare tax on 959.63 = 13.91

19. 59.50 + 13.91 = 73.41

20. Social Security tax on 1000 = 62.00
Social Security tax on 800 = 49.60
Social Security tax on 63.79 = 3.95
Social Security tax on 1863.79= 115.55

21. Medicare tax on 1000 = 14.50
Medicare tax on 800 = 11.60
Medicare tax on 63.79 = .92
Medicare tax on 1863.79 = 27.02

22. 115.55 + 27.02 = 142.57

23. Social Security tax on 3000
        = 3(62.00) =   186.00
     Social Security tax on 100 =   6.20
     Social Security tax on 72.25 =   4.48
     Social Security tax on 3172.25= 196.68

24. Medicare tax on 3000
        = 3(14.50) =   43.50
     Medicare tax on 100 =   1.45
     Medicare tax on 72.25 =   1.05
     Medicare tax on 3172.25 =   46.00

25. 196.68 + 46.00 = 242.68

26. 57,600 - 53,535.15 = 4064.85
     Social Security tax on 4000
        = 4(62.00) =   248.00
     Social Security tax on 64.85 =   4.02
     Social Security tax on 2064.85 = 252.02

27. Medicare tax on 4000
        = 4(14.50) =   58.00
     Medicare tax on 900 =   13.05
     Medicare tax on 81.98 =   1.19
     Medicare tax on 4981.98 =   72.24

28. 252.02 + 72.24 = 324.26

29. Strategy
     To find the amount subject to Social
     Security tax:
     • Find the accumulated earnings
       through November by multiplying the
       monthly salary by 11.
     • Subtract the accumulated earnings
       from $57,600.

     Solution
     4810(11) = 52,910
     57,600 - 52,910 = 4690

     The amount subject to Social Security
     tax is $4690.

30. Strategy
     To find the amount subject to Social
     Security tax:
     • Find the accumulated earnings
       through November by multiplying the
       monthly salary by 11.
     • Subtract the accumulated earnings
       from $57,600.

     Solution
     5175(11) = 56,925
     57,600 - 56,925 = 675

     The amount subject to Social Security
     tax is $675.

31. Strategy
     To find the FICA tax to be withheld:
     • Find the Social Security tax on
       $900 and on $62.44.
     • Find the Medicare tax on $900 and
       on $62.44.
     • Add the four amounts.

     Solution
     Social Security tax on 900 =   55.80
     Social Security tax on 62.44 =   3.87
     Medicare tax on 900 =   13.05
     Medicare tax on 62.44 =   .91
     FICA tax =   73.63

     The FICA tax to be withheld is $73.63.

32. Strategy
     To find the FICA tax to be withheld:
     • Find the Social Security tax on
       $600 and on $84.55.
     • Find the Medicare tax on $600 and
       on $84.55.
     • Add the four amounts.

     Solution
     Social Security tax on 600 =   37.20
     Social Security tax on 84.55 =   5.24
     Medicare tax on 600 =   8.70
     Medicare tax on 84.55 =   1.23
     FICA tax =   52.37

     The FICA tax to be withheld is $52.37.

33. Strategy
    To find the FICA tax to be withheld:
    • Find the amount subject to Social
      Security tax.
    • Find the Social Security tax on the
      amount subject to Social Security
      tax.
    • Find the Medicare tax on $3000, on
      $400, and on $56.78.
    • Add the Social Security taxes and
      the Medicare taxes.

    Solution
    57,600 - 55,235.67 = 2364.33

    $2364.33 is subject to Social Security
    tax.

    Social Security tax on 2000
      = 2(62.00) =   124.00
    Social Security tax on 300 =   18.60
    Social Security tax on 64.33 =   3.99
    Medicare tax on 3000
      = 3(14.50) =   43.50
    Medicare tax on 400 =   5.80
    Medicare tax on 56.78 =   .82
    FICA tax =   196.71

    The FICA tax to be withheld is
    $196.71.

34. Strategy
    To find the FICA tax to be withheld:
    • Find the amount subject to Social
      Security tax.
    • Find the Social Security tax on the
      amount subject to Social Security
      tax.
    • Find the Medicare tax on $4000, on
      $200, and on $85.54.
    • Add the Social Security taxes and
      the Medicare taxes.

    Solution
    57,600 - 54,521.54 = 3078.46

    $3078.46 is subject to Social Security
    tax.

    Social Security tax on 3000
      = 3(62.00) =   186.00
    Social Security tax on 78.46 =   4.86
    Medicare tax on 4000
      = 4(14.50) =   58.00
    Medicare tax on 200 =   2.90
    Medicare tax on 85.54 =   1.24
    FICA tax =   253.00

    The FICA tax to be withheld is
    $253.00.

35. Strategy
    To find the FICA tax to be withheld,
    multiply the gross pay by 0.0765.

    Solution
    732.95(0.0765) ≈ 56.07

    The FICA tax to be withheld is $56.07.

36. Strategy
    To find the FICA tax to be withheld,
    multiply the gross pay by 0.0765.

    Solution
    518.50(0.0765) ≈ 39.67

    The FICA tax to be withheld is $39.67.

37. Strategy
    To find the Social Security tax,
    multiply the gross pay by 0.062.
    To find the Medicare tax, multiply the
    gross pay by 0.0145.

    Solution
    5675(0.062) = 351.85
    5675(0.0145) ≈ 82.29

    The Social Security tax is $351.85.
    The Medicare tax is $82.29.

38. Strategy
    To find the Social Security tax,
    multiply the gross pay by 0.062.
    To find the Medicare tax, multiply the
    gross pay by 0.0145.

    Solution
    850.75(0.062) ≈ 52.75
    850.75(0.0145) ≈ 12.34

    The Social Security tax is $52.75.
    The Medicare tax is $12.34.

39. Strategy
    To find the Social Security tax:
    • Find the amount subject to Social
      Security tax.
    • Multiply the amount subject to
      Social Security tax by 0.062.
    To find the Medicare tax, multiply the
    gross pay by 0.0145.

    Solution
    4985(11) = 54,835
    57,600 - 54,835 = 2765
    2765(0.062) = 171.43

    The Social Security tax is $171.43.

    4985(0.0145) ≈ 72.28

    The Medicare tax is $72.28.

40. Strategy
    To find the Social Security tax:
    • Find the amount subject to Social
      Security tax.
    • Multiply the amount subject to
      Social Security tax by 0.062.
    To find the Medicare tax, multiply the
    gross pay by 0.0145.

    Solution
    4850(11) = 53,350
    57,600 - 53,350 = 4250
    4250(0.062) = 263.50

    The Social Security tax is $263.50.

    4850(0.0145) ≈ 70.33

    The Medicare tax is $70.33.

41. Withholding allowance = 4(195.83)
                          = 783.32
    Federal earnings = 3327 - 783.32
                     = 2543.68

42. FIT = 0.15(2543.68 - 517) = 304.00

43. Withholding allowance = 2(195.83)
                          = 391.66
    Federal earnings = 4156.45 - 391.66
                     = 3764.79

44. FIT = 261.60 + 0.28(3764.79 - 1954)
        = 261.60 + 507.02 = 768.62

45. Withholding allowance = 1(45.19)
                          = 45.19
    Federal earnings = 549 - 45.19
                     = 503.81

46. FIT = 60.30 + 0.28(503.81 - 451)
        = 60.30 + 14.79 = 75.09

47. Withholding allowance = 3(45.19)
                          = 135.57
    Federal earnings = 913.37 - 135.57
                     = 777.80

48. FIT = 0.15(777.80 - 119) = 98.82

49. Withholding allowance = 5(90.38)
                          = 451.90
    Federal earnings = 1307.70 - 451.90
                     = 855.80

50. FIT = 0.15(855.80 - 238) = 92.67

51. Withholding allowance = 4(97.92)
                          = 391.68
    Federal earnings = 2083.33 - 391.68
                     = 1691.65

52. FIT = 130.80 + 0.28(1691.65 - 977)
        = 130.80 + 200.10 = 330.90

53. $377   54. $385   55. $117   56. $147   57. $746   58. $223

59. Strategy
    To find the federal earnings:
    • Use Table 9.3 to find the withholding allowance.
    • Subtract the withholding allowance from the monthly salary.
    To find the FIT, use Table 9.4.

    Solution
    Withholding allowance
    = 2(195.83) = 391.66
    Federal earnings = 7166.67 - 391.66
                     = 6775.01

    The federal earnings are $6775.01.

    FIT = 1376.85 + 0.31(6775.01 - 6771)
    = 1376.85 + 1.24 = 1378.09

    The FIT to be withheld is $1378.09.

60. Strategy
    To find the federal earnings:
    • Use Table 9.3 to find the withholding allowance.
    • Subtract the withholding allowance from the monthly salary.
    To find the FIT, use Table 9.4.

    Solution
    Withholding allowance
    = 3(45.19) = 135.57
    Federal earnings = 1424 - 135.57
                     = 1288.43

    The federal earnings are $1288.43.

    FIT = 197.78 + 0.31(1288.43 - 942)
    = 197.78 + 107.39 = 305.17

    The FIT to be withheld is $305.17.

61. Strategy
    To find the FIT to be withheld:
    • Use Table 9.3 to find the withholding allowance.
    • Subtract the withholding allowance from the weekly salary to find the federal earnings.
    • Use Table 9.4 to calculate the FIT.

    Solution
    Withholding allowance = 1(90.38)
                          = 90.38
    Federal earnings = 2375 - 90.38
                     = 2284.62
    FIT = 199.35 + 0.28(2284.62 - 1567)
    = 199.35 + 200.93 = 400.28

    The FIT to be withheld is $400.28.

62. Strategy
    To find the FIT to be withheld:
    • Use Table 9.3 to find the withholding allowance.
    • Subtract the withholding allowance from the weekly salary to find the federal earnings.
    • Use Table 9.4 to calculate the FIT.

    Solution
    Withholding allowance = 1(97.92)
                          = 97.92
    Federal earnings = 3125 - 97.92
                     = 3027.08
    FIT = 216.00 + 0.28(3027.08 - 1698)
    = 216.00 + 372.14 = 588.14

    The FIT to be withheld is $588.14.

63. Strategy
    To find the FIT to be withheld:
    • Use Table 9.3 to find the withholding allowance.
    • Subtract the withholding allowance from the weekly salary to find the federal earnings.
    • Use Table 9.4 to calculate the FIT.

    Solution
    Withholding allowance = 2(97.92)
                          = 195.84
    Federal earnings = 947.50 - 195.84
                     = 751.66
    FIT = 0.15(751.66 - 105) = 97.00

    The FIT to be withheld is $97.00.

64. Strategy
    To find the FIT to be withheld:
    • Use Table 9.3 to find the withholding allowance.
    • Subtract the withholding allowance from the weekly salary to find the federal earnings.
    • Use Table 9.4 to calculate the FIT.

    Solution
    Withholding allowance = 0
    Federal earnings = 947.50
    FIT = 120.75 + 0.28(947.50 - 902)
    = 120.75 + 12.74 = 133.49

    The FIT to be withheld is $133.49.

65. Strategy
To find the FIT to be deducted, use
Table 9.5.

Solution
The amount deducted for FIT is $63.

66. Strategy
To find the FIT to be deducted, use
Table 9.6.

Solution
The amount deducted for FIT is $277.

67. Strategy
To find the FIT to be deducted using
the percentage method:
• Use Table 9.3 to find the
  withholding allowance.
• Subtract the withholding allowance
  from the weekly salary to find the
  federal earnings.
• Use Table 9.4 to calculate the FIT.

Solution
Withholding allowance = 4(195.83)
$$= 783.32$$
Federal earnings = 4210 - 783.32
$$= 3426.68$$
FIT = 431.85 + 0.28(3426.68 - 3396)
$$= 431.85 + 8.59 = 440.44$$

Using the percentage method, the FIT
to be withheld is $440.44.

Using the wage bracket method, the
amount to be deducted for FIT is $443.

68. Strategy
To find the FIT to be deducted using
the percentage method:
• Use Table 9.3 to find the
  withholding allowance.
• Subtract the withholding allowance
  from the weekly salary to find the
  federal earnings.
• Use Table 9.4 to calculate the FIT.

Solution
Withholding allowance = 2(45.19) =
$$= 90.38$$
Federal earnings = 945 - 90.38
$$= 854.62$$
FIT = 60.38 + 0.28(854.62 - 451)
$$= 60.30 + 113.01 = 173.31$$

Using the percentage method, the FIT
to be withheld is $173.31.

Using the wage bracket method, the
amount to be deducted for FIT is $173.

Section 9.3, pages 269–272

1. (a) FICA tax = 844(0.0765) = $64.57
   (b) Withholding allowance = 3(45.19) = $135.57
       Federal earnings = 844 - 135.57 = $708.43
       FIT = 0.15(708.43 - 119) = $88.41
   (c) Net pay = 844 - (64.57 + 88.41) = 844 - 152.98 = $691.02

2. (a) FICA tax = 788(0.0765) = $60.28
   (b) Withholding allowance = 2(45.19) = $90.38
       Federal earnings = 788 - 90.38 = $697.62
       FIT = 0.15(697.62 - 119) = $86.79
   (c) Net pay = 788 - (60.28 + 86.79) = 788 - 147.07 = $640.93

3. (a) FICA tax = 610(0.0765) = $46.67
   (b) FIT = $68
   (c) Net pay = 610 - (46.67 + 68) = 610 - 114.67 = $495.33

4. (a) FICA tax = 750(0.0765) = $57.38
   (b) FIT = $120
   (c) Net pay = 750 - (57.38 + 120) = 750 - 177.38 = $572.62

5. FICA = 3650(0.0765) = $279.23
   FIT = $325
   State disability taxes = 3650(0.005) = $18.25
   Investment account = $150
   Net pay = 3650 - (279.23 + 325 + 18.25 + 150) = 2650 - 772.48 = $2877.52

6. FICA = 4066(0.0765) = $311.05
    FIT = $414
    State disability taxes = 4066(0.01) = $40.66
    Investment account = $100
    Net pay = 4066 - (311.05 + 414 + 40.66 + 100) = 4066 - 865.71 = $3200.29

7. FICA = 4450(0.0765) = $340.43
    Withholding allowance = 1(195.83) = $195.83
    Federal earnings = 4450 - 195.83 = $4254.17
    FIT = 857.16 + 0.31(4254.17 - 4081) = 857.16 + 53.68 = $910.84
    Union dues = $36
    Hospitalization insurance = $49.50
    Net pay = 4450 - (340.43 + 910.84 + 36 + 49.50) = 4450 - 1336.77 = $3113.23

8. FICA = 3940(0.0765) = $301.41
    Withholding allowance = 2(195.83) = $391.66
    Federal earnings = 3940 - 391.66 = $3548.34
    FIT = 261.60 + 0.28(3548.34 - 1954) = 261.60 + 446.42 = $708.02
    Union dues = $44
    Hospitalization insurance = $64.50
    Net pay = 3940 - (301.41 + 708.02 + 44 + 64.50) = 3940 - 1117.93 = $2822.07

9. FICA = 2040(0.0765) = $156.06
    Withholding allowance = 3(90.38) = $271.14
    Federal earnings = 2040 - 271.14 = $1768.86
    FIT = 199.35 + 0.28(1768.86 - 1567) = 199.35 + 56.52 = $255.87
    State income tax = 2040(0.03) = $61.20
    Health insurance = $72.13
    Net pay = 2040 - (156.06 + 255.87 + 61.20 + 72.13) = 2040 - 545.26 = $1494.74

10. FICA = 2150(0.0765) = $164.48
    Withholding allowance = 3(97.92) = $293.76
    Federal earnings = 2150 - 293.76 = $1856.24
    FIT = 216 + 0.28(1856.24 - 1698) = 216 + 44.31 = $260.31
    State income tax = 2150(0.04) = $86
    Health insurance = $68.75
    Net pay = 2150 - (164.48 + 260.31 + 86 + 68.75) = 2150 - 579.54 = $1570.46

11. (a) Gross pay = 40(18.50) + 12(18.50)(1.5) = 740 + 333 = $1073
    (b) FICA = 1073(0.0765) = $82.08
    (c) Withholding allowance = 3(45.19) = $135.57
        Federal earnings = 1073 - 135.57 = $937.43
        FIT = 99.75 + 0.28(937.43 - 784) = 99.75 + 42.96 = $142.71
    (d) Net pay = 1073 - (82.08 + 142.71) = 1073 - 224.79 = $848.21

12. (a) Gross pay = 40(19.60) + 8(19.60)(1.5) = 784 + 235.20 = $1019.20
    (b) FICA = 1019.20(0.0765) = $77.97
    (c) Withholding allowance = 4(45.19) = $180.76
        Federal earnings = 1019.20 - 180.76 = $838.44
        FIT = 99.75 + 0.28(838.44 - 784) = 99.75 + 15.24 = $114.99
    (d) Net pay = 1019.20 - (77.97 + 114.99) = 1019.20 - 192.96 = $826.24

13. (a) Gross pay = 250 + (0.03)(37,500) = 250 + 1125 = $1375
    (b) FICA = 1375(0.0765) = $105.19
    (c) Withholding allowance = 2(45.19) = $90.38
        Federal earnings = 1375 - 90.38 = $1284.62
        FIT = 197.78 + 0.31(1284.62 - 942) = 197.78 + 106.21 = $303.99
    (d) Net pay = 1375 - (105.19 + 303.99) = 1375 - 409.18 = $965.82

14. (a) Gross pay = 300 + (0.02)(52,000) = 300 + 1040 = $1340
    (b) FICA = 1340(0.0765) = $102.51
    (c) Withholding allowance = 1(45.19) = $45.19
        Federal earnings = 1340 - 45.19 = $1294.81
        FIT = 197.78 + 0.31(1294.81 - 942) = 197.78 + 109.37 = $307.15
    (d) Net pay = 1340 - (102.51 + 307.15) = 1340 - 409.66 = $930.34

15. Accumulated earnings = 4820(11) = $53,020
    Amount subject to Social Security tax = 57,600 - 53,020 = $4580
    Social Security tax = 4580(0.062) = $283.96
    Medicare tax = 4820(0.0145) = $69.89
    Withholding allowance = 1(195.83) = $195.83
    Federal earnings = 4820 - 195.83 = $4624.17
    FIT = 857.16 + 0.31(4624.17 - 4081) = 857.16 + 168.38 = $1025.54
    City income tax = 4820(0.015) = $72.30
    Net pay = 4820 - (283.96 + 69.89 + 1025.54 + 72.30) = 4820 - 1451.69 = $3368.31

16. Accumulated earnings = 5140(11) = $56,540
    Amount subject to Social Security tax = 57,600 - 56,540 = $1060
    Social Security tax = 1060(0.062) = $65.72
    Medicare tax = 5140(0.0145) = $74.53
    Withholding allowance = 3(195.83) = $587.49
    Federal earnings = 5140 - 587.49 = $4552.51
    FIT = 857.16 + 0.31(4552.51 - 4081) = 857.16 + 146.17 = $1003.33
    City income tax = 5140(0.0125) = $64.25
    Net pay = 5140 - (65.72 + 74.53 + 1003.33 + 64.25) = 5140 - 1207.83 = $3932.17

17. Accumulated earnings = 4970(11) = $54,670
    Amount subject to Social Security tax = 57,600 - 54,670 = $2930
    Social Security tax = 2930(0.062) = $181.66
    Medicare tax = 4970(0.0145) = $72.07
    FIT = $766
    State disability tax = 4970(0.02) = $99.40
    Net pay = 4970 - (181.66 + 72.07 + 766 + 99.40) = 4970 - 1119.13 = $3850.87

18. Accumulated earnings = 5350(10) = $53,500
    Amount subject to Social Security tax = 57,600 - 53,500 = $4100
    Social Security tax = 4100(0.062) = $254.20
    Medicare tax = 5350(0.0145) = $77.58
    FIT = $757
    State income tax = 5350(0.04) = $214
    Net pay = 5350 - (254.20 + 77.58 + 757 + 214) = 5350 - 1302.78 = $4047.22

19. Earnings = 40(12.60) + 6(18.90)
              = 504 + 113.40 = 617.40

20. FICA = 617.40(0.0765) = 47.23

21. FIT = 81

22. Total deductions = 47.23 + 81 = 128.23

23. Net pay = 617.40 - 128.23 = 489.17

24. Earnings = 40(12.60) + 10(18.90)
             = 504 + 189.00 = 693.00

25. FICA = 693.00(0.0765) = 53.01

26. FIT = 103

27. Total deductions = 53.01 + 103
                     = 156.01

28. Net pay = 693.00 - 156.01 = 536.99

29. Earnings = 40(12.60) + 14(18.90)
             = 504 + 264.60 = 768.60

30. FICA = 768(0.0765) = 58.80

31. FIT = 123

32. Total deductions = 58.80 + 123
                     = 181.80

33. Net pay = 768.60 - 181.80 = 586.80

34. Earnings = 40(12.60) + 5(18.90)
    = 504 + 94.50 = 598.50

35. FICA = 598.50(0.0765) = 45.79

36. FIT = 75

37. Total deductions = 45.79 + 75 = 120.79

38. Net pay = 598.50 - 120.79 = 477.71

39. Earnings = 250 + 0.02(8640)
    = 250 + 172.80 = 422.80

40. FICA/OASI = 422.80(0.062) = 26.21

41. FICA/MED = 422.80(0.0145) = 6.13

42. Withholding allowance = 3(45.19) = 135.57
    Federal earnings = 422.80 - 135.57 = 287.23
    FIT = 0.15(287.23 - 119) = 25.23

43. Total deductions = 26.21 + 6.13 + 25.23 = 57.57

44. Net pay = 422.80 - 57.57 = 365.23

45. Earnings = 250 + 0.02(12,500)
    = 250 + 250 = 500

46. FICA/OASI = 500(0.062) = 31

47. FICA/MED = 500(0.0145) = 7.25

48. Withholding allowance = 3(45.19) = 135.57
    Federal earnings = 500 - 135.57 = 364.43
    FIT = 0.15(364.43 - 119) = 36.81

49. Total deductions = 31 + 7.25 + 36.81
    = 75.06

50. Net pay = 500 - 75.06 = 424.94

51. Earnings = 250 + 0.02(19,250)
    = 250 + 385 = 635

52. FICA/OASI = 635(0.062) = 39.37

53. FICA/MED = 635(0.0145) = 9.21

54. Withholding allowance = 3(45.19) = 135.57
    Federal earnings = 635 - 135.57 = 499.43
    FIT = 0.15(499.43 - 119) = 57.06

55. Total deductions = 39.37 + 9.21 + 57.06 = 105.64

56. Net pay = 635 - 105.64 = 529.36

57. Earnings = 250 + 0.02(24,420)
    = 250 + 488.40 = 738.40

58. FICA/OASI = 738.40(0.062) = 45.78

59. FICA/MED = 738.40(0.0145) = 10.71

60. Withholding allowance = 3(45.19) = 135.57
    Federal earnings = 738.40 - 135.57 = 602.83
    FIT = 0.15(602.83 - 119) = 72.57

61. Total deductions = 45.78 + 10.71 + 72.57 = 129.06

62. Net pay = 738.40 - 129.06 = 609.34

63. Earnings = 0.03(142,000) = 4260

64. Accumulated earnings = 42,570 + 4260 = 46,830
    FICA = 4260(0.062) + 4260(0.0145) = 264.12 + 61.77 = 325.89

65. FIT = 455

66. Total deductions = 325.89 + 455
    = 780.89

67. Net pay = 4260 - 780.89 = 3479.11

68. Earnings = 0.03(108,300) = 3249

69. Accumulated earnings = 46,830 + 3249 = 50,079
    FICA = 3249(0.062) + 3249(0.0145) = 201.44 + 47.11 = 248.55

70. FIT = 294

71. Total deductions = 248.55 + 294
                     = 542.55

72. Net pay = 3249 - 542.55 = 2706.45

73. Earnings = 0.03(167,500) = 5025

74. Accumulated earnings = 50,079 + 5025 = 55,104
    FICA = 5025(0.062) + 5025(0.0145) = 311.55 + 72.86 = 384.41

75. FIT = 667

76. Total deductions = 384.41 + 667
                     = 1051.41

77. Net pay = 5025 - 1051.41 = 3973.59

78. Earnings = 0.03(132,000) = 3960

79. Accumulated earnings = 55,104 + 3960 = 59,064
    Amount subject to Social Security tax = 57,600 - 55,104 = 2496
    FICA = 2496(0.062) + 3960(0.0145) = 154.75 + 57.42 = 212.17

80. FIT = 402

81. Total deductions = 212.17 + 402
                     = 614.17

82. Net pay = 3960 - 614.17 = 3345.83

83. FICA = 4873(0.0765) = 372.78

84. Withholding allowance = 3(195.83) = 587.49
    Federal earnings = 4873 - 587.49 = 4285.51
    FIT = 857.16 + 0.31(4285.51 - 4081) = 857.16 + 63.40 = 920.56

85. State withholding tax = 4873(0.025)
                          = 121.83

86. Retirement fund deduction = 150

87. Total deductions = 372.78 + 920.56 + 121.83 + 150 = 1565.17

88. Net pay = 4873 - 1565.17 = 3307.83

Business Case Study

1a. Barbara: Hours worked = 8 + 8 + 9 + 8 + 10 = 43
              Gross pay = (40 hours x $6 per hour) + (3 hours x $9 per hour)
                        = $240 + $27 = $267

    Todd: Hours worked = 8 + 8 + 8 + 8 + 8 = 40
              Gross pay = 40 hours x $7.50 per hour = $300

    Allen: Hours worked = 7 + 9 + 8 + 8 + 10 = 42
              Gross pay = (40 hours x $6.25 per hour) + (2 hours x $9.375 per hour)
                        = $250 + $18.75 = $268.75

 b. John: Gross pay = $1600

    Carol: Gross pay = $1550

    Tony: Gross pay = $500 + 0.05($5000) + 0.06($2500) + 0.07($1025)
                        = $500 + $250 + $150 + $71.75 = $971.75

    Mary: Gross pay = $500 + 0.05($5000) + 0.06($2500) + 0.07($2230)
                        = $500 + $250 + $150 + $156.10 = $1056.10

Randy: Gross pay = $500 + 0.05($5000) + 0.06($1990)
= $500 + $250 + $119.40 = $869.40

c. John: Gross pay = $1600

Carol: Gross pay = $1550

Mike: Gross pay = $2400

Sue: Gross pay = $1800

Larry: Gross pay = $1800

2. Barbara: FICA = 0.0765 x $267 = $20.43
Federal income tax deduction = $45.19 x 3 = $135.57
Federal earnings = $267 - $135.57 = $131.43
FIT = 0.15($131.43 - $119) = 0.15($12.43) = $1.87

Todd: FICA = 0.0765 x $300 = $22.95
Federal income tax deduction = $45.19 x 5 = $225.95
Federal earnings = $300 - $225.95 = $74.05
FIT = $0

Allen: FICA = 0.0765 x $268.75 = $20.56
Federal income tax deduction = $45.19 x 1 = $45.19
Federal earnings = $268.75 - $45.19 = $223.56
FIT = 0.15($223.56 - $49) = 0.15($174.56) = $26.18

John: FICA = 0.0765 x $1600 = $122.40
Federal income tax deduction = $97.92 x 4 = $391.68
Federal earnings = $1600 - $391.68 = $1208.32
FIT = 0.15($1208.32 - $517) = 0.15($691.32) = $103.70

Carol: FICA = 0.0765 x $1550 = $118.58
Federal income tax deduction = $97.92 x 2 = $195.84
Federal earnings = $1550 - $195.84 = $1354.16
FIT = 0.15($1354.16 - $517) = 0.15($837.16) = $125.57

Tony: FICA = 0.0765 x $971.75 = $74.34
Federal income tax deduction = $97.92 x 1 = $97.92
Federal earnings = $971.75 - $97.92 = $873.83
FIT = 0.15($873.83 - $105) = 0.15($768.83) = $11.52

Mary: FICA = 0.0765 x $1056.10 = $80.79
Federal income tax deduction = $97.92 x 2 = $195.84
Federal earnings = $1056.10 - $195.84 = $860.26
FIT = 0.15($860.26 - $258) = 0.15($602.26) = $90.34

Randy: FICA = 0.0765 x $869.40 = $66.51
Federal income tax deduction = $97.92 x 0 = $0
Federal earnings = $869.40 - $0 = $869.40
FIT = 0.15($869.40 - $105) = 0.15($764.40) = $114.66

John: FICA = 0.0765 x $1600 = $122.40
Federal income tax deduction = $97.92 x 4 = $391.68
Federal earnings = $1600 - $391.68 = $1208.32
FIT = 0.15($1208.32 - $517) = 0.15($691.32) = $103.70

Carol: FICA = 0.0765 x $1550 = $118.58
Federal income tax deduction = $97.92 x 2 = $195.84
Federal earnings = $1550 - $195.84 = $1354.16
FIT = 0.15($1354.16 - $517) = 0.15($837.16) = $125.57

Mike: FICA = 0.0765 x $2400 = $183.60
        Federal income tax deduction = $195.83 x 3 = $587.49
        Federal earnings = $2400 - $587.49 = $1812.51
        FIT = 0.15($1812.51 - $517) = 0.15($1295.51) = $194.33

Sue: FICA = 0.0765 x $1800 = $137.70
        Federal income tax deduction = $195.83 x 1 = $195.83
        Federal earnings = $1800 - $195.83 = $1604.17
        FIT = 0.15($1604.17 - $517) = 0.15($1087.17) = $163.08

Larry: FICA = 0.0765 x $1800 = $137.70
        Federal income tax deduction = $195.83 x 0 = $0
        Federal earnings = $1800 - $0 = $1800
        FIT = 0.15($1800 - $210) = 0.15($1590) = $238.50

3. Barbara: Net pay = $267 - ($20.43 + $1.87) = $244.70

    Todd: Net pay = $300 - ($22.95 + $0) = $277.05

    Allen: Net pay = $268.75 - ($20.56 + $26.18) = $222.01

    John: Net pay = $1600 - ($122.40 + $103.70) = $1373.90

    Carol: Net pay = $1550 - ($118.58 + $125.57) = $1305.85

    Tony: Net pay = $971.75 - ($74.34 + $11.52) = $885.89

    Mary: Net pay = $1056.10 - ($80.79 + $90.34) = $884.97

    Randy: Net pay = $869.40 - ($66.51 + $114.66) = $688.23

    John: Net pay = $1600 - ($122.40 + $103.70) = $1373.90

    Carol: Net pay = $1550 - ($118.58 + $125.57) = $1305.85

    Mike: Net pay = $2400 - ($183.60 + $194.33) = $2022.07

    Sue: Net pay = $1800 - ($137.70 + $163.08) = $1499.22

    Larry: Net pay = $1800 - ($137.70 + $238.50) = $1423.80

Review/Test, pages 277–278

1. Strategy
    To find the gross pay:
    • Find the total number of hours
      worked.
    • Multiply the number of hours worked
      by the rate per hour.

    Solution
    $6\frac{1}{2} + 8 + 7\frac{1}{4} + 12 = 33\frac{3}{4}$
    Gross pay = $33\frac{3}{4}(9.50) = 320.63$

    The clerk's gross pay for the week is
    $320.63.

2. Strategy
    To find the gross pay:
    • Find the regular pay.
    • Find the overtime pay.
    • Add the regular pay to the overtime
      pay.

    Solution
    Regular pay = 40 x 18.20 = 728
    Overtime pay = 18.20(1.5)(50-40)
                 = 18.20(1.5)(10) = 273
    Gross pay = 728 + 273 = 1001

    The carpenter's gross pay for this
    week is $1001.

3. Strategy
   To find the gross pay, multiply the
   selling price by the commission rate.

   Solution
   132,500(0.03) = 3975.

   The agent's gross pay is $3975.

4. Strategy
   To find the gross pay:
   • Multiply the hourly rate by the
     number of hours worked.
   • Multiply the sales by the
     commission rate.
   • Add the hourly rate and the
     commission.

   Solution
   8.65 x 35 = 302.75
   6000(0.02) = 120
   302.75 + 120 = 422.75

   The clerk's gross pay is $422.75.

5. Strategy
   To find the weekly pay, multiply the
   rate per box by the number of boxes
   picked.

   Solution
   0.95(324) = 307.80

   The worker's weekly pay is $307.80.

6. Strategy
   To find the gross pay for the week:
   • Find the hourly pay by multiplying
     the number of hours worked by the
     rate per hour.
   • Find the piecework pay by
     multiplying the rate per unit by
     the number of units produced.
   • Add the hourly pay and the
     piecework pay.

   Solution
   6.50(40) = 260
   0.80(400) = 320
   260 + 320 = 580

   The technician's gross pay for the
   week is $580.

7. Strategy
   To find the amount due:
   • Add the pay for the first $20,000
     in sales and the pay for the sales
     in excess of $20,000
     (35,000 - 20,000 = 15,000) to find
     the commission.
   • Subtract the drawings from the
     commission.

   Solution
   20,000 x 0.03 = 600
   15,000 x 0.04 = 600
   Commission = 600 + 600 = 1200
   1200 - 700 = 500

   The amount due is $500.

8. Strategy
   To find the gross pay:
   • Find the pay for the first 1200
     welds.
   • Find the pay for the welds over
     1200.
   • Add the two amounts.

   Solution
   0.70(1200) = 840
   0.90(1400 - 1200) = 0.90(200) = 180
   840 + 180 = 1020

   The welder's gross pay is $1020.

9. Strategy
   To find the FICA tax, multiply the gross earnings by 7.65%.

   Solution
   $814.56(0.0765) \approx 62.31$

   The FICA tax is $62.31.

10. Strategy
    To find the Social Security tax:
    • Find the amount subject to Social Security tax.
    • Multiply the amount subject to Social Security tax by 0.062.
    To find the Medicare tax, multiply the gross pay by 0.0145.

    Solution
    $53,892 + 4328 = 58,220$
    $57,600 - 53,892 = 3708$
    $3708(0.062) = 229.90$

    The Social Security tax is $229.90.

    $4328(0.0145) = 62.76$

    The Medicare tax is $62.76.

11. Strategy
    To find the FIT deduction, use Table 9.6.

    Solution
    The FIT deduction is $598.

12. Strategy
    To find the FIT deduction:
    • Use Table 9.3 to find the withholding allowance.
    • Subtract the withholding allowance from the gross pay to find the federal earnings.
    • Use Table 9.4 to calculate the FIT.

    Solution
    Withholding allowance $= 3(90.38)$
    $\qquad = 271.14$
    Federal earnings $= 2236 - 271.14$
    $\qquad = 1964.86$
    $FIT = 199.35 + 0.28(1964.86 - 1567)$
    $\quad = 199.35 + 111.40 = 310.75$

    The FIT deduction is $310.75.

13. Strategy
    To find the net pay:
    • Multiply the gross pay by 7.65% to find the FICA deduction.
    • Use Table 9.5 to find the FIT deduction.
    • Subtract the FICA deduction and the FIT deduction from the gross pay.

    Solution
    $FICA = 862(0.0765) = 65.94$
    Withholding allowance $= 151$
    $FIT = 862 - (65.94 + 151)$
    $\quad = 862 - 216.94 = 645.06$

    The net pay is $645.06.

14. $FICA = 942(0.0765) = \$72.06$
    Withholding allowance $= 4(45.19)$
    $\qquad = \$180.76$
    Federal earnings $= 942 - 180.76$
    $\qquad = \$761.24$
    $FIT = 0.15(761.24 - 119) = \$96.34$
    State income tax $= 942(0.035) = \$32.97$
    Health insurance $= \$58.40$
    Net pay $= 942 - (72.06 + 96.34 + 32.97$
    $\qquad + 58.40) = 942 - 259.77$
    $\qquad = \$682.23$

    The net pay is $682.23.

15. $FICA = 1027(0.0765) = 78.57$

16. Withholding allowance $= 2(45.19) = 90.38$
    Federal earnings $= 1027 - 90.38 = 936.62$
    $FIT = 99.75 + 0.28(936.62 - 784) = 99.75 + 42.73 = 142.48$

17. State withholding tax = 1027(0.015) = 15.41

18. Other deduction = saving deduction = 200

19. Total deductions = 78.57 + 142.48 + 15.41 + 200 = 436.46

20. Net pay = 1027 - 436.46 = 590.54

CHAPTER 10
Simple and Compound Interest

Section 10.1, pages 287–290

1. I = Prt
    $I = 16,000(0.065)\left(\frac{8}{12}\right) \approx 693.33$

2. I = Prt
    $I = 15,000(0.0825)\left(\frac{9}{12}\right) \approx 928.13$

3. I = Prt
    $I = 10,000(0.069)\left(\frac{120}{360}\right) = 230$

4. I = Prt
    $I = 17,500(0.084)\left(\frac{60}{360}\right) = 245$

5.   I = Prt
    $750 = P(0.075)\left(\frac{3}{12}\right)$
    $750 = P(0.01875)$
    $40,000 = P$

6.   I = Prt
    $148.75 = P(0.085)\left(\frac{6}{12}\right)$
    $148.75 = P(0.0425)$
    $3500 = P$

7.   I = Prt
    $280 = 12,000(r)\left(\frac{4}{12}\right)$
    $280 = 4000r$
    $0.07 = r$
    $7\% = r$

8.   I = Prt
    $1350 = 25,000(r)\left(\frac{9}{12}\right)$
    $1350 = 18,7500r$
    $0.072 = r$
    $7.2\% = r$

9.   I = Prt
    $770 = 27,500(0.084)t$
    $770 = 2310t$
    $\left(\frac{1}{3}\right) = t$

    $\frac{1}{3}(12 \text{ months}) = 4 \text{ months}$

10.   I = Prt
    $326.25 = 9000(0.0725)t$
    $326.25 = 652.50t$
    $0.5 = t$

    $0.5(12 \text{ months}) = 6 \text{ months}$

11.   I = Prt
    $665 = 35,000(0.076)t$
    $665 = 2660t$
    $0.25 = t$

    $0.25(360 \text{ days}) = 90 \text{ days}$

12.   I = Prt
    $229.50 = 8500(0.0081)t$
    $229.50 = 688.50t$
    $\left(\frac{1}{3}\right) = t$

    $\frac{1}{3}(360 \text{ days}) = 120 \text{ days}$

13. Strategy
    To find the simple interest, use the
    formula I = Prt.
    P = 25,000, r = 0.094, t = $\frac{120}{360}$.

    Solution
    I = Prt
    I = 25,000(0.094) $\left(\frac{120}{360}\right)$ = 783.33

    The simple interest is $783.33.

14. Strategy
    To find the simple interest, use the
    formula I = Prt.
    P = 8000, r = 0.085, t = $\frac{75}{360}$.

    Solution
    I = Prt
    I = 8000(0.085) $\left(\frac{75}{360}\right)$ = 141.67

    The interest is $141.67.

15. Strategy
    To find the simple interest, use the
    formula I = Prt.
    P = 1500, r = 0.112, t = $\frac{9}{12}$.

    Solution
    I = Prt
    I = 1500(0.112) $\left(\frac{9}{12}\right)$ = 126

    The simple interest is $126.

16. Strategy
    To find the simple interest, use the
    formula I = Prt.
    P = 4000, r = 0.098, t = $\frac{4}{12}$.

    Solution
    I = Prt
    I = 4000(0.098) $\left(\frac{4}{12}\right)$ = 130.67

    The simple interest is $130.67.

17. Strategy
    To find the simple interest, use the
    formula I = Prt.
    P = 4500, r = 0.09, t = $\frac{75}{360}$.

    Solution
    I = Prt
    I = 4500(0.09) $\left(\frac{75}{360}\right)$ = 84.38

    The simple interest is $84.38.

18. Strategy
    To find the simple interest, use the
    formula I = Prt.
    P = 20,000, r = 0.074, t = $\frac{20}{360}$.

    Solution
    I = Prt
    I = 20,000(0.074) $\left(\frac{20}{360}\right)$ = 82.22

    The simple interest is $82.22.

19. Strategy
    To find the simple interest, use the
    formula I = Prt.
    P = 7500, r = 0.078, t = $\frac{3}{12}$.

    Solution
    I = Prt
    I = 7500(0.078) $\left(\frac{3}{12}\right)$ = 146.25

    The simple interest is $146.25.

20. Strategy
    To find the simple interest, use the
    formula I = Prt.
    P = 14,000, r = 0.086, t = $\frac{4}{12}$.

    Solution
    I = Prt
    I = 14,000(0.086) $\left(\frac{4}{12}\right)$ = 401.33

    The simple interest is $401.33.

21. Strategy
    To find the interest rate, solve the
    simple interest formula I = Prt for r.
    I = 462, P = 12,000, t = $\frac{6}{12}$.

    Solution
    $$I = Prt$$
    $$462 = 12,000\left(\frac{6}{12}\right)r$$
    $$462 = 6000r$$
    $$r = 0.077 = 7.7\%$$

    The interest rate is 7.7%.

22. Strategy
    To find the interest rate, solve the
    simple interest formula I = Prt for r.
    I = 148.50, P = 1800, t = $\frac{9}{12}$.

    Solution
    $$I = Prt$$
    $$148.50 = 1800\left(\frac{9}{12}\right)r$$
    $$148.50 = 1350r$$
    $$r = 0.011 = 11\%$$

    The interest rate is 11%.

23. Strategy
    To find the interest rate, solve the
    simple interest formula I = Prt for r.
    I = 450, P = 24,000, t = $\frac{90}{360}$.

    Solution
    $$I = Prt$$
    $$450 = 24,000\left(\frac{90}{360}\right)r$$
    $$450 = 6000r$$
    $$r = 0.075 = 7.5\%$$

    The rate is 7.5%.

24. Strategy
    To find the interest rate, solve the
    simple interest formula I = Prt for r.
    I = 136, P = 8000, t = $\frac{60}{360}$.

    Solution
    $$I = Prt$$
    $$136 = 8000\left(\frac{60}{360}\right)r$$
    $$136 = \frac{4000}{3}r$$
    $$r = 0.102 = 10.2\%$$

    The rate is 10.2%.

25. Strategy
    To find the amount borrowed, solve the
    simple interest formula I = Prt for P.
    I = 375, r = 0.08, t = $\frac{6}{12}$.

    Solution
    $$I = Prt$$
    $$375 = P(0.08)\left(\frac{6}{12}\right)$$
    $$375 = 0.04P$$
    $$9375 = P$$

    The amount borrowed was $9375.

26. Strategy
    To find the amount borrowed, solve the
    simple interest formula I = Prt for P.
    I = 225, r = 0.075, t = $\frac{9}{12}$.

    Solution
    $$I = Prt$$
    $$225 = P(0.075)\left(\frac{9}{12}\right)$$
    $$225 = 0.05625P$$
    $$4000 = P$$

    The amount borrowed was $4000.

27. Strategy
    To find the amount borrowed, solve the
    simple interest formula I = Prt for P.
    I = 96, r = 0.064, t = $\frac{90}{360}$.

    Solution
    $$I = Prt$$
    $$96 = P(0.064)\left(\frac{90}{360}\right)$$
    $$96 = 0.016P$$
    $$6000 = P$$

    The amount borrowed was $6000.

28. Strategy
    To find the amount borrowed, solve the
    simple interest formula I = Prt for P.
    I = 348, r = 0.087, t = $\frac{120}{360}$.

    Solution
    $$I = Prt$$
    $$348 = P(0.087)\left(\frac{120}{360}\right)$$
    $$348 = 0.029P$$
    $$12,000 = P$$

    The amount borrowed was $12,000.

29. Strategy
    To find the time of the loan:
    • Solve the simple interest formula
      for t.
      I = 375, P = 10,000, r = 0.075.
    • Convert the time of the loan to
      months by multiplying the value of
      t by 12.
    • Convert the time of the loan to
      days by multiplying the value of t
      by 360.

    Solution
    $$I = Prt$$
    375 = 10,000(0.075)t
    375 = 750t
    0.5 = t

    0.5(12 months) = 6 months
    0.5(360 days) = 180 days

    The time of the loan is (a) 6 months
    or (b) 180 days.

30. Strategy
    To find the time of the loan:
    • Solve the simple interest formula
      for t.
      I = 510, P = 30,000, r = 0.068.
    • Convert the time of the loan to
      months by multiplying the value of
      t by 12.
    • Convert the time of the loan to
      days by multiplying the value of t
      by 360.

    Solution
    $$I = Prt$$
    510 = 30,000(0.068)t
    510 = 2040t
    0.25 = t

    0.25(12 months) = 3 months
    0.25(360 days) = 90 days

    The time of the loan is (a) 3 months
    or (b) 90 days.

31. Strategy
    To find the time of the loan:
    • Solve the simple interest formula
      for t.
      I = 372, P = 12,000, r = 0.093.
    • Convert the time of the loan to
      months by multiplying the value of
      t by 12.
    • Convert the time of the loan to
      days by multiplying the value of t
      by 360.

    Solution
    $$I = Prt$$
    372 = 12,000(0.093)t
    372 = 1116t
    $\frac{1}{3} = t$

    $\frac{1}{3}$(12 months) = 4 months
    $\frac{1}{3}$(360 days) = 120 days

    The time of the loan is (a) 4 months
    or (b) 120 days.

32. Strategy
    To find the time of the loan:
    • Solve the simple interest formula
      for t.
      I = 828, P = 16,000, r = 0.069.
    • Convert the time of the loan to
      months by multiplying the value of
      t by 12.
    • Convert the time of the loan to
      days by multiplying the value of t
      by 360.

    Solution
    $$I = Prt$$
    828 = 16,000(0.069)t
    828 = 1104t
    0.75 = t

    0.75(12 months) = 9 months
    0.75(360 days) = 270 days

    The time of the loan is (a) 9 months
    or (b) 270 days.

33. Strategy
    The term is in months. The maturity
    date is the corresponding date 6
    months from August.

    Solution
    The month six months from August is
    February.

    The maturity date is February 3.

34. Strategy
    The term is in months. The maturity
    date is the corresponding date three
    months from May.

    Solution
    The month three months from May is
    August.

    The maturity date is August 14.

35. Strategy
    To find the maturity date:
    - Locate July 10 on the Day of the Year table.
    - Add the number of days in the loan to the day of the year.
    - Use the table to find the date corresponding to this sum.

    Solution
    July 10 is day   191
    Term is 90 days   90
    ─────
    281

    Day 281 is October 8.

    The maturity date is October 8.

36. Strategy
    To find the maturity date:
    - Locate April 4 on the Day of the Year table.
    - Add the number of days in the loan to the day of the year.
    - Use the table to find the date corresponding to this sum.

    Solution
    April 4 is day   94
    Term of loan   120
    ─────
    214

    Day 214 is August 2.

    The maturity date is August 2.

37. Strategy
    To find the due date:
    - Locate March 20 on the Day of the Year table.
    - Add the number of days in the loan to the day of the year.
    - Use the table to find the date corresponding to this sum.

    Solution
    March 20 is day   79
    Term of loan   15
    ─────
    94

    Day 94 is April 4.

    The due date is April 4.

38. Strategy
    To find the due date:
    - Locate December 8 on the Day of the Year table.
    - Add the number of days in the loan to the day of the year.
    - Use the table to find the date corresponding to this sum.

    Solution
    December 8 is day   342
    Term of loan   45
    ─────
    387
    Subtract 365   365
    ─────
    22

    Day 22 is January 22.

    The due date is January 22.

39. Strategy
    To find the maturity value:
    - Find the simple interest. Use the formula I = Prt.
      $P = 10{,}000 \; r = 0.08, \; t = \frac{90}{360}$.
    - Use the maturity value formula M = P + I.

    Solution
    I = Prt
    $I = 10{,}000(0.08)\left(\frac{90}{360}\right) = 200$
    M = P + I
    M = 10,000 + 200 = 10,200

    The maturity value of the note is $10,200.

40. Strategy
    To find the maturity value:
    - Find the simple interest. Use the formula I = Prt.
      $P = 25{,}000 \; r = 0.075, \; t = \frac{30}{360}$.
    - Use the maturity value formula M = P + I.

    Solution
    I = Prt
    $I = 25{,}000(0.075)\left(\frac{30}{360}\right) = 156.25$
    M = P + I
    M = 25,000 + 156.25 = 25,156.25

    The maturity value of the note is $25,156.25.

41. Strategy
    To find the maturity value:
    - Find the simple interest. Use the
      formula I = Prt.
      $P = 40,000 \quad r = 0.085, \quad t = \frac{60}{360}$.
    - Use the maturity value formula
      M = P + I.

    Solution
    I = Prt
    $I = 40,000(0.085)\left(\frac{60}{360}\right) \approx 566.67$

    M = P + I
    M = 40,000 + 566.67 = 40,566.67

    The maturity value of the note is
    $40,566.67.

42. Strategy
    To find the maturity value:
    - Find the simple interest. Use the
      formula I = Prt.
      $P = 90,000 \quad r = 0.095, \quad t = \frac{9}{12}$.
    - Use the maturity value formula
      M = P + I.

    Solution
    I = Prt
    $I = 90,000(0.095)\left(\frac{9}{12}\right) = 6412.50$

    M = P + I
    M = 90,000 + 6412.50 = 96,412.50

    The maturity value of the note is
    $96,412.50.

43. Strategy
    To find the maturity date:
    - Find the date 45 days from
      September 18.
    To find the maturity value:
    - Find the simple interest by solving
      the simple interest formula for I.
      $P = 12,000, \quad r = 0.085, \quad t = \frac{45}{360}$.
    - Use the maturity value formula
      M = P + I.

    Solution
    September 18 is day 261.
    261 + 45 = 306
    Day 306 is November 2.

    The maturity date of the note is
    November 2.

    I = Prt
    $I = 12,000(0.085)\left(\frac{45}{360}\right) = 127.50$

    M = P + I
    M = 12,000 + 127.50 = 12,127.50

    The maturity value of the note is
    $12,127.50.

44. Strategy
    To find the maturity date:
    - Find the date 120 days from
      February 16.
    To find the maturity value:
    - Find the simple interest by solving
      the simple interest formula for I.
      $P = 750, \quad r = 0.075, \quad t = \frac{120}{360}$.
    - Use the maturity value formula
      M = P + I.

    Solution
    February 16 is day 47.
    47 + 120 = 167
    Day 167 is June 16.

    The maturity date of the note is
    June 16.

    I = Prt
    $I = 750(0.075)\left(\frac{120}{360}\right) = 18.75$

    M = P + I
    M = 750 + 18.75 = 768.75

    The maturity value of the note is
    $768.75.

45. Strategy
    To find the maturity date:
    • Find the date 90 days from June 14.
    To find the maturity value:
    • Find the simple interest by solving
    the simple interest formula for I.
    $P = 20,000$, $r = 0.0925$, $t = \frac{90}{360}$.
    • Use the maturity value formula
    $M = P + I$.

    Solution
    June 14 is day 165.
    $165 + 190 = 255$
    Day 255 is September 12.

    The maturity date of the note is
    September 12.

    $I = Prt$
    $I = 20,000(0.0925)\left(\frac{90}{360}\right) = 462.50$

    $M = P + I$
    $M = 20,000 + 462.50 = 20,462.50$

    The maturity value of the note is
    $20,462.50.

46. Strategy
    To find the maturity date:
    • Find the date 45 days from July 20.
    To find the maturity value:
    • Find the simple interest by solving
    the simple interest formula for I.
    $P = 15,000$, $r = 0.0875$, $t = \frac{45}{360}$.
    • Use the maturity value formula
    $M = P + I$.

    Solution
    July 20 is day 201.
    $201 + 45 = 246$
    Day 246 is September 3.

    The maturity date of the note is
    September 3.

    $I = Prt$
    $I = 15,000(0.0875)\left(\frac{45}{360}\right) \approx 164.06$

    $M = P + I$
    $M = 15,000 + 164.06 = 15,164.06$

    The maturity value of the note is
    $15,164.06.

Section 10.2, pages 295–298

1. Strategy
   To find the discount, use the formula
   $D = Mdt$.
   $M = 8000$, $d = 0.075$, $t = \frac{60}{360}$.

   Solution
   $D = Mdt$
   $D = 8000(0.075)\left(\frac{60}{360}\right) = 100$

   The discount is $100.

2. Strategy
   To find the discount, use the formula
   $D = Mdt$.
   $M = 2000$, $d = 0.09$, $t = \frac{45}{360}$.

   Solution
   $D = Mdt$
   $D = 2000(0.09)\left(\frac{45}{360}\right) = 22.50$

   The discount is $22.50.

3. Strategy
   To find the discount, use the formula
   $D = Mdt$.
   $M = 14,000$, $d = 0.075$, $t = \frac{9}{12}$.

   Solution
   $D = Mdt$
   $D = 14,000(0.075)\left(\frac{9}{12}\right) = 787.50$

   The discount is $787.50.

4. Strategy
   To find the discount, use the formula
   $D = Mdt$.
   $M = 1800$, $d = 0.10$, $t = \frac{3}{12}$.

   Solution
   $D = Mdt$
   $D = 1800(0.010)\left(\frac{3}{12}\right) = 45$

   The discount is $45.

5. Strategy
   To find the term of the note, find the number of days from March 25 to May 9. To find the discount, use the simple discount formula D = Mdt.
   M = 2000, d = 0.075.

   Solution
   March 25 is day 84.
   May 9 is day 129.
   129 - 84 = 45

   The term of the note is 45 days.

   D = Mdt
   $D = 2000(0.075)\left(\frac{45}{360}\right) = 18.75$

   The discount is $18.75.

6. Strategy
   To find the term of the note, find the number of days from July 18 to August 17. To find the discount, use the simple discount formula D = Mdt.
   M = 5000, d = 0.08.

   Solution
   July 18 is day 199.
   August 17 is day 229.
   229 - 199 = 30

   The term of the note is 30 days.

   D = Mdt
   $D = 5000(0.08)\left(\frac{30}{360}\right) \approx 33.33$

   The discount is $33.33.

7. Strategy
   To find the discount, use the simple discount formula D = Mdt.
   M = 3300, d = 0.12, $t = \frac{2}{12}$.
   To find the proceeds, use the formula p = M - D.

   Solution
   D = Mdt
   $D = 3300(0.12)\left(\frac{2}{12}\right) = 66$

   The discount is $66.

   p = M - D
   p = 3300 - 66 = 3234

   The proceeds are $3234.

8. Strategy
   To find the discount, use the simple discount formula D = Mdt.
   M = 4500, d = 0.12, $t = \frac{10}{360}$.
   To find the proceeds, use the formula p = M - D.

   Solution
   D = Mdt
   $D = 4500(0.12)\left(\frac{10}{360}\right) = 15$

   The discount is $15.

   p = M - D
   p = 4500 - 15 = 4485

   The proceeds are $4485.

9. Strategy
   To find the term of the note, find the number of days from April 14 to May 14. To find the discount, use the simple discount formula D = Mdt.
   M = 2500, d = 0.09.
   To find the proceeds, use the formula p = M - D.

   Solution
   May 14 is 1 month from April 14.
   The term of the note is 1 month.

   D = Mdt
   $D = 2500(0.09)\left(\frac{1}{12}\right) = 18.75$
   The discount is $18.75.

   p = M - D
   p = 2500 - 18.75 = 2481.25
   The proceeds are $2481.25.

10. Strategy
    To find the term of the note, find the number of days from February 22 to May 22. To find the discount, use the simple discount formula D = Mdt.
    M = 11,000, d = 0.084.
    To find the proceeds, use the formula p = M - D.

    Solution
    May 22 is 3 months from February 22.
    The term of the note is 3 months.

    D = Mdt
    $D = 11,000(0.084)\left(\frac{3}{12}\right) = 231$
    The discount is $231.

    p = M - D
    p = 11,000 - 231 = 10,769
    The proceeds are $10,769.

11. Strategy
    To find the discount rate, solve the
    formula D = Mdt for d.
    $D = 88$, $M = 4500$, $t = \frac{60}{360}$.

    Solution
    $D = Mdt$
    $88 = 4500(d)\left(\frac{60}{360}\right)$
    $88 = 750d$
    $0.117 \approx d$

    The discount rate is 11.7%.

12. Strategy
    To find the discount rate, solve the
    formula D = Mdt for d.
    $D = 50$, $M = 5000$, $t = \frac{45}{360}$.

    Solution
    $D = Mdt$
    $50 = 5000(d)\left(\frac{45}{360}\right)$
    $50 = 625d$
    $0.08 \approx d$

    The discount rate is 8%.

13. Strategy
    To find the discount rate:
    • Find the term of the note.
    • Solve the formula D = Mdt for d.
      $D = 200$, $M = 7500$.

    Solution
    April 12 is 4 months after
    December 12.

    The term of the note is 4 months.

    $D = Mdt$
    $200 = 7500(d)\left(\frac{4}{12}\right)$
    $200 = 2500d$
    $0.08 = d$

    The discount rate is 8%.

14. Strategy
    To find the discount rate:
    • Find the term of the note.
    • Solve the formula D = Mdt for d.
      $D = 115.50$, $M = 6600$.

    Solution
    November 8 is 3 months after August 8.

    The term of the note is 3 months.

    $D = Mdt$
    $115.50 = 6600(d)\left(\frac{3}{12}\right)$
    $115.50 = 1650d$
    $0.07 = d$

    The discount rate is 7%.

15. Strategy
    To find the proceeds:
    • Find the term of the note.
    • Use the formula D = Mdt to find the
      discount.
      $M = 3000$, $d = 0.08$.
    • Use the formula p = M − D.

    Solution
    June 23 is day 194.
    August 22 is day 234.
    $234 - 174 = 60$

    The term of the note is 60 days.

    $D = Mdt$
    $D = 3000(0.08)\left(\frac{60}{360}\right) = 40$

    $p = M - D$
    $p = 3000 - 40 = 2960$

    The proceeds are $2960.

16. Strategy
    To find the proceeds:
    • Find the term of the note.
    • Use the formula D = Mdt to find the
      discount.
      $M = 8000$, $d = 0.085$.
    • Use the formula p = M − D.

    Solution
    April 13 is 6 months after October 13.

    The term of the note is 6 months.

    $D = Mdt$
    $D = 8000(0.085)\left(\frac{6}{12}\right) = 340$

    $p = M - D$
    $p = 8000 - 340 = 7660$

    The proceeds are $7660.

17. Strategy
    To find the maturity value, use the
    formula M = P + I, where I = Prt.
    P = 25,000, r = 0.08, t = 5.
    To find the discount, use the simple
    discount formula D = Mdt to find the
    discount on a 2-year, 10% note. The
    maturity value is the value found in
    Step 1.
    To find the proceeds, use the formula
    p = M - D.

    Solution
    M = P + I
    M = 25,000 + 25,000(0.08)(5)
      = 25,000 + 10,000 = 35,000

    The maturity value is $35,000.

    D = Mdt
    D = 35,000(0.10)(2) = 7000

    The discount is $7000.

    p = M - D
    p = 35,000 - 7000 = 28,000

    The proceeds are $28,000.

18. Strategy
    To find the maturity value, use the
    formula M = P + I, where I = Prt.
    P = 6000, r = 0.09, t = 2.
    To find the discount, use the simple
    discount formula D = Mdt to find the
    discount on a 1.5-year, 10% note. The
    maturity value is the value found in
    Step 1.
    To find the proceeds, use the formula
    p = M - D.

    Solution
    M = P + I
    M = 6000 + 6000(0.09)(2)
      = 6000 + 1080 = 7080

    The maturity value is $7080.

    D = Mdt
    D = 7080(0.10)(1.5) = 1062

    The discount is $1062.

    p = M - D
    p = 7080 - 1062 = 6018

    The proceeds are $6018.

19. Strategy
    To find the amount the bank will pay
    for the note:
    • Use the formula M = P + I to find
      the maturity value. (I = Prt)
      P = 5000, r = 0.10, t = 5.
    • Use the formula D = Mdt to find the
      discount on a 3-year, 8% note. The
      maturity value is the value found
      in Step 1.
    • Use the formula p = M - D to find
      the proceeds.

    Solution
    M = P + I
    M = 5000 + 5000(0.10)(5)
      = 5000 + 2500 = 7500

    D = Mdt
    D = 7500(0.08)(3) = 1800

    p = M - D
    p = 7500 - 1800 = 5700

    The bank will pay $5700 for the note.

20. Strategy
    To find the amount the bank will pay
    for the note:
    • Use the formula M = P + I to find
      the maturity value, (I = Prt)
      P = 2500, r = 0.09, t = 3.
    • Use the formula D = Mdt to find the
      discount on a 2-year, 10% note. The
      maturity value is the value found
      in Step 1.
    • Use the formula p = M - D to find
      the proceeds.

    Solution
    M = P + I
    M = 2500 + 2500(0.09)(3)
      = 2500 + 675 = 3175

    D = Mdt
    D = 3175(0.10)(2) = 635

    p = M - D
    p = 3175 - 635 = 2540

    The bank will pay $2540 for the note.

21. Strategy
    To find the maturity value:
    • Find the number of days until the maturity date.
    • Use the formula M = P + I, where I = Prt.

    $P = 18,000$, $r = 0.08$, $t = \frac{120}{360}$.

    To find the discount, use the simple formula D = Mdt to find the discount on a 60-day, 8.8% note. The maturity value is the value found in Step 1. To find the proceeds, use the formula p = M − D.

    Solution
    November 27 is day 331.
    January 26 is day 26.
    (365 − 331) + 26 = 34 + 26 = 60

    60 days of the 120-day note have passed.

    120 − 60 = 60

    There are 60 days until the maturity date of the note.

    M = P + I
    $M = 18,000 + 18,000(0.08)\left(\frac{120}{360}\right)$
    $= 18,000 + 480 = 18,480$

    The maturity value is $18,480.

    D = Mdt
    $D = 18,480(0.08)\left(\frac{60}{360}\right) = 271.04$

    The discount is $271.04.

    p = M − D
    p = 18,480 − 271.04 = 18,208.96

    The proceeds are $18,208.96.

22. Strategy
    To find the maturity value:
    • Find the number of days until the maturity date.
    • Use the formula M = P + I, where I = Prt.

    $P = 12,000$, $r = 0.09$, $t = \frac{90}{360}$.

    To find the discount, use the simple formula D = Mdt to find the discount on a 30-day, 10% note. The maturity value is the value found in Step 1. To find the proceeds, use the formula p = M − D.

    Solution
    June 30 is day 181.
    August 29 is day 241.
    241 − 181 = 60

    60 days of the 90-day note have passed.

    90 − 60 = 30

    There are 30 days until the maturity date of the note.

    M = P + I
    $M = 12,000 + 12,000(0.09)\left(\frac{90}{360}\right)$
    $= 12,000 + 270 = 12,270$

    The maturity value is $12,270.

    D = Mdt
    $D = 12,270(0.10)\left(\frac{30}{360}\right) = 102.25$

    The discount is $102.25.

    p = M − D
    p = 12,270 − 102.25 = 12,167.75

    The proceeds are $12,167.75.

23. Strategy
To find the proceeds:
* Find the number of days until the maturity date.
* Use the formula M = P + I, where I = Prt, to find the maturity value.
  P = 6000, r = 0.06, t = $\frac{180}{360}$.
* Use the simple discount formula D = Mdt to find the discount on a 120-day, 6.6% note.
* Use the formula p = M − D.

Solution
March 4 is day 63.
May 3 is day 123.
123 − 63 = 60

60 days of the 180-day note have passed.

180 − 60 = 120

There are 120 days until the maturity date of the note.

M = P + I
M = 6000 + 6000(0.06) $\left(\frac{180}{360}\right)$
  = 6000 + 180 = 6180

D = Mdt
M = 6180(0.06) $\left(\frac{120}{360}\right)$ = 135.96

p = M − D
p = 6180 − 135.96 = 6044.04

The proceeds are $6044.04.

24. Strategy
To find the proceeds:
* Find the number of days until the maturity date.
* Use the formula M = P + I, where I = Prt, to find the maturity value.
  P = 4000, r = 0.05, t = $\frac{60}{360}$.
* Use the simple discount formula D = Mdt to find the discount on a 30-day, 6% note.
* Use the formula p = M − D.

Solution
June 28 is day 179.
July 28 is day 209.
209 − 179 = 30

30 days of the 60-day note have passed.

60 − 30 = 30

There are 30 days until the maturity date of the note.

M = P + I
M = 4000 + 4000(0.05) $\left(\frac{60}{360}\right)$
  = 4000 + 33.33 = 4033.33

D = Mdt
M = 4033.33(0.06) $\left(\frac{30}{360}\right)$ = 20.17

p = M − D
p = 4033.33 − 20.17 = 4013.16

The proceeds are $4013.16.

25. Strategy
To find the proceeds:
* Find the number of days until the maturity date.
* Use the formula M = P + I, where I = Prt, to find the maturity value.
  P = 9000, r = 0.08, t = $\frac{210}{360}$.
* Use the simple discount formula D = Mdt to find the discount on a 210-day, 6% note.
* Use the formula p = M − D.

Solution
November 3 is day 307.
September 18 is day 261.
307 − 261 = 46

46 days of the 210-day note have passed.

219 − 46 = 164

There are 164 days until the maturity date of the note.

M = P + I

M = 9000 + 9000(0.08) $\left(\frac{210}{360}\right)$ = 9000 + 420 = 9420

D = Mdt

M = 9420(0.09) $\left(\frac{164}{360}\right)$ = 386.22

p = M - D

p = 9420 - 386.22 = 9033.78

The proceeds are $9033.78.

Section 10.3, pages 309–312

1. Strategy
    To find the future value, use the
    formula FV = PV x compounding factor.
    PV = 10,000, i% = 8%, daily
    compounding for 2 years.

    Solution
    FV = PV x compounding factor
    FV = 10,000(1.173490) = 11,734.90

    The future value of the investment is
    $11,734.90.

2. Strategy
    To find the future value, use the
    formula FV = PV x compounding factor.
    PV = 3500, i% = $\frac{12\%}{12}$ = 1%,
    n = 12 x 3 = 36.

    Solution
    FV = PV x compounding factor
    FV = 3500(1.430769) ≈ 5007.69

    The future value of the investment is
    $5007.69.

3. Strategy
    To find the future value, use the
    formula FV = PV x compounding factor.
    PV = 2300, i% = $\frac{10\%}{4}$ = 2.5,
    n = 6 x 4 = 24.

    Solution
    FV = PV x compounding factor
    FV = 2300(1.808726) ≈ 4160.07

    The future value of the investment is
    $4160.07.

4. Strategy
    To find the future value, use the
    formula FV = PV x compounding factor.
    PV = 3200, i% = 10% daily compounding
    for 5 years.

    Solution
    FV = PV x compounding factor
    FV = 3200(1.648607) = 5275.542

    The future value of the investment is
    $5275.54.

5. Strategy
    To find the future value, use the
    formula FV = PV x compounding factor.
    PV = 4500, i% = 8% daily compounding
    for 4 years.

    Solution
    FV = PV x compounding factor
    FV = 4500(1.377079) = 6196.8555

    The future value of the investment is
    $6196.86.

6. Strategy
    To find the future value, use the
    formula FV = PV x compounding factor.
    PV = 4.35, i% = $\frac{10\%}{1}$, n = 5.

    Solution
    FV = PV x compounding factor
    FV = 4.35(1.610510) ≈ 7.0057

    The future value of the investment is
    $7.01.

7. Strategy
   To find the future value, use the
   formula FV = PV x compounding factor.

   PV = 6.24, i% = $\frac{8\%}{1}$ = 8%, n = 3.

   Solution
   FV = PV x compounding factor
   FV = 6.24(1.259712) ≈ 7.8606

   The future value of the investment is
   $7.86.

8. Strategy
   To find the interest:
   • Find the future value of the
     investment. Use the formula
     FV = PV x compounding factor.
   • Find the interest. Use the formula
     CI = FV - PV.

   P = 3200, i% = $\frac{9\%}{12}$ = 0.75,

   n = 12·4 = 48.

   Solution
   FV = PV x compounding factor
   FV = 3200(1.431405) = 4580.496

   The future value is $4580.50.

   CI = FV - PV
   CI = 4580.50 - 3200 = 1380.50

   The interest earned is $1380.50.

9. Strategy
   To find the interest:
   • Find the future value of the
     investment. Use the formula
     FV = PV x compounding factor.
   • Find the interest. Use the formula
     CI = FV - PV.

   PV = 8500, i% = $\frac{9\%}{360}$, n = 5.

   Solution
   FV = PV x compounding factor
   FV = 8500(1.568224) = 13,329.904

   The future value is $13,329.90.

   CI = FV - PV
   CI = 13,329.90 - 8500 = 4829.90

   The interest earned is $4829.90.

10. Strategy
    To find the interest:
    • Find the future value of the
      investment. Use the formula
      FV = PV x compounding factor.
    • Find the interest. Use the formula
      CI = FV - PV.

    PV = 5500, i% = $\frac{7\%}{360}$, n = 4.

    Solution
    FV = PV x compounding factor
    FV = 5500(1.323094) = 7277.017

    The future value is $7277.02.

    CI = FV - PV
    CI = 7277.02 - 5500 = 1777.02

    The interest earned is $1777.02.

11-20. Strategy
       Use the formula FV = PV x compounding factor.
       PV = 1000, i% = 8%, n = 1 year.

       Solution

Compounding Period	Compounding Factor	Present Value	Future Value
Annually	1.080000	$1000	$1080.00
Semiannually	1.081600	$1000	$1081.60
Quarterly	1.082432	$1000	$1082.43
Monthly	1.083000	$1000	$1083.00
Daily	1.083277	$1000	$1083.28

21. Strategy
    To find the difference in the amount
    of interest earned, subtract the
    future value by compounding annually
    from the future value by compounding
    daily.

    Solution
    1083.28 - 1080 = $3.28

23. Strategy
    To find the present value, use the
    formula FV = FV + compounding factor.
    FV = 2000, i% = 9% daily compounding
    for 5 years.

    Solution
    PV = FV + compounding factor
    PV = 2000 ÷ 1.568224 = 1275.328

    The amount to be deposited is
    $1275.33.

25. Strategy
    To find the present value, use the
    formula FV = FV + compounding factor.
    FV = 15,000, i% = 8% daily compounding
    for 4 years.

    Solution
    PV = FV + compounding factor
    PV = 15,000 ÷ 1.377079 = 10,892.621

    The amount to be invested is
    $10,892.62.

27. Strategy
    To find the present value, use the
    formula FV = FV + compounding factor.
    FV = 5000, i% = $\frac{8\%}{2}$ = 4%, n = 10.

    Solution
    PV = FV + compounding factor
    PV = 5000 ÷ 1.480244 = 3377.8215

    The amount to be invested is $3377.82.

22. Strategy
    To find the difference in the amount
    of interest earned, subtract the
    future value by compounding annually
    from the future value by compounding
    monthly.

    Solution
    1083.28 - 1083 = $.28

24. Strategy
    To find the present value, use the
    formula FV = FV + compounding factor.
    FV = 5000, i% = $\frac{6\%}{4}$ = $1\frac{1}{2}$%,
    n = 4 · 4 = 16.

    Solution
    PV = FV + compounding factor
    PV = 5000 ÷ 1.268986 = 3940.1538

    The amount to be invested is $3940.15.

26. Strategy
    To find the present value, use the
    formula FV = FV + compounding factor.
    FV = 35,000, i% = $\frac{8\%}{4}$ = 2%, n = 8.

    Solution
    PV = FV + compounding factor
    PV = 35,000 ÷ 1.171659 = 29,872.173

    The amount to be invested is
    $29,872.17.

28. Strategy
    To find the present value, use the
    formula FV = FV + compounding factor.
    FV = 10,000, i% = $\frac{6\%}{2}$ = 3%, n = 20.

    Solution
    PV = FV + compounding factor
    PV = 10,000 ÷ 1.806111 = 5536.768

    The present value of the investment is
    $5536.76.

29.   Strategy
      To find the present value, use the
      formula FV = FV + compounding factor.
      FV = 5000, 7% daily compounding for 5
      years.

      Solution
      PV = FV + compounding factor
      PV = 5000 + 1.419019 = 3523.561

      The present value of the investment is
      $3523.56.

30.   Strategy
      To find the present value, use the
      formula FV = FV + compounding factor.
      FV = 2500, i% = $\frac{9\%}{12}$ = 0.75%, n = 36.

      Solution
      PV = FV + compounding factor
      PV = 2500 + 1.308645 = 1910.3729

      The present value of the investment is
      $1910.37.

31.   Strategy
      To find the investment with the
      greater present value:
      • Find the present value of each
        investment. Use the formula
        PV = FV + compounding factor.
      • Compare the present values to
        determine the greater present
        value.
        First investment:
        FV = 10,000, 7% daily compounding
            for 8 years.
        Second investment:
        FV = 7500, 7% daily compounding for
            6 years.

      Solution
      PV = FV + compounding factor
      First investment:
      PV = 10,000 + 1.750577 ≈ 5712.40
      Second investment:
      PV = 7500 + 1.521899 ≈ 4928.05

      The $10,000 investment has the greater
      present value.

32.   Strategy
      To find the investment with the
      greater present value:
      • Find the present value of each
        investment. Use the formula
        PV = FV + compounding factor.
      • Compare the present values to
        determine the greater present
        value.
        First investment:
        FV = 5000, 8% daily compounding for
            6 years.
        Second investment:
        FV = 9000, 8% daily compounding for
            10 years.

      Solution
      PV = FV + compounding factor
      First investment:
      PV = 5000 + 1.615988 ≈ 3094.08
      Second investment:
      PV = 9000 + 2.225343 ≈ 4044.32

      The $9000 investment has a larger
      present value.

33. Strategy
     To find the investment with the
     greater present value:
     • Find the present value of each
       investment. Use the formula
       PV = FV ÷ compounding factor.
     • Compare the present values to
       determine the greater present
       value.
       First investment:
       FV = 5000, 9% daily compounding for
            5 years.
       Second investment:
       FV = 7500, 9% daily compounding for
            8 years.

     Solution
     PV = FV ÷ compounding factor
     First investment:
     PV = 5000 ÷ 1.568224 ≈ 3188.32
     Second investment:
     PV = 7500 ÷ 2.054248 ≈ 3650.97

     The second certificate of $7500 has
     the larger present value.

34. Strategy
     To find the effective interest rate:
     • Find the future value of $100. Use
       the future value formula
       FV = PV x compounding factor.
     • Find the interest earned. Use the
       formula CI = FV - PV.

     Solution
     FV = PV x compounding factor
     FV = 100(1.072501) = 107.2501
     CI = FV - PV
     CI = 107.2501 - 100 = 7.2501

     The effective rate is 7.25%.

35. Strategy
     To find the effective interest rate:
     • Find the future value of $100. Use
       the future value formula
       FV = PV x compounding factor.
     • Find the interest earned. Use the
       formula CI = FV - PV.

     Solution
     FV = PV x compounding factor
     FV = 100(1.082432) = 108.2432
     CI = FV - PV
     CI = 108.2432 - 100 = 8.2432

     The effective rate is 8.24%.

36. Strategy
     To find the effective interest rate:
     • Find the future value of $100. Use
       the future value formula
       FV = PV x compounding factor.
     • Find the interest earned. Use the
       formula CI = FV - PV.

     Solution
     FV = PV x compounding factor
     FV = 100(1.083000) = 108.3000
     CI = FV - PV
     CI = 108.3000 - 100 = 8.3000

     The effective rate is 8.30%.

37. Strategy
     To find the effective interest rate:
     • Find the future value of $100. Use
       the future value formula
       FV = PV x compounding factor.
     • Find the interest earned. Use the
       formula CI = FV - PV.

     Solution
     FV = PV x compounding factor
     FV = 100(1.061678) = 106.1678
     CI = FV - PV
     CI = 106.1678 - 100 = 6.1678

     The effective rate is 6.17%.

38–52. Strategy
Use the compound interest table to find the compounding factor. Use the formula
FV = PV x compounding factor.

Solution

Compounding Period	Compounding Factor	Present Value	Future Value	Effective Rate
Annually	1.080000	$1.00	$1.08000	8%
Semiannually	1.081600	$1.00	$1.08160	8.16%
Quarterly	1.082432	$1.00	$1.08243	8.24%
Monthly	1.083000	$1.00	$1.08300	8.3%
Daily	1.083277	$1.00	$1.08328	8.33%

53. Strategy
To determine which has the higher effective annual rate:
• Calculate the effective annual rate of 6% compounded quarterly.
• Calculate the effective annual rate of 6.25% compounded semiannually.
• Compare the two effective rates.

Solution
$$FV = PV(1 + i)^n$$
$$= 100(1 + 0.015)^4$$
$$= 106.13636$$

$$CI = FV - PV$$
$$= 106.13636 - 100$$
$$= 6.13636$$

The effective rate of 6% compounded quarterly is 6.14%.

$$FV = PV(1 + i)^n$$
$$= 100(1 + 0.03125)^2$$
$$= 106.34766$$

$$CI = FV - PV$$
$$= 106.34766 - 100$$
$$= 6.34766$$

The effective rate of 6.25% compounded semiannually is 6.35%.

6.35% is greater than 6.14%.

6.25% compounded semiannually has the higher effective annual rate.

54. Strategy
To determine which has the higher effective annual rate:
• Calculate the effective annual rate of 7.8% compounded monthly.
• Calculate the effective annual rate of 7.5% compounded daily.
• Compare the two effective rates.

Solution
$$FV = PV(1 + i)^n$$
$$= 100(1 + 0.0065)^{12}$$
$$= 108.08498$$

$$CI = FV - PV$$
$$= 108.08498 - 100$$
$$= 8.08498$$

The effective rate of 7.8% compounded monthly is 8.08%.

$$FV = PV(1 + i)^n$$
$$= 100 \left(1 + \frac{0.075}{360}\right)^{360}$$
$$= 107.78757$$

$$CI = FV - PV$$
$$= 107.78757 - 100$$
$$= 7.78757$$

The effective rate of 7.5% compounded daily is 7.79%.

8.08% is greater than 7.79%.

7.8% compounded monthly has the higher effective annual rate.

Business Case Study

1. Cash discount on $300,000 @ 2% discount rate = $6000
   Cash discount on $150,000 @ 3% discount rate = $4500

   $6000 + $4500 = $10,500

   $10,500 would not have been spent on merchandise if the company had taken advantage of the cash discounts available.

2. Principal + interest = $37,500(1.093807) = $41,017.76

   Interest earned = $41,017.76 - $37,500 = $3517.76

   $3517.76 would have been lost to the business by not earning interest on the $37,500.

3. $10,500 - $3517.76 = $6982.24

   The difference is $6982.24.

4. Yes, the accountant's advice should be taken.

Review/Test, pages 317–318

1. Strategy
   To find the simple interest, use the simple interest formula.
   P = 3000, r = 0.0875, t = $\frac{45}{360}$.

   Solution
   I = Prt
   $= 3000(0.0875)\left(\frac{45}{360}\right) = 32.8125$

   The interest is $32.81.

2. Strategy
   To find the simple interest, use the simple interest formula.
   P = 2700, r = 0.07, t = $\frac{3}{12}$.

   Solution
   I = Prt
   $= 2700(0.07)\left(\frac{3}{12}\right) = 47.25$

   The interest is $47.25.

3. Strategy
   To find the maturity date of the note:
   • Locate March 14 in the table. The day of the year appears below the date (73).
   • Add the number of days in the loan to the day of the year.
   • Use the table to find the date which corresponds to the sum.

   Solution
   ```
     73
   +90
   ───
    163
   ```
   Day 163 is June 12.

   The maturity date of the loan is June 12.

4. Strategy
   To find the maturity date of the note, find the corresponding day 4 months from July 31.

   Solution
   4 months from July 31 is November 30.

   The maturity date is November 30.

5. **Strategy**
   To find the maturity value of the note:
   • Find the simple interest.
     $P = 5000$, $r = 0.096$, $t = \frac{60}{160}$.
   • Use the maturity value formula $M = P + I$.

   Solution
   $I = Prt$
   $= 5000(0.096)\left(\frac{60}{360}\right) = 80$

   $M = P + I$
   $= 5000 + 80 = 5080$

   The maturity value of the note is $5080.

6. **Strategy**
   To find the maturity value of the note:
   • Find the simple interest.
     $P = 25{,}000$, $r = 0.10$, $t = \frac{9}{12}$.
   • Use the maturity value formula $M = P + I$.

   Solution
   $I = Prt$
   $= 25{,}000(0.10)\left(\frac{9}{12}\right) = 1875$

   $M = P + I$
   $= 25{,}000 + 1875 = 26{,}875$

   The maturity value of the note is $26,875.

7. **Strategy**
   To find the proceeds of the note:
   • Use the discount formula to find the discount.
     $M = 8000$, $d = 0.09$, $t = \frac{6}{12}$.
   • Use the proceeds formula $p = M - D$.

   Solution
   $D = Mdt = 8000(0.09)\left(\frac{6}{12}\right) = 360$
   $p = M - D = 8000 - 360 = 7640$

   The proceeds are $7640.

8. **Strategy**
   To find the proceeds of the note:
   • Use the discount formula to find the discount.
     $M = 3400$, $d = 0.07$,
     $t = \frac{\text{number of days}}{360}$.
   • Use the proceeds formula $p = M - D$.

   Solution
   April 23 = day 113; June 7 = day 158;
   $158 - 113 = 45$ days
   $D = Mdt = 3400(0.07)\left(\frac{45}{360}\right) = 29.75$
   $p = M - D = 3400 - 29.75 = 3370.25$

   The proceeds are $3370.25.

9. **Strategy**
   To find the future value, use the future value formula
   FV = PV x compounding factor.
   PV = 5000, 8% daily compounding for 4 years.

   Solution
   FV = PV x compounding factor
   $= 5000(1.377079) = 6885.395$

   The future value of the investment is $6885.40.

10. **Strategy**
    To find the amount in the account after 10 years, use the compound interest formula
    FV = PV x compounding factor.
    $PV = 1000$, $i\% = \frac{6}{4}\%$, $n = 4 \cdot 15 = 60$.

    Solution
    FV = PV x compounding factor
    $= 1000(2.443220) = 2443.22$

    The amount in the account after 10 years is $2443.22.

11. Strategy
    To find the amount, use the present
    value formula
    PV = FV ÷ compounding factor.
    FV = 40,000, i% = $\frac{8}{12}$% = $\frac{2}{3}$%,
    n = 12 · 2 = 24.

    Solution
    PV = FV ÷ compounding factor
       = 40,000 ÷ 1.172888 = 34,103.85

    $34,103.85 should be placed into the
    account.

13. Strategy
    To find the present value, use the
    present value formula
    PV = FV ÷ compounding factor.
    FV = 10,000, i% = $\frac{10}{2}$% = 5%,
    n = 2 · 3 = 6

    Solution
    PV = FV ÷ compounding factor
       = 10,000 ÷ 1.340096 = 7462.152

    The present value of the investment is
    $7462.15.

12. Strategy
    To find the amount of money, use the
    present value formula
    PV = FV ÷ compounding factor.
    FV = 80,000, i% = $\frac{9}{12}$% ,
    n = 12 · 4 = 48.

    Solution
    PV = FV ÷ compounding factor
       = 80,000 ÷ 1.431405 = 55,889.144

    $55,889.14 must be deposited in the
    account.

14. Strategy
    To find the effective rate:
    • Use the future value formula and
      the daily compounding table to find
      the future value of $100.
      PV = 1, i% = 9%, n = 1.
    • Use the formula CI = FV - PV to
      find the interest earned.

    Solution
    FV = PV x compounding factor
       = 100(1.094162) = 109.4162

    CI = 109.4162 - 100 = 9.4162

    The effective rate is 9.42%.

15. Strategy
    To find the effective rate:
    • Use the future value formula and
      the daily compounding table to find
      the future value of $100.
      PV = 1, i% = 11%, n = 1.
    • Use the formula CI = FV - PV to
      find the interest earned.

    Solution
    FV = PV x compounding factor
       = 100(1.116259) = 111.6259

    CI = 111.6259 - 100 = 11.6259

    The effective rate is 11.63%.

CHAPTER 11
Annuities

Section 11.1, pages 329–332

1. PMT = 400, i% = $\frac{r}{c}$ = $\frac{4\%}{4}$ = 1%, n = 4·15 = 60

   FV = PMT·$s\,\overline{_n}|_i$

   FV = 400(81.669670) ≈ \$32,667.87

2. PMT = 2000, i% = $\frac{r}{c}$ = $\frac{5\%}{2}$ = 2.5%, n = 2·8 = 16

   FV = PMT·$s\,\overline{_n}|_i$

   FV = 2000(19.380225) = \$38,760.45

3. PMT – 5000, i% = $\frac{r}{c}$ – $\frac{7\%}{1}$ = 7%, n – 1·12 = 12, 1 + i = 1 + 0.07 = 1.07

   FV = PMT·$s\,\overline{_n}|_i$(1 + i)

   FV = 5000(17.888451)(1.07) = \$95,703.21

4. PMT = 600, i% = $\frac{r}{c}$ = $\frac{6\%}{12}$ = 0.5%, n = 12·12 = 120, 1 + i = 1 + 0.005 = 1.005

   FV = PMT·$s\,\overline{_n}|_i$(1 + i)

   FV = 600(163.879347)(1.005) = \$98,819.25

5. Strategy
   To find the future value, use the formula for the future value of an ordinary annuity, FV = PMT·$s\,\overline{_n}|_i$.

   PMT = 3000, i% = $\frac{8\%}{4}$ = 2%,
   n = 4·5 = 20.

   Solution
   FV = PMT·$s\,\overline{_n}|_i$

   = 3000(24.297370) = 72,892.11

   The future value is \$72,892.11.

6. Strategy
   To find the future value, use the formula for the future value of an annuity due, FV = PMT·$s\,\overline{_n}|_i$(1 + i).

   PMT = 50, i% = $\frac{9\%}{12}$,
   1 + i = 1.0075, n = 12·10 = 120.

   Solution
   FV = PMT·$s\,\overline{_n}|_i$(1 + i)

   = 50(193.514277)(1.0075) ≈ 9748.28

   The future value is \$9748.28.

7. Strategy
   To find the future value, use the formula for the future value of an annuity due, $FV = PMT \cdot s\,\overline{n}|_i(1 + i)$.

   $PMT = 75$, $i\% = \frac{8\%}{12} = \frac{2}{3}\%$.

   $1 + i = 1.0066667$, $n = 12 \cdot 10 = 120$.

   Solution
   $FV = PMT \cdot s\,\overline{n}|_i(1 + i)$

   $= 75(182.946039)(1.0066667)$

   $\approx 13,812.43$

   The future value is $13,812.43.

8. Strategy
   To find the future value, use the formula for the future value of an ordinary annuity, $FV = PMT \cdot s\,\overline{n}|_i$.

   $PMT = 500$, $i\% = \frac{6\%}{4} = 1.5\%$,

   $n = 4 \cdot 3 = 12$.

   Solution
   $FV = PMT \cdot s\,\overline{n}|_i$

   $= 500(13.041211) = 6520.6055$

   The future value is $6520.61.

9. Strategy
   To find the future value, use the formula for the future value of an ordinary annuity, $FV = PMT \cdot s\,\overline{n}|_i$.

   $PMT = 113.28$, $i\% = \frac{6\%}{12} = 0.5\%$,

   $n = 12 \cdot 5 = 60$.

   Solution
   $FV = PMT \cdot s\,\overline{n}|_i$

   $= 113.28(69.770031) = 7903.5491$

   The future value is $7903.55.

10. Strategy
    To find the future value, use the formula for the future value of an annuity due, $FV = PMT \cdot s\,\overline{n}|_i(1 + i)$.

    $PMT = 2500$, $i\% = \frac{10\%}{4} = 2.5\%$,

    $1 + i = 1.025$, $n = 4 \cdot 1 = 4$.

    Solution
    $FV = PMT \cdot s\,\overline{n}|_i(1 + i)$

    $= 2500(4.152516)(1.025)$
    $= 10,640.822$

    The future value is $10,640.82.

11. Strategy
    To find the larger future value of the two ordinary annuities, compare the future values of the annuities. Use the formula $FV = PMT \cdot s\,\overline{n}|_i$.

    For annuity (1),
    $PMT = 300$, $i\% = \frac{12\%}{4} = 3\%$,
    $n = 4 \cdot 5 = 20$.
    For annuity (2),
    $PMT = 100$, $i\% = \frac{12\%}{12} = 1\%$,
    $n = 12 \cdot 5 = 60$.

    Solution
    (1) $FV = PMT \cdot s\,\overline{n}|_i$

    $= 300(26.870374) \approx 8061.11$
    (2) $FV = PMT \cdot s\,\overline{n}|_i$

    $= 100(81.669670) \approx 8166.97$

    8166.97 is greater than 8061.11.

    Annuity (2) has the larger future value.

12. Strategy
    To find the larger future value of the two ordinary annuities, compare the future values of the annuities. Use the formula $FV = PMT \cdot s\,\overline{n}|_i(1 + i)$.

    For annuity (1),
    $PMT = 1000$, $i\% = \frac{10\%}{1} = 10\%$,
    $1 + i = 1.1$, $n = 1 \cdot 5 = 5$.
    For annuity (2),
    $PMT = 500$, $i\% = \frac{10\%}{2} = 5\%$,
    $1 + i = 1.05$, $n = 2 \cdot 5 = 10$.

    Solution
    (1) $FV = PMT \cdot s\,\overline{n}|_i(1 + i)$

    $= 1000(6.105100)(1.1)$
    ≈ 6715.61
    (2) $FV = PMT \cdot s\,\overline{n}|_i(1 + i)$

    $= 500(12.577893)(1.05)$
    ≈ 6603.39

    6715.61 is greater than 6603.39.

    Annuity (1) has the larger future value.

13. Strategy
    To find the future value of the annuity, use the formula for the future value of an annuity due.
    PMT = 1200, i% = $\frac{r}{c}$ = $\frac{7\%}{1}$ = 7%, n = 1·15 = 15, 1 + i = 1 + 0.07 = 1.07.
    To find the total of his payments, multiply the number of payments (15) times the amount of each payment (1200).
    To find the total amount of interest earned, subtract the total of his payments from the future value of the annuity.

    Solution
    FV = PMT·$s_{\overline{n}|i}$(1 + i)

    FV = 1200(25.129022)(1.07) = 32,265.66

    The future value of the annuity is $32,265.66.

    Total of the payments = 15(1200) = 18,000

    The total of the payments is $18,000.

    32,265.66 - 18,000 = 14,265.66

    The total amount of interest earned is $14,265.66.

14. Strategy
    To find the future value of the annuity, use the formula for the future value of an ordinary annuity.
    PMT = 2500, i% = $\frac{r}{c}$ = $\frac{5\%}{1}$ = 5%, n = 1·20 = 20.
    To find the total of her payments, multiply the number of payments (20) times the amount of each payment (2500).
    To find the total amount of interest earned, subtract the total of her payments from the future value of the annuity.

    Solution
    FV = PMT·$s_{\overline{n}|i}$

    FV = 2500(33.065954) = 82,664.89

    The future value of the annuity is $82,664.89.

    Total of the payments = 20(2500) = 50,000

    The total of the payments is $50,000.

    82,664.89 - 50,000 = 32,664.89

    The total amount of interest earned is $32,664.89.

15. Strategy
    To find the interest earned:
    • Find the total of the annuity payments.
    • Find the future value of the ordinary annuity by using the formula for the future value of an ordinary annuity,
    $FV = PMT \cdot s_{\overline{n}|i}$.

    $PMT = 500$, $i\% = \dfrac{8\%}{2} = 4\%$,
    $n = 2 \cdot 4 = 8$.
    • Subtract the total of the annuity payments from the future value.

    Solution
    $500(8) = 4000$
    $FV = PMT \cdot s_{\overline{n}|i}$

        $= 500(9.214226) \approx 4607.11$
    $4607.11 - 4000 = 607.11$

    The interest earned is $607.11.

16. Strategy
    To find the interest earned:
    • Find the total of the annuity payments.
    • Find the future value of the ordinary annuity by using the formula for the future value of an annuity due,
    $FV = PMT \cdot s_{\overline{n}|i}(1 + i)$.

    $PMT = 500$, $i\% = \dfrac{8\%}{2} = 4\%$,
    $n = 2 \cdot 4 = 8$.
    • Subtract the total of the annuity payments from the future value.

    Solution
    $500(8) = 4000$
    $FV = PMT \cdot s_{\overline{n}|i}$

        $= 500(9.214226)(1.04) \approx 4791.40$
    $4791.40 - 4000 = 791.40$

    The interest earned is $791.40.

17. $FV = 25,000$, $i\% = \dfrac{r}{c} = \dfrac{10\%}{4} = 2.5\%$, $n = 4 \cdot 5 = 20$
    $PMT = FV \cdot s_{\overline{n}|i}$
    $PMT = 25,000 \div 25.544658 = \$978.68$

18. $FV = 30,000$, $i\% = \dfrac{r}{c} = \dfrac{4\%}{2} = 2\%$, $n = 2 \cdot 10 = 20$
    $PMT = FV \cdot s_{\overline{n}|i}$
    $PMT = 30,000 \div 24.297370 = \$1234.70$

19. $FV = 17,500$, $i\% = \dfrac{r}{c} = \dfrac{9\%}{1} = 9\%$, $n = 1 \cdot 14 = 14$, $1 + i = 1 + 0.09 = 1.09$
    $PMT = FV \cdot [s_{\overline{n}|i}(1 + i)]$
    $PMT = 17,500 \div [26.019189(1.09)] = \$617.05$

20. $FV = 6000$, $i\% = \dfrac{r}{c} = \dfrac{8\%}{12} = \dfrac{2}{3}\%$, $n = 12 \cdot 3 = 36$, $1 + i \approx 1 + 0.00667 = 1.00667$
    $PMT = FV \cdot [s_{\overline{n}|i}(1 + i)]$
    $PMT = 6000 \div [40.535558(1.00667)] = \$147.04$

21. Strategy
    To find the amount that should be deposited, use the formula for the sinking fund payment for an ordinary annuity, $PMT = FV \div s_{\overline{n}|i}$.

    $FV = 40,000$, $i\% = \dfrac{6\%}{12} = 0.5\%$,
    $n = 12 \cdot 10 = 120$.

    Solution
    $PMT = FV \div s_{\overline{n}|i}$

        $= 40,000 \div 163.879347 \approx 244.08$

    The monthly deposit would be $244.08.

22. Strategy
    To find the amount that should be deposited, use the formula for the sinking fund payment for an ordinary annuity, $PMT = FV \div s_{\overline{n}|i}$.

    $FV = 60,000$, $i\% = \dfrac{8\%}{12} = \dfrac{2}{3}\%$,
    $n = 12 \cdot 10 = 120$.

    Solution
    $PMT = FV \div s_{\overline{n}|i}$

        $= 60,000 \div 182.946039 \approx 327.97$

    The monthly deposit would be $327.97.

23. Strategy
    To find the amount that should be
    deposited, use the formula for the
    sinking fund payment for an ordinary
    annuity, $PMT = FV \div s_{\overline{n}|i}$.

    $FV = 100,000$, $i\% = \frac{8\%}{4} = 2\%$,
    $n = 4 \cdot 5 = 20$.

    Solution
    $PMT = FV \div s_{\overline{n}|i}$

    $\quad = 100,000 \div 24.297370 \approx 4115.67$

    The quarterly deposit would be
    $4115.67.

24. Strategy
    To find the amount that should be
    deposited, use the formula for the
    sinking fund payment for an annuity
    due, $PMT = FV \div s_{\overline{n}|i}(1 + i)$.

    $FV = 50,000$, $i\% = \frac{6\%}{4} = 1.5\%$,
    $1 + i = 1.015$, $n = 4 \cdot 4 = 16$.

    Solution
    $PMT = FV \div [s_{\overline{n}|i}(1 + i)]$

    $\quad = 50,000 \div [17.932370(1.015)]$
    $\quad = 50,000 \div [18.201356] \approx 2747.05$

    The quarterly deposit would be
    $2747.05.

25. Strategy
    To find the amount that should be
    deposited, use the formula for the
    sinking fund payment for an annuity
    due, $PMT = FV \div [s_{\overline{n}|i}(1 + i)]$.

    $FV = 10,000$, $i\% = \frac{12\%}{12} = 1\%$,
    $1 + i = 1.01$, $n = 12 \cdot 3 = 36$.

    Solution
    $PMT = FV \div [s_{\overline{n}|i}(1 + i)]$

    $\quad = 10,000 \div [43.0776878(1.01)]$
    $\quad = 10,000 \div [43.507647] = 229.8447$

    The monthly deposit would be $229.84.

26. Strategy
    To find the amount of each deposit,
    use the formula for the sinking fund
    payment for an annuity due,
    $PMT = FV \div [s_{\overline{n}|i}(1 + i)]$.

    $FV = 60,000$, $i\% = \frac{8\%}{4} = 2\%$,
    $1 + i = 1.02$, $n = 4 \cdot 4 = 16$.

    Solution
    $PMT = FV \div [s_{\overline{n}|i}(1 + i)]$

    $\quad = 60,000 \div [18.639285(1.02)]$
    $\quad = 60,000 \div [19.012071] \approx 3155.8898$

    The amount of each deposit is
    $3155.89.

27. Strategy
    To find the amount of each deposit,
    use the formula for the sinking fund
    payment for an annuity due,
    $PMT = FV \div [s_{\overline{n}|i}(1 + i)]$.

    $FV = 50,000$, $i\% = \frac{9\%}{12} = 0.75\%$,
    $1 + i = 1.0075$, $n = 12 \cdot 5 = 60$.

    Solution
    $PMT = FV \div [s_{\overline{n}|i}(1 + i)]$

    $\quad = 50,000 \div [75.424137(1.0075)]$
    $\quad = 50,000 \div [75.989818] \approx 657.98289$

    The amount of each deposit is $657.98.

28. Strategy
    To find the amount that should be
    deposited, use the formula for the
    sinking fund payment for an ordinary
    annuity, $PMT = FV \div s_{\overline{n}|i}$.

    $FV = 1,000,000$, $i\% = \frac{8\%}{12} = \frac{2}{3}\%$,
    $n = 12 \cdot 3 = 36$.

    Solution
    $PMT = FV \div s_{\overline{n}|i}$

    $\quad = 1,000,000 \div 40.535558$
    $\quad = 24,669.669$

    The monthly deposit would be
    $24,669.70.

29. Strategy
    To find the semiannual payment, use
    the formula for the sinking fund
    payment for an ordinary annuity,
    $PMT = FV \div s_{\overline{n}|i}.$

    $FV = 100,000$, $i\% = \dfrac{8\%}{2} = 4\%$,
    $n = 2 \cdot 5 = 10.$

    Solution
    $PMT = FV \div s_{\overline{n}|i}$
    $\qquad = 100,000 \div 12.006107 = 8329.0945$

    The semiannual payment is $8329.09.

30. Strategy
    To find the semiannual payment, use
    the formula for the sinking fund
    payment for an ordinary annuity,
    $PMT = FV \div s_{\overline{n}|i}.$

    $FV = 75,000$, $i\% = \dfrac{6\%}{2} = 3\%$,
    $n = 2 \cdot 4 = 8.$

    Solution
    $PMT = FV \div s_{\overline{n}|i}$
    $\qquad = 75,000 \div 8.892336 = 8434.2292$

    The semiannual payment is $8434.23.

Section 11.2, pages 341–344

1. $PMT = 5000$, $i\% = \dfrac{r}{c} = \dfrac{7\%}{1} = 7\%$,
    $n = 1 \cdot 10 = 10$
    $PV = PMT \cdot a_{\overline{n}|i}$
    $PV = 5000(7.0023582) = \$35,117.91$

2. $PMT = 2500$, $i\% = \dfrac{r}{c} = \dfrac{5\%}{2} = 2.5\%$,
    $n = 2 \cdot 5 = 10$
    $PV = PMT \cdot a_{\overline{n}|i}$
    $PV = 2500(8.752064) = \$21,880.16$

3. $PMT = 400$, $i\% = \dfrac{r}{c} = \dfrac{6\%}{12} = 0.5\%$,
    $n = 12 \cdot 4 = 48$,
    $1 + i = 1 + 0.005 = 1.005$
    $PV = PMT \cdot a_{\overline{n}|i}(1 + i)$
    $PV = 400(42.580318)(1.005)$
    $\qquad = \$17,117.29$

4. $PMT = 600$, $i\% = \dfrac{r}{c} = \dfrac{8\%}{4} = 2\%$,
    $n = 4 \cdot 3 = 12$, $1 + i = 1 + 0.02 = 1.02$
    $PV = PMT \cdot a_{\overline{n}|i}(1 + i)$
    $PV = 600(10.575341)(1.02)$
    $\qquad = \$6472.11$

5. Strategy
    To find the present value, use the
    formula for the present value of an
    ordinary annuity, $PV = PMT \cdot a_{\overline{n}|i}.$

    $PMT = 300$, $i\% = \dfrac{8\%}{12} = \dfrac{2}{3}\%$,
    $n = 12 \cdot 20 = 240.$

    Solution
    $PV = PMT \cdot a_{\overline{n}|i}$
    $\qquad = 300(119.554288) = 35,866.287$

    The present value is $35,866.29.

6. Strategy
    To find the present value, use the
    formula for the present value of an
    annuity due, $PV = PMT \cdot a_{\overline{n}|i}(1 + i).$

    $PMT = 500$, $i\% = \dfrac{8\%}{4} = 2\%$,
    $1 + i = 1.02$, $n = 4 \cdot 15 = 60.$

    Solution
    $PV = PMT \cdot a_{\overline{n}|i}(1 + i)$
    $\qquad = 500(34.760887)(1.02) = 17,728.052$

    The present value is $17,728.05.

158　*Chapter 11*

7. **Strategy**
To find the present value, use the
formula for the present value of an
annuity due, $PV = PMT \cdot a_{\overline{n}|i}(1 + i)$.

$PMT = 540$, $i\% = \dfrac{9\%}{12} = 0.75\%$,
$1 + i = 1.0075$, $n = 12 \cdot 2 = 24$.

Solution
$$PV = PMT \cdot a_{\overline{n}|i}(1 + i)$$
$$= 540(21.889146)(1.0075)$$
$$= 11,908.79$$

The present value is \$11,908.79.

8. **Strategy**
To find the present value, use the
formula for the present value of an
annuity due, $PV = PMT \cdot a_{\overline{n}|i}(1 + i)$.

$PMT = 420$, $i\% = \dfrac{8\%}{12} = \dfrac{2}{3}\%$,
$1 + i = 1.0066667$, $n = 12 \cdot 4 = 48$.

Solution
$$PV = PMT \cdot a_{\overline{n}|i}(1 + i)$$
$$= 420(40.961913)(1.0066667)$$
$$= 17,318.697$$

The present value is \$17,318.70.

9. **Strategy**
To find the present value, use the
formula for the present value of an
ordinary annuity, $PV = PMT \cdot a_{\overline{n}|i}$.

$PMT = 12,000$, $i\% = \dfrac{7\%}{1} = 7\%$,
$n = 1 \cdot 20 = 20$.

Solution
$$PV = PMT \cdot a_{\overline{n}|i}$$
$$= 12,000(10.594014) = 127,128.17$$

The present value is \$127,128.17.

10. **Strategy**
To find the present value, use the
formula for the present value of an
ordinary annuity, $PV = PMT \cdot a_{\overline{n}|i}$.

$PMT = 800$, $i\% = \dfrac{10\%}{1} = 10\%$,
$n = 1 \cdot 20 = 20$.

Solution
$$PV = PMT \cdot a_{\overline{n}|i}$$
$$= 800(8.513564) = 6810.8512$$

The present value is \$6810.85.

11. **Strategy**
To find the amount owed for the loan,
use the formula for the present value
of an ordinary annuity,
$PV = PMT \cdot a_{\overline{n}|i}$, to find the present
value of the remaining payments.
$PMT = 265.71$, $i\% = \dfrac{12\%}{12} = 1\%$,
$n = $ number of payments remaining
$= 36 - 18 = 18$.

Solution
$$PV = PMT \cdot a_{\overline{n}|i}$$
$$= 265.71(16.398269) = 4357.1841$$

The amount owed for the loan is
\$4357.18.

12. **Strategy**
To find the amount owed for the loan,
use the formula for the present value
of an ordinary annuity,
$PV = PMT \cdot a_{\overline{n}|i}$, to find the present
value of the remaining payments.
$PMT = 281.82$, $i\% = \dfrac{6\%}{12} = 0.5\%$,
$n = $ number of payments remaining
$= 48 - 24 = 24$.

Solution
$$PV = PMT \cdot a_{\overline{n}|i}$$
$$= 281.82(22.562866) = 6358.6669$$

The amount owed for the loan is
\$6358.67.

13. Strategy
    To find the remaining balance, use the
    formula for the present value of an
    ordinary annuity, $PV = PMT \cdot a\overline{\,_n}|_i$, to
    find the present value of the
    remaining payments.
    $PMT = 1528.92$, $i\% = \frac{8\%}{4} = 2\%$,
    n = number of payments remaining
    $= 20 - 12 = 8$.

    Solution
    $PV = PMT \cdot a\overline{\,_n}|_i$
    $= 1528.92(7.325481) = 11,200.07$

    The remaining balance is $11,200.07.

14. Strategy
    To find the remaining balance, use the
    formula for the present value of an
    ordinary annuity, $PV = PMT \cdot a\overline{\,_n}|_i$, to
    find the present value of the
    remaining payments.
    $PMT = 4853.01$, $i\% = \frac{10\%}{4} = 2.5\%$,
    n = number of payments remaining
    $= 60 - 40 = 20$.

    Solution
    $PV = PMT \cdot a\overline{\,_n}|_i$
    $= 4853.01(15.589162) = 75,654.36$

    The remaining balance is $75,654.36.

15. Strategy
    To find the larger present value of
    the two ordinary annuities, compare
    the present values of the annuities.
    Use the formula $PV = PMT \cdot a\overline{\,_n}|_i$.

    For the first investment, $PMT = 1500$,
    $i\% = \frac{8\%}{4} = 2\%$, $n = 4 \cdot 5 = 20$.
    For the second investment, $PMT = 500$,
    $i\% = \frac{8\%}{12} = \frac{2}{3}\%$, $n = 12 \cdot 5 = 60$.

    Solution
    (1) $PV = PMT \cdot a\overline{\,_n}|_i$
    $= 1500(16.351433) = 24,527.15$
    (2) $PV = PMT \cdot a\overline{\,_n}|_i$
    $= 500(49.318433) = 24,659.22$

    $24,659.22$ is greater than $24,527.15$.

    The investment that pays $500 at the
    end of each month has the greater
    present value.

16. Strategy
    To find the larger present value of
    the two ordinary annuities, compare
    the present values of the annuities.
    Use the formula $PV = PMT \cdot a\overline{\,_n}|_i(1 + i)$.

    For the first investment, $PMT = 1100$,
    $i\% = \frac{12\%}{1} = 12\%$, $1 + i = 1.12$,
    $n = 1 \cdot 5 = 5$.
    For the second investment, $PMT = 100$,
    $i\% = \frac{12\%}{12} = 1\%$, $1 + i = 1.01$,
    $n = 12 \cdot 5 = 60$.

    Solution
    (1) $PV = PMT \cdot a\overline{\,_n}|_i(1 + i)$
    $= 1100(3.604776)(1.12)$
    $= 4441.08$
    (2) $PV = PMT \cdot a\overline{\,_n}|_i(1 + i)$
    $= 100(44.955038)(1.01)$
    $= 4540.46$

    4540.46 is greater than 4441.08.

    Investment (2) has the greater present
    value.

17. $PV = 15,000$, $i\% = \frac{12\%}{4} = 3\%$,
    $n = 4 \cdot 12 = 48$
    $PMT = PV \div a\overline{\,_n}|_i$
    $PMT = 15,000 \div 25.666707 = \$593.67$

18. $PV = 100,000$, $i\% = \frac{9\%}{1} = 9\%$,
    $n = 1 \cdot 15 = 15$
    $PMT = PV \div a\overline{\,_n}|_i$
    $PMT = 100,000 \div 8.060688 = \$12,405.89$

19. $PV = 9750$, $i\% = \frac{8\%}{12} = \frac{2}{3}\%$,
    $n = 12 \cdot 3 = 36$
    $PMT = PV \div a\overline{\,_n}|_i$
    $PMT = 9750 \div 31.911805 = \$305.53$

20. $PV = 32,000$, $i\% = \frac{10\%}{2} = 5\%$,
    $n = 2 \cdot 4 = 8$
    $PMT = PV \div a\overline{\,_n}|_i$
    $PMT = 32,000 \div 6.463213 = \$4951.10$

21. Strategy
    To find the monthly payment, use the equation $PMT = PV \div a_{\overline{n}|i}$.

    $PV = 30,000$, $i\% = \frac{9\%}{12} = 0.75\%$,
    $n = 12 \cdot 5 = 60$.

    Solution
    $PMT = PV \div a_{\overline{n}|i}$
    $= 30,000 \div 48.173374 = 622.7506$

    The monthly payment is $622.75.

22. Strategy
    To find the quarterly payment, use the equation $PMT = PV \div a_{\overline{n}|i}$.

    $PV = 75,000$, $i\% = \frac{8\%}{4} = 2\%$,
    $n = 4 \cdot 4 = 16$.

    Solution
    $PMT = PV \div a_{\overline{n}|i}$
    $= 75,000 \div 13.577709 = 5523.7596$

    The quarterly payment is $5523.76.

23. Strategy
    To find the semiannual payment, use the equation $PMT = PV \div a_{\overline{n}|i}$.

    $PV = 600,000$, $i\% = \frac{10\%}{2} = 5\%$,
    $n = 2 \cdot 10 = 20$.

    Solution
    $PMT = PV \div a_{\overline{n}|i}$
    $= 600,000 \div 12.462210 = 48,145.554$

    The semiannual payment is $48,145.55.

24. Strategy
    To find the monthly payment, use the equation $PMT = PV \div a_{\overline{n}|i}$.

    $PV = 150,000$, $i\% = \frac{8\%}{12} = \frac{2}{3}\%$,
    $n = 12 \cdot 5 = 60$.

    Solution
    $PMT = PV \div a_{\overline{n}|i}$
    $= 150,000 \div 49.318433 = 3041.4592$

    The monthly payment is $3041.46.

25. Strategy
    (a) To find the monthly payment, use the equation $PMT = PV \div a_{\overline{n}|i}$.

    $PV = 25,000$, $i\% = \frac{9\%}{12} = 0.75\%$,
    $n = 12 \cdot 5 = 60$.
    (b) To find the total amount of interest paid, subtract the present value from the total amount repaid (number of months x PMT).

    Solution
    $PMT = PV \div a_{\overline{n}|i}$
    $= 25,000 \div 48.173374 \approx 518.96$

    The monthly payment is $518.96.

    Interest paid
    $= $ (number of months x PMT) $- PV$
    $= (60 \times 518.96) - 25,000$
    $= 31,137.60 - 25,000 = 6137.60$

    The interest paid is $6137.60.

26. Strategy
    (a) To find the monthly payment, use the equation $PMT = PV \div a_{\overline{n}|i}$.

    $PV = 6000$, $i\% = \frac{6\%}{12} = 0.5\%$,
    $n = 12 \cdot 4 = 48$.
    (b) To find the total amount of interest paid, subtract the present value from the total amount repaid (number of months x PMT).

    Solution
    $PMT = PV \div a_{\overline{n}|i}$
    $= 6000 \div 42.580318 \approx 140.91$

    The monthly payment is $140.91.

    Interest paid
    $= $ (number of months x PMT) $- PV$
    $= (48 \times 140.91) - 6000$
    $= 6763.68 - 6000 = 763.68$

    The interest paid is $763.68.

27. Strategy
To find which of the two loans has the smaller monthly payment:
- Use the equation PMT = PV $\div$ $a_{\overline{n}|i}$ for each loan.
  For the first loan, PV = 6000, i% = $\frac{8\%}{12}$ = $\frac{2}{3}\%$, n = 12·4 = 48.
  For the second loan, PV = 6000, i% = $\frac{9\%}{12}$ = 0.75%, n = 12·5 = 60.
- Compare the two monthly payments.

Solution
(1) PMT = PV $\div$ $a_{\overline{n}|i}$
  = 6000 $\div$ 40.961913 $\approx$ 146.48
(2) PMT = PV $\div$ $a_{\overline{n}|i}$
  = 6000 $\div$ 48.173374 $\approx$ 124.55
124.55 is less than 146.48.

The 9%, 5-year loan has the smaller monthly payment.

28. Strategy
To find the difference between the monthly payments on the two loans:
- Calculate the monthly payment on the first loan.
  PV = 1000, i% = $\frac{9\%}{12}$ = 0.75%, n = 1·12 = 12
- Calculate the monthly payment on the second loan.
  PV = 1000, i% = $\frac{8\%}{12}$ = $\frac{2}{3}\%$, n = 2·12 = 24
- Subtract the smaller monthly payment from the larger.

Solution
PMT = PV $\div$ $a_{\overline{n}|i}$
PMT = 1000 $\div$ 11.434913 = 87.45

PMT = PV $\div$ $a_{\overline{n}|i}$
PMT = 1000 $\div$ 22.110544 = 45.23

87.45 - 45.23 = 42.22

The difference between the monthly payments is $42.22.

29. Strategy
To find the amount that is interest, use the simple interest formula I = Prt.
To find the amount that is principal:
- Use the formula PMT = PV $\div$ $a_{\overline{n}|i}$ to find the annual payment.
  PV = 40,000, i% = $\frac{7\%}{1}$ = 7%, n = 1·15 = 15
- Subtract the amount that is interest from the annual payment.

Solution
I = Prt
I = 40,000(0.07)(1) = 2800

For the first annual payment, $2800 is interest.

PMT = PV $\div$ $a_{\overline{n}|i}$
PMT = 40,000 $\div$ 9.107914 = 4391.79
PMT - interest = 4391.78 - 2800
  = 1591.79

For the first annual payment, $1591.79 is principal.

30. Strategy
To find the amount that is interest, use the simple interest formula I = Prt.
To find the amount that is principal:
- Use the formula PMT = PV $\div$ $a_{\overline{n}|i}$ to find the annual payment.
  PV = 75,000, i% = $\frac{9\%}{1}$ = 9%, n = 1·20 = 20
- Subtract the amount that is interest from the annual payment.

Solution
I = Prt
I = 75,000(0.09)(1) = 6750

For the first annual payment, $6750 is interest.

PMT = PV $\div$ $a_{\overline{n}|i}$
PMT = 75,000 $\div$ 9.128546 = 8215.99
PMT - interest = 8215.99 - 6750
  = 1465.99

For the first annual payment, $1465.99 is principal.

31. Strategy
    To find the amount that is interest
    and the amount that is principal:
    • Use the formula $PMT = PV \div a_{\overline{n}|i}$ to
      find the quarterly payment.
      $PV = 50,000$, $i\% = \frac{8\%}{4} = 2\%$,
      $n = 4 \cdot 6 = 24$.
    • Use the simple interest formula
      $I = Prt$ to find the interest for the
      first payment.
    • Subtract the interest from the
      quarterly payment to find the
      amount that is principal.

    Solution
    $PMT = PV \div a_{\overline{n}|i}$
    $\quad = 50,000 \div 18.913926 \approx 2643.55$

    $I = Prt$
    $\quad = 50,000(0.08)\left(\frac{1}{4}\right) = 1000$

    The interest for the first quarter is
    $1000.

    Payment - interest = 2643.55 - 1000
    $\qquad\qquad\qquad\quad = 1643.55$

    The amount that is principal is
    $1643.55.

32. Strategy
    To find the amount that is interest
    and the amount that is principal:
    • Use the formula $PMT = PV \div a_{\overline{n}|i}$ to
      find the quarterly payment.
      $PV = 25,000$, $i\% = \frac{9\%}{12} = 0.75\%$,
      $n = 12 \cdot 5 = 60$.
    • Use the simple interest formula
      $I = Prt$ to find the interest for the
      first payment.
    • Subtract the interest from the
      quarterly payment to find the
      amount that is principal.

    Solution
    $PMT = PV \div a_{\overline{n}|i}$
    $\quad = 25,000 \div 48.173374 \approx 518.96$

    $I = Prt$
    $\quad = 25,000(0.09)\left(\frac{1}{12}\right) = 187.50$

    The interest for the first quarter is
    $187.50.

    Payment - interest = 518.96 - 187.50
    $\qquad\qquad\qquad\quad = 331.46$

    The amount that is principal is
    $331.46.

Business Case Study

1. $PMT = PV \div a_{\overline{n}|i} = (12,000 - 1200) \div 31.446805 = 10,800 \div 31.446805 \approx 343.44$
   The monthly payment on the car loan would be $343.44.

2. PV (monthly payments) $= PMT \cdot a_{\overline{n}|i} = 343.44(31.911805) = 10,959.79$
   PV (maintenance costs) $= PMT \cdot a_{\overline{n}|i} = 20(31.911805) \approx 638.24$
   Present value of monthly payments and maintenance costs
   $= \$10,959.79 + \$638.24 = \$11,598.03$

3. $PV = PV \div$ compounding factor $= 5000 \div 1.270237 \approx 3936.27$
   The present value of the car's resale value is $3936.27.

4. $PV = \$1200 + \$11,598.03 - \$3936.27 = \$8861.76$
   The present value of the purchase option is $8861.76.

5. $PV = PMT \cdot [a_{\overline{n}|i}(1 + i)] = 325[31.911805(1.0067)] = 325(32.125614) \approx 10,440.83$
   The present value of the monthly payments for leasing the car is $10,440.83.

6. Since $8861.76 is less than $10,440.83, buying would cost less than leasing.

Review/Test, pp. 349–350

1. Strategy
   To find the future value, use the formula for the future value of an ordinary annuity, $FV = PMT \cdot s_{\overline{n}|i}$.

   $PMT = 250$, $i\% = \frac{9\%}{12} = 0.75\%$,
   $n = 12 \cdot 5 = 60$.

   Solution
   $FV = PMT \cdot s_{\overline{n}|i}$
   $\quad = 250(75.424137) \approx 18,856.03$

   The future value is $18,856.03.

2. Strategy
   To find the future value, use the formula for the future value of an annuity due, $FV = PMT \cdot s_{\overline{n}|i}(1 + i)$.

   $PMT = 200$, $i\% = \frac{8\%}{4} = 2\%$, $1 + i = 1.02$,
   $n = 4 \cdot 15 = 60$.

   Solution
   $FV = PMT \cdot s_{\overline{n}|i}(1 + i)$
   $\quad = 200(114.051539)(1.02) \approx 23,266.51$

   The future value is $23,266.51.

3. Strategy
   To find the amount that should be deposited, use the formula for the sinking fund payment for an annuity due, $PMT = FV \div [s_{\overline{n}|i}(1 + i)]$.

   $FV = 100,000$, $i\% = \frac{8\%}{4} = 2\%$,
   $1 + i = 1.02$, $n = 4 \cdot 12 = 48$.

   Solution
   $PMT = FV \div [s_{\overline{n}|i}(1 + i)]$
   $\quad = 100,000 \div [79.353519(1.02)]$
   $\quad = 100,000 \div [80.940589] \approx 1235.47$

   The quarterly deposit would be $1235.47.

4. Strategy
   To find the amount that should be deposited, use the formula for the sinking fund payment for an ordinary annuity.

   $FV = 120,000$, $i\% = \frac{9\%}{12} = 0.75\%$,
   $n = 12 \cdot 10 = 120$.

   Solution
   $PMT = FV \div s_{\overline{n}|i}$
   $PMT = 120,000 \div 193.514277 = 620.11$

   $620.11 should be deposited at the end of each month.

5. Strategy
   To find the present value, use the formula for the present value of an ordinary annuity, $PV = PMT \cdot a_{\overline{n}|i}$.

   $PMT = 1000$, $i\% = \frac{8\%}{4} = 2\%$,
   $n = 4 \cdot 12 = 48$.

   Solution
   $PV = PMT \cdot a_{\overline{n}|i}$
   $\quad = 1000(30.673120) \approx 30,673.12$

   The present value is $30,673.12.

6. Strategy
   To find the present value, use the formula for the present value of an ordinary annuity,
   $PV = PMT \cdot a_{\overline{n}|i}(1 + i)$.

   $PMT = 150$, $i\% = \frac{6\%}{12} = 0.5\%$,
   $1 + i = 1.005$, $n = 12 \cdot 10 = 120$.

   Solution
   $PV = PMT \cdot a_{\overline{n}|i}(1 + i)$
   $\quad = 150(90.073453)(1.005)$
   $\quad \approx 13,578.57$

   The present value is $13,578.57.

7. Strategy
    To find the monthly payment, use the
    equation $PMT = PV \div a\,\overline{_n}|_i$.

    $PV = 4425$, $i\% = \frac{9\%}{12} = 0.75\%$,
    $n = 12 \cdot 2 = 24$.

    Solution
    $PMT = PV \div a\,\overline{_n}|_i$
    $= 4425 \div 21.889146 \approx 202.15$

    The monthly payment is $202.15.

8. Strategy
    To find the amount that is interest
    and the amount that is principal:
    *   Use the simple interest formula
        $I = Prt$ to find the interest for
        the first payment.

        $P = 1000$, $r = 0.12$, $t = \frac{1}{12}$
    *   Subtract the interest from the
        monthly payment to find the amount
        that is principal.

    Solution
    $I = Prt$

    $= 1000(0.12)\left(\frac{1}{12}\right) = 10$

    The amount of the first month's
    payment that is interest is $10.

    $Principal = PMT - I = 88.85 - 10$
    $\qquad\qquad\qquad = 78.85$

    The amount that is principal is
    $78.85.

9. Strategy
    To find the monthly payment, use the
    equation $PMT = PV \div a\,\overline{_n}|_i$.

    $PV = 14,000$, $i\% = \frac{8\%}{12} = \frac{2}{3}\%$,
    $n = 12 \cdot 4 = 48$.

    Solution
    $PMT = PV \div a\,\overline{_n}|_i$
    $= 14,000 \div 40.961913 \approx 341.78$

    The monthly payment is $341.78.

10. Strategy
    To find the remaining loan balance,
    use the formula $PV = PMT \cdot a\,\overline{_n}|_i$ to find
    the present value of the remaining
    payments.

    $PMT = 109.52$, $i\% = \frac{6\%}{12} = 0.5\%$,
    $n =$ the number of payments remaining
    $= 36 - 24 = 12$.

    Solution
    $PV = PMT \cdot a\,\overline{_n}|_i$
    $= 109.52(11.618932) \approx 1272.51$

    The remaining loan balance is
    $1272.51.

11. Strategy
    To find the remaining loan balance:
    • Use the formula $PMT = PV \div a_{\overline{n}|i}$ to
      find the monthly payment.
      $PV = 9500$, $i\% = \frac{8\%}{12} = \frac{2}{3}\%$,
      $n = 12 \cdot 5 = 60$.
    • Use the formula $PV = PMT \cdot a_{\overline{n}|i}$ to
      find the present value of the
      remaining payments.

      n = number of payments remaining
         $= 60 - 36 = 24$.

    Solution
    $PMT = PV \div a_{\overline{n}|i}$

    $\quad = 9500 \div 49.318433 \approx 192.63$

    $PV = PMT \cdot a_{\overline{n}|i}$

    $\quad = 192.63(22.110544) \approx 4259.15$

    The remaining loan balance is
    $4259.15.

12. Strategy
    To find the amount of interest that
    will be repaid:
    • Use the equation $PMT = PV \div a_{\overline{n}|i}$ to
      find the monthly payment.
      $PV = 10,000$, $i\% \frac{8\%}{12} = \frac{2}{3}\%$, $n = 48$.
    • Multiply the monthly payment by the
      number of payments to find the
      total of all payments.
    • Subtract the present value from the
      total of all payments.

    Solution
    $PMT = PV \div a_{\overline{n}|i}$

    $\quad = 10,000 \div 40.961913 \approx 244.13$

    Total of all payments = PMT x n
    $= 244.13 \times 48 = 11,718.24$

    Interest paid
    = total of all payments - PV
    $= 11,718.24 - 10,000 = 1718.24$

    The interest paid is $1718.24.

CHAPTER 12
Business and Consumer Loans

Section 12.1, pages 357–358

1. **Strategy**
   To find the commission, solve the
   basic percent equation for part.
   Base = 130, Rate = 2.2%

   Solution
   Part = base x rate
   = 130 x 0.022 = 2.86

   The commission is $2.86.

2. **Strategy**
   To find the commission, solve the
   basic percent equation for part.
   Base = 275, Rate = 1.8%

   Solution
   Part = base x rate
   = 275 x 0.018 = 4.95

   The commission is $4.95.

3. **Strategy**
   Since the bill was paid before the due
   date of October 1, there is no finance
   charge.

   Solution
   The finance charge is $0.

4. **Strategy**
   Since the bill was paid before the due
   date of September 5, there is no
   finance charge.

   Solution
   The finance charge is $0.

5. **Strategy**
   To find the average daily balance:
   • Find the total amount owed each day of the month.
   • Divide the total amount owed each day of the month by the number of days in the
     billing period.

   Solution

Date	Payments or Purchases	Daily Balance	Number of Days	Days x Amount
July 5-12		149	8	1192
July 13-Aug. 4	82	231	23	5313
	Total owed each day of the month			6505

   There are 31 days in the billing period.
   Average daily balance = 6505 ÷ 31 ≈ 209.84

   The average daily balance was $209.84.

6. Strategy
   To find the average daily balance:
   • Find the total amount owed each day of the month.
   • Divide the total amount owed each day of the month by the number of days in the billing period.

   Solution

Date	Payments or Purchases	Daily Balance	Number of Days	Days x Amount
March 1-11		316	11	3,476
March 12-31	115	431	20	8,620
Total owed each day of the month				12,096

   There are 31 days in the billing period.
   Average daily balance = 12,096 ÷ 31 ≈ 390.19

   The average daily balance was $390.19.

7. Strategy
   To find the average daily balance:
   • Find the total amount owed each day of the month.
   • Divide the total amount owed each day of the month by the number of days in the billing period.

   Solution

Date	Payments or Purchases	Daily Balance	Number of Days	Days x Amount
June 5-19		512	15	7,680
June 20-July 4	-150	362	15	5,430
Total owed each day of the month				13,110

   There are 30 days in the billing period.
   Average daily balance = 13,110 ÷ 30 = 437

   The average daily balance was $437.00.

8. Strategy
   To find the average daily balance:
   • Find the total amount owed each day of the month.
   • Divide the total amount owed each day of the month by the number of days in the billing period.

   Solution

Date	Payments or Purchases	Daily Balance	Number of Days	Days x Amount
Dec. 10-21		819	12	9,828
Dec. 22-Jan. 9	-200	619	19	11,761
Total owed each day of the month				21,589

   There are 31 days in the billing period.
   Average daily balance = 21,589 ÷ 31 ≈ 696.42

   The average daily balance was $696.42.

9. Strategy
    To find the average daily balance:
    • Find the total amount owed each day of the month.
    • Divide the total amount owed each day of the month by the number of days in the billing period.

    Solution

Date	Payments or Purchases	Daily Balance	Number of Days	Days x Amount
March 5-11		244	7	1,708
March 12-27	152	396	16	6,336
March 28-April 4	-100	296	8	2,368
	Total owed each day of the month			10,412

    There are 31 days in the billing period.
    Average daily balance = 10,412 ÷ 31 ≈ 335.87

    The average daily balance was $335.87.

10. Strategy
    To find the average daily balance:
    • Find the total amount owed each day of the month.
    • Divide the total amount owed each day of the month by the number of days in the billing period.

    Solution

Date	Payments or Purchases	Daily Balance	Number of Days	Days x Amount
April 1-4		768	4	3,072
April 5-17	316	1084	13	14,092
April 18-30	-200	884	13	11,492
	Total owed each day of the month			28,656

    There are 30 days in the billing period.
    Average daily balance = 28,656 ÷ 30 ≈ 955.20

    The average daily balance was $955.20.

11. Strategy
    To find the finance charge:
    • Find the total amount owed each day of the month.
    • Find the average daily balance.
    • Multiply the average daily balance by the interest rate per month.

    Solution

Date	Payments or Purchases	Daily Balance	Number of Days	Days x Amount
May 5-16		944	12	11,328
May 17-19	255	1199	3	3,597
May 20-June 4	-150	1049	16	16,784
	Total owed each day of the month			31,709

    Average daily balance = 31,709 ÷ 31 ≈ 1022.87
    Finance charge = 1022.87 x 0.015 ≈ 15.34

    The finance charge is $15.34.

12. Strategy
    To find the finance charge:
    • Find the total amount owed each day of the month.
    • Find the average daily balance.
    • Multiply the average daily balance by the interest rate per month.

    Solution

Date	Payments or Purchases	Daily Balance	Number of Days	Days x Amount
June 1-14		655	14	9,170
June 15-16	-250	405	2	810
June 17-30	98	503	14	7,042
	Total owed each day of the month			17,022

    Average daily balance = 17,022 + 30 = 567.40
    Finance charge = 567.40 x 0.012 ≈ 6.81

    The finance charge is $6.81.

13. Strategy
    To find the amount due:
    • Find the total amount owed each day of the month.
    • Find the average daily balance.
    • Find the finance charges.
    • Find the amount due
      (previous balance + new purchases + finance charges - amount paid).

    Solution

Date	Payments or Purchases	Daily Balance	Number of Days	Days x Amount
Aug. 10-14		345	5	1,725
Aug. 15-26	56			
	-75	326	12	3,912
Aug. 27-Sept. 9	157	483	14	6,762
	Total owed each day of the month			12,399

    Average daily balance = 12,399 + 31 ≈ 399.97
    Finance charge = 399.97 x 0.0125 ≈ 5.00
    New balance = 345 + 56 + 157 + 5 - 75 = 488

    The amount due is $488.00.

14. Strategy
    To find the amount due:
    • Find the total amount owed each day of the month.
    • Find the average daily balance.
    • Find the finance charges.
    • Find the amount due
      (previous balance + new purchases + finance charges - amount paid).

    Solution

Date	Payments or Purchases	Daily Balance	Number of Days	Days x Amount
May 1-4		189	4	756
May 5-20	213	402	16	6,432
May 21-24	102	504	4	2,016
May 25-31	-150	354	7	2,478
Total owed each day of the month				11,682

    Average daily balance = 11,682 ÷ 31 ≈ 376.84
    Finance charge = 376.84 x 0.015 ≈ 5.65
    New balance = 189 + 213 + 102 + 5.65 - 150 = 359.65

    The amount due is $359.65.

15. Strategy
    To find the balance due:
    • Find the total amount owed each day of the month.
    • Find the average daily balance.
    • Find the finance charges.
    • Find the amount due
      (previous balance + new purchases + finance charges - amount paid).

    Solution

Date	Payments or Purchases	Daily Balance	Number of Days	Days x Amount
July 5-12		611	8	4,888
July 13-19	116	727	7	5,089
July 20-24	77	804	5	4,020
July 25-Aug. 4	-150	654	11	7,194
Total owed each day of the month				21,191

    Average daily balance = 21,191 ÷ 31 ≈ 683.58
    Finance charge = 683.58 x 0.0175 ≈ 11.96
    New balance = 611 + 116 + 77 + 11.96 - 150 = 665.96

    The balance due is $665.96.

16. Strategy
     To find the balance due:
     • Find the total amount owed each day of the month.
     • Find the average daily balance.
     • Find the finance charges.
     • Find the amount due
       (previous balance + new purchases + finance charges - amount paid).

     Solution

Date	Payments or Purchases	Daily Balance	Number of Days	Days x Amount
March 10-14		423	5	2,115
March 15-16	-200	223	2	446
March 17-28	129	352	12	4,224
March 29-April 9	47	399	12	4,788
Total owed each day of the month				11,573

     Average daily balance = 11,573 ÷ 31 ≈ 373.32
     Finance charge = 373.32 x 0.016 ≈ 5.97
     New balance = 423 + 129 + 47 + 5.97 - 200 = 404.97

     The balance due is $404.97.

Section 12.2, pages 369-372

1. Strategy
    To find the add-on interest:
    • Find the amount financed.
    • Find the finance charge.
    To find the annual percentage rate:
    • Find the finance charge per $100.
    • Use the APR Table. The term is 6 months.

    Solution
    Amount financed
     = cash price - down payment
     = 850 - 125 = 725

    Finance charge
     = amount financed x interest rate
       x time
     = 725 x 0.095 x $\frac{6}{12}$ = 34.44

    The add-on interest is $34.44.

    Finance charge per $100
     = $\frac{34.44}{725}$ x 100 = 4.75

    The APR is 16.00%.

2. Strategy
    To find the add-on interest:
    • Find the amount financed.
    • Find the finance charge.
    To find the annual percentage rate:
    • Find the finance charge per $100.
    • Use the APR Table. The term is 12 months.

    Solution
    Amount financed
     = cash price - down payment
     = 1240 - 300 = 940

    Finance charge
     = amount financed x interest rate
       x time
     = 940 x 0.10 x $\frac{12}{12}$ = 94.00

    The add-on interest is $94.00.

    Finance charge per $100
     = $\frac{94.00}{940}$ x 100 = 10

    The APR is 18.00%.

3. Strategy
   To find the finance charge:
   • Find the amount financed.
   • Multiply the amount financed by the
     interest rate by the time.
   To find the annual percentage rate:
   • Find the finance charge per $100.
   • Use the APR table. The term is 24
     months.

   Solution
   Amount financed
    = cash price - down payment
    = 2580 - 500 = 2080

   Finance charge
    = amount financed x interest rate
      x time
    = 2080 x 0.09 x 2 = 374.40

   The finance charge is $374.40.

   Finance charge per $100
    = $\frac{374.40}{2080}$ x 100 = 18

   The APR is 16.50%.

4. Strategy
   To find the finance charge:
   • Find the amount financed.
   • Multiply the amount financed by the
     interest rate by the time.
   To find the annual percentage rate:
   • Find the finance charge per $100.
   • Use the APR table. The term is 6
     months.

   Solution
   Amount financed
    = cash price - down payment
    = 800 - 160 = 640

   Finance charge
    = amount financed x interest rate
      x time
    = 640 x 0.105 x $\frac{6}{12}$ = 33.60

   The finance charge is $33.60.

   Finance charge per $100
    = $\frac{33.60}{640}$ x 100 = 5.25

   The APR is 17.75%.

5. Strategy
   To find the monthly payment:
   • Find the amount financed.
   • Find the finance charge.
   • Find the total of the installment payments.
   • Divide the total of the installment payments by the number of monthly payments.
   To find the annual percentage rate:
   • Find the finance charge per $100.
   • Use the APR table. The term is 6 months.

   Solution
   Amount financed
   = cash price - down payment
   = 757 - 150 = 607

   Finance charge
   = amount financed x interest rate x time
   = $607 \times 0.075 \times \frac{6}{12} \approx 22.76$

   Total of installment payments
   = amount financed + finance charges
   = 607 + 22.76 = 629.76

   Monthly payment = $\frac{629.76}{6}$ = 104.96

   The monthly payment is $104.96.

   Finance charge per $100
   = $\frac{22.76}{607} \times 100 \approx 3.75$

   The APR is 12.75%.

6. Strategy
   To find the monthly payment:
   • Find the amount financed.
   • Find the finance charge.
   • Find the total of the installment payments.
   • Divide the total of the installment payments by the number of monthly payments.
   To find the annual percentage rate:
   • Find the finance charge per $100.
   • Use the APR table. The term is 18 months.

   Solution
   Amount financed
   = cash price - down payment
   = 950 - 200 = 750

   Finance charge
   = amount financed x interest rate x time
   = $750 \times 0.08 \times \frac{18}{12} = 90$

   Total of installment payments
   = amount financed + finance charges
   = 750 + 90 = 840

   Monthly payment = $\frac{840}{18} \approx 46.67$

   The monthly payment is $46.67.

   Finance charge per $100
   = $\frac{90}{750} \times 100 = 12$

   The APR is 14.75%.

7. Strategy
    To find the annual percentage rate:
    • Find the amount financed.
    • Find the finance charge.
    • Find the finance charge per $100.
    • Use the APR table. The term is 18
      months.

    Solution
    Amount financed
     = cash price - down payment
     = 2260 - 200 = 2060

    Finance charge
     = amount financed x interest rate
       x time
     = 2060 x 0.068 x $\frac{18}{12}$ = 210.12

    Finance charge per $100
     = $\frac{210.12}{2060}$ x 100 = 10.2

    The APR is 12.50%.

8. Strategy
    To find the annual percentage rate:
    • Find the amount financed.
    • Find the finance charge.
    • Find the finance charge per $100.
    • Use the APR table. The term is 12
      months.

    Solution
    Amount financed
     = cash price - down payment
     = 1680 - 300 = 1380

    Finance charge
     = amount financed x interest rate
       x time
     = 1380 x 0.085 x $\frac{12}{12}$ = 117.30

    Finance charge per $100
     = $\frac{117.30}{1380}$ x 100 = 8.50

    The APR is 15.25%.

9. Strategy
    To find the annual percentage rate:
    • Find the amount financed.
    • Find the finance charge.
    • Find the finance charge per $100.
    • Use the APR table. The term is 6
      months.

    Solution
    Amount financed
     = cash price - down payment
     = 580 - 50 = 530

    Finance charge
     = amount financed x interest rate
       x time
     = 530 x 0.09 x $\frac{6}{12}$ = 23.85

    Finance charge per $100
     = $\frac{23.85}{530}$ x 100 = 4.50

    The APR is 15.25%.

10. Strategy
    To find the annual percentage rate:
    • Find the amount financed.
    • Find the finance charge.
    • Find the finance charge per $100.
    • Use the APR table. The term is 6
      months.

    Solution
    Amount financed
     = cash price - down payment
     = 425 - 75 = 350

    Finance charge
     = amount financed x interest rate
       x time
     = 350 x 0.08 x $\frac{6}{12}$ = 14

    Finance charge per $100
     = $\frac{14}{350}$ x 100 = 4

    The APR is 13.50%.

11. Strategy
    To find the annual percentage rate:
    • Find the amount financed.
    • Find the finance charge.
    • Find the finance charge per $100.
    • Use the APR table. The term is 18 months.

    Solution
    Amount financed
    = cash price − down payment
    = 1240 − 240 = 1000

    Finance charge
    = amount financed × interest rate × time
    = $1000 \times 0.07 \times \frac{18}{12} = 105$

    Finance charge per $100
    = $\frac{105}{1000} \times 100 = 10.5$

    The APR is 12.75%.

12. Strategy
    To find the annual percentage rate:
    • Find the amount financed.
    • Find the finance charge.
    • Find the finance charge per $100.
    • Use the APR table. The term is 24 months.

    Solution
    Amount financed
    = cash price − down payment
    = 1450 − 300 = 1150

    Finance charge
    = amount financed × interest rate × time
    = 1150 × 0.085 × 2 = 195.50

    Finance charge per $100
    = $\frac{195.50}{1150} \times 100 = 17.00$

    The APR is 15.50%.

13. Strategy
    To find the monthly payment:
    • Find the amount financed.
    • Use the equation $PMT = PV \div a_{\overline{n}|i}$.

    PV = amount financed,
    $i\% = \frac{12\%}{12} = 1\%$, $n = 24$.

    Solution
    Amount financed = 1840 − 400 = 1440
    $PMT = PV \div a_{\overline{n}|i}$
        = 1440 ÷ 21.243387 ≈ 67.79

    The monthly payment is $67.79.

14. Strategy
    To find the monthly payment:
    • Find the amount financed.
    • Use the equation $PMT = PV \div a_{\overline{n}|i}$.

    PV = amount financed,
    $i\% = \frac{8\%}{12} = \frac{2}{3}\%$, $n = 15$.

    Solution
    Amount financed = 1400 − 250 = 1150
    $PMT = PV \div a_{\overline{n}|i}$
        = 1150 ÷ 14.229338 ≈ 80.82

    The monthly payment is $80.82.

15. Strategy
    To find the monthly payment:
    • Find the amount financed.
    • Use the equation $PMT = PV \div a_{\overline{n}|i}$.

    PV = amount financed,
    $i\% = \frac{8\%}{12} = \frac{2}{3}\%$, $n = 24$.

    Solution
    Amount financed = 2200 − 200 = 2000
    $PMT = PV \div a_{\overline{n}|i}$
        = 2000 ÷ 22.110544 ≈ 90.45

    The monthly payment is $90.45.

16. Strategy
    To find the monthly payment:
    • Find the amount financed.
    • Use the equation $PMT = PV \div a_{\overline{n}|i}$.

    PV = amount financed,
    $i\% = \frac{12\%}{12} = 1\%$, $n = 18$.

    Solution
    Amount financed = 1050 − 150 = 900
    $PMT = PV \div a_{\overline{n}|i}$
        = 900 ÷ 16.398269 ≈ 54.88

    The monthly payment is $54.88.

17. Strategy
    To find the monthly payment:
    • Find the amount financed.
    • Use the equation PMT = PV ÷ $a_{\overline{n}|i}$.

    PV = amount financed,
    i% = $\frac{9\%}{12}$ = 0.75%, n = 48.

    Solution
    Amount financed = 11,400 - 2280 = 9120
    PMT = PV ÷ $a_{\overline{n}|i}$

      = 9120 ÷ 40.184782 ≈ 226.95

    The monthly payment is $226.95.

18. Strategy
    To find the monthly payment:
    • Find the amount financed.
    • Use the equation PMT = PV ÷ $a_{\overline{n}|i}$.

    PV = amount financed,
    i% = $\frac{8\%}{12}$ = $\frac{2}{3}$%, n = 48.

    Solution
    Amount financed = 17,800 - 3000
                    = 14,800
    PMT = PV ÷ $a_{\overline{n}|i}$

      = 14,800 ÷ 40.961913 ≈ 361.31

    The monthly payment is $361.31.

19. Strategy
    To find the monthly payment:
    • Find the amount financed.
    • Use the equation PMT = PV ÷ $a_{\overline{n}|i}$.

    PV = amount financed,
    i% = $\frac{8\%}{12}$ = $\frac{2}{3}$%, n = 120.

    Solution
    Amount financed = 18,000 - 1800
                    = 16,200
    PMT = PV ÷ $a_{\overline{n}|i}$

      = 16,200 ÷ 82.421479 ≈ 196.55

    The monthly payment is $196.55.

20. Strategy
    To find the monthly payment:
    • Find the amount financed.
    • Use the equation PMT = PV ÷ $a_{\overline{n}|i}$.

    PV = amount financed,
    i% = $\frac{12\%}{12}$ = 1%, n = 120.

    Solution
    Amount financed = 21,500 - 2150
                    = 19,350
    PMT = PV ÷ $a_{\overline{n}|i}$

      = 19,350 ÷ 69.700522 ≈ 277.62

    The monthly payment is $277.62.

21. Strategy
    (a) To find the monthly payment, use the equation PMT = PV ÷ $a\overline{_n}|_i$.

    PV = 80,000

    $i = \frac{9\%}{12} = 0.75\%$, n = 9.

    (b) To find the amount of interest paid the first month, use the simple interest formula, I = Prt.
    (c) To find the amount of principal repaid the first month, subtract the interest owed for the first month from the monthly payment.

    Solution
    PMT = PV ÷ $a\overline{_n}|_i$

    = 80,000 ÷ 8.671576 ≈ 9225.54

    The monthly payment is $9225.54.

    Interest paid = 80,000(0.09)$\left(\frac{1}{12}\right)$

    = 600

    The interest paid the first month is $600.

    Principal paid = 9225.54 - 600
    = 8625.54

    The amount of principal paid the first month is $8625.54.

22. Strategy
    (a) To find the monthly payment, use the equation PMT = PV ÷ $a\overline{_n}|_i$.

    PV = 45,000

    $i = \frac{12\%}{12} = 1\%$, n = 6.

    (b) To find the amount of interest paid the first month, use the simple interest formula, I = Prt.
    (c) To find the amount of principal repaid the first month, subtract the interest owed for the first month from the monthly payment.

    Solution
    PMT = PV ÷ $a\overline{_n}|_i$

    = 45,000 ÷ 5.795476 ≈ 7764.68

    The monthly payment is $7764.68.

    Interest paid = 45,000(0.12)$\left(\frac{1}{12}\right)$

    = 450

    The interest paid the first month is $450.

    Principal paid = 7764.68 - 450
    = 7314.68

    The amount of principal paid the first month is $7314.68.

23. Strategy
    To find the loan payoff:
    • Use the equation PMT = PV ÷ $a\overline{_n}|_i$ to find the monthly payment.

    PV = 100,000, i% = $\frac{10\%}{4}$ = 2.5%, n = 16.

    • Use the equation PV = PMT·$a\overline{_n}|_i$

    n = 16 - 12 = 4.

    Solution
    PMT = PV ÷ $a\overline{_n}|_i$

    = 100,000 ÷ 13.055003 ≈ 7659.90

    PV = PMT·$a\overline{_n}|_i$

    = 7659.90(3.761974) ≈ 28,816.35

    The loan payoff is $28,816.35.

24. Strategy
    To find the loan payoff:
    • Use the equation PMT = PV ÷ $a\overline{_n}|_i$ to find the monthly payment.

    PV = 50,000, i% = $\frac{12\%}{12}$ = 1%, n = 24.

    • Use the equation PV = PMT·$a\overline{_n}|_i$

    n = 24 - 14 = 10.

    Solution
    PMT = PV ÷ $a\overline{_n}|_i$

    = 50,000 ÷ 21.243387 ≈ 2353.67

    PV = PMT·$a\overline{_n}|_i$

    = 2353.67(9.471305) ≈ 22,292.33

    The loan payoff is $22,292.33.

25. Strategy
    (a) To find the amount of the loan payoff:
      * Use the equation $PMT = PV \div a_{\overline{n}|i}$ to find the monthly payment.

      $$PV = 12,000, \quad i\% = \frac{9\%}{12} = 0.75\%, \quad n = 9.$$

      * Use the equation $PV = PMT \cdot a_{\overline{n}|i}$, $n = 9 - 5 = 4$.

    (b) To find the unearned finance charge:
      * Find the total of the remaining payments by multiplying the monthly payment by the number of remaining payments.
      * Subtract the loan payoff from the total of the remaining payments.

    Solution
    $PMT = PV \div a_{\overline{n}|i} = 12,000 \div 8.671576 \approx 1383.83$

    $PV = PMT \cdot a_{\overline{n}|i} = 1383.83(3.926110) \approx 5433.07$

    The loan payoff is $5433.07.
    Total of remaining payments = 1383.83(4) = 5535.32
    Unearned finance charge = 5535.32 - 5433.07 = 102.25
    The unearned finance charge is $102.25.

26. Strategy
    (a) To find the amount of the loan payoff:
      * Use the equation $PMT = PV \div a_{\overline{n}|i}$ to find the monthly payment.

      $$PV = 2600, \quad i\% = \frac{12\%}{12} = 1\%, \quad n = 6.$$

      * Use the equation $PV = PMT \cdot a_{\overline{n}|i}$, $n = 6 - 4 = 2$.

    (b) To find the unearned finance charge:
      * Find the total of the remaining payments by multiplying the monthly payment by the number of remaining payments.
      * Subtract the loan payoff from the total of the remaining payments.

    Solution
    $PMT = PV \div a_{\overline{n}|i} = 2600 \div 5.795476 \approx 448.63$

    $PV = PMT \cdot a_{\overline{n}|i} = 448.63(1.970395) \approx 883.98$

    The loan payoff is $883.98.
    Total of remaining payments = 448.63(2) = 897.26
    Unearned finance charge = 897.26 - 883.98 = 13.28
    The unearned finance charge is $13.28.

27. Strategy
    To find the unearned finance charge:
    * Use the equation $PMT = PV \div a_{\overline{n}|i}$ to find the monthly payment.

    $$PV = 25,000, \quad i\% = \frac{8\%}{12} = \frac{2}{3}\%, \quad n = 12.$$

    * Use the equation $PV = PMT \cdot a_{\overline{n}|i}$ to find the loan payoff, $n = 12 - 7 = 5$.

    * Find the total of the remaining payments by multiplying the monthly payment by the number of remaining payments.
    * Subtract the loan payoff from the total of the remaining payments.

    Solution
    $PMT = PV \div a_{\overline{n}|i} = 25,000 \div 11.495782 \approx 2174.71$

    $PV = PMT \cdot a_{\overline{n}|i} = 2174.71(4.091535) \approx 10,659.42$

    Total of remaining payments = 2174.71(5) = 10,873.55
    Unearned finance charge = 10,873.55 - 10,659.42 = 214.13
    The unearned finance charge is $214.13.

28. Strategy
     To find the unearned finance charge:
     • Use the equation PMT = PV ÷ $a\,\overline{_n}|_i$ to find the monthly payment.

     PV = 40,000, i% = $\frac{8\%}{12}$ = $\frac{2}{3}\%$, n = 18.
     • Use the equation PV = PMT·$a\,\overline{_n}|_i$ to find the loan payoff, n = 18 - 10 = 8.

     • Find the total of the remaining payments by multiplying the monthly payment by the
       number of remaining payments.
     • Subtract the loan payoff from the total of the remaining payments.

     Solution
     PMT = PV ÷ $a\,\overline{_n}|_i$ = 40,000 ÷ 16.908944 ≈ 2365.61
     PV = PMT·$a\,\overline{_n}|_i$ = 2365.61(7.765237) ≈ 18,369.52

     Total of remaining payments = 2365.61(8) = 18,924.88
     Unearned finance charge = 18,924.88 - 18,369.52 = 555.36
     The unearned finance charge is $555.36.

Section 12.3, pages 377–380

1. Strategy
    To find the charge for points, solve
    the basic percent equation for part.

    Solution
    Part = base x rate
         = 325,000 x 0.015 = 4875

    The charge for points is $4875.

2. Strategy
    To find the charge for points, solve
    the basic percent equation for part.

    Solution
    Part = base x rate
         = 285,000 x 0.0225 = 6412.50

    The charge for points is $6412.50.

3. Strategy
    To find the fee for points, solve the
    basic percent equation for part.

    Solution
    Part = base x rate
         = 125,000 x 0.025 = 3125

    The charge for points is $3125.

4. Strategy
    To find the charge for points, solve
    the basic percent equation for part.

    Solution
    Part = base x rate
         = 95,000 x 0.0175 = 1662.50

    The charge for points is $1662.50.

5. Strategy
    To find the initial costs:
    • Find the amount paid for points by
      solving the basic percent equation
      for part.
    • Add the amount paid for points to
      the amounts paid for the other
      closing costs.

    Solution
    Part = base x rate
         = 72,000 x 0.015 = 1080

    Closing costs
         = 1080 + 120 + 240 + 125 + 179
         = 1744

    The initial costs are $1744.

6. Strategy
    To find the total closing costs:
    • Find the amount paid for points by
      solving the basic percent equation
      for part.
    • Add the amount paid for points to
      the amounts paid for the other
      closing costs.

    Solution
    Part = base x rate
         = 112,000 x 0.02 = 2240

    Closing costs
         = 2240 + 35 + 315 + 150 + 30 + 422
         = 3192

    The total closing costs are $3192.

180   *Chapter 12*

7. Strategy
   (a) To find the amount of the
       mortgage:
       • Find the amount of the down
         payment by solving the basic
         percent equation for part.
       • Subtract the down payment from
         the purchase price.
   (b) To find the amount paid for
       points, solve the basic percent
       equation for part.

   Solution
   Part = base x rate
        = 75,000 x 0.20 = 15,000

   Mortgage = 75,000 - 15,000 = 60,000

   The amount of the mortgage is $60,000.

   Part = base x rate
        = 60,000 x 0.02 = 1200

   The amount paid for points is $1200.

8. Strategy
   (a) To find the amount of the
       mortgage:
       • Find the amount of the down
         payment by solving the basic
         percent equation for part.
       • Subtract the down payment from
         the purchase price.
   (b) To find the amount paid for
       points, solve the basic percent
       equation for part.

   Solution
   Part = base x rate
        = 90,000 x 0.25 = 22,500

   Mortgage = 90,000 - 22,500 = 67,500

   The amount of the mortgage is $67,500.

   Part = base x rate
        = 67,500 x 0.0225 = 1518.75

   The amount paid for points is
   $1518.75.

9. Strategy
   (a) To find the amount of the
       mortgage:
       • Find the amount of the down
         payment by solving the basic
         percent equation for part.
       • Subtract the down payment from
         the purchase price.
   (b) To find the amount paid for
       points, solve the basic percent
       equation for part.

   Solution
   Part = base x rate
        = 225,000 x 0.15 = 33,750

   Mortgage = 225,000 - 33,750 = 191,250

   The amount of the mortgage is
   $191,250.

   Part = base x rate
        = 191,250 x 0.02 = 3825

   The amount paid for points is $3825.

10. Strategy
    (a) To find the amount of the
        mortgage:
        • Find the amount of the down
          payment by solving the basic
          percent equation for part.
        • Subtract the down payment from
          the purchase price.
    (b) To find the amount paid for
        points, solve the basic percent
        equation for part.
    (c) To find the total initial costs,
        add the amount paid for points to
        the amounts paid for the other
        initial costs.

    Solution
    Part = base x rate
         = 54,000 x 0.20 = 10,800

    Mortgage = 54,000 - 10,800 = 43,200

    The amount of the mortgage is $43,200.

    Part = base x rate
         = 43,200 x 0.03 = 1296

    The amount paid for points is $1296.

    Initial costs
        = 1296 + 268 + 213 + 350 + 25
        + 10,800
        = 12,952

    The total initial costs are $12,952.

11. Strategy
    (a) To find the amount of the
        mortgage:
        • Find the amount of the down
          payment by solving the basic
          percent equation for part.
        • Subtract the down payment from
          the purchase price.
    (b) To find the amount paid for
        points, solve the basic percent
        equation for part.
    (c) To find the total initial costs,
        add the amount paid for points to
        the amounts paid for the other
        initial costs.

    Solution
    Part = base x rate
         = 160,000 x 0.15 = 24,000

    Mortgage = 160,000 - 24,000 = 136,000

    The amount of the mortgage is
    $136,000.

    Part = base x rate
         = 136,000 x 0.015 = 2040

    The amount paid for points is $2040.

    Initial costs
         = 2040 + 435 + 1460 + 840 + 100
         + 24,000
         = 28,875

    The total initial costs are $28,875.

12. Strategy
    (a) To find the amount of the
        mortgage:
        • Find the amount of the down
          payment by solving the basic
          percent equation for part.
        • Subtract the down payment from
          the purchase price.
    (b) To find the amount paid for
        points, solve the basic percent
        equation for part.
    (c) To find the total initial costs,
        add the amount paid for points to
        the amounts paid for the other
        initial costs.

    Solution
    Part = base x rate
         = 65,000 x 0.18 = 11,700

    Mortgage = 65,000 - 11,700 = 53,300

    The amount of the mortgage is $53,300.

    Part = base x rate
         = 53,300 x 0.02 = 1066

    The amount paid for points is $1066.

    Initial costs
         = 1066 + 375 + 110 + 213 + 180
         + 25 + 100 + 11,700
         = 13,769

    The total initial costs are $13,769.

13. Strategy
    To find the amount of interest paid,
    use the equation I = Prt.

    Solution
    I = Prt
      $= 225,000(0.12)\left(\frac{1}{12}\right) = 2250$

    The first month's interest is $2250.

14. Strategy
    To find the amount of interest paid,
    use the equation I = Prt.

    Solution
    I = Prt
      $= 190,000(0.09)\left(\frac{1}{12}\right) = 1425$

    The first month's interest is $1425.

15. Strategy
    To find the monthly mortgage payment,
    use the equation PMT = PV ÷ $a_{\overline{n}|i}$.

    PV = 850,000, i% = $\frac{8\%}{12} = \frac{2}{3}\%$,
    n = 12·20 = 240.

    Solution
    PMT = PV ÷ $a_{\overline{n}|i}$
        = 850,000 ÷ 119.554288 ≈ 7109.74

    The monthly mortgage payment is
    $7109.74.

16. Strategy
    To find the monthly mortgage payment,
    use the equation PMT = PV ÷ $a_{\overline{n}|i}$.

    PV = 415,000, i% = $\frac{8\%}{12} = \frac{2}{3}\%$,
    n = 12·30 = 360.

    Solution
    PMT = PV ÷ $a_{\overline{n}|i}$
        = 415,000 ÷ 136.283489 ≈ 3045.12

    The monthly mortgage payment is
    $3045.12.

17. Strategy
    To find the monthly mortgage payment,
    use the equation $PMT = PV \div a_{\overline{n}|i}$.

    $PV = 92,500$, $i\% = \dfrac{8\%}{12} = \dfrac{2}{3}\%$,
    $n = 12 \cdot 30 = 360$.

    Solution
    $PMT = PV \div a_{\overline{n}|i}$
    $\quad = 92,500 \div 136.283489 \approx 678.73$

    The monthly mortgage payment is
    $678.73.

18. Strategy
    To find the monthly mortgage payment,
    use the equation $PMT = PV \div a_{\overline{n}|i}$.

    $PV = 88,000$, $i\% = \dfrac{9\%}{12} = 0.75\%$,
    $n = 12 \cdot 20 = 240$.

    Solution
    $PMT = PV \div a_{\overline{n}|i}$
    $\quad = 88,000 \div 111.144954 \approx 791.76$

    The monthly mortgage payment is
    $791.76.

19. Strategy
    To find the monthly mortgage payment,
    use the equation $PMT = PV \div a_{\overline{n}|i}$.

    $PV = 105,000$, $i\% = \dfrac{9\%}{12} = 0.75\%$,
    $n = 12 \cdot 20 = 240$.

    Solution
    $PMT = PV \div a_{\overline{n}|i}$
    $\quad = 105,000 \div 111.144954 \approx 944.71$

    The monthly mortgage payment is
    $944.71.

20. Strategy
    To find the monthly mortgage payment,
    use the equation $PMT = PV \div a_{\overline{n}|i}$.

    $PV = 88,000$, $i\% = \dfrac{8\%}{12} = \dfrac{2}{3}\%$,
    $n = 12 \cdot 30 = 360$.

    Solution
    $PMT = PV \div a_{\overline{n}|i}$
    $\quad = 88,000 \div 136.283489 \approx 645.71$

    The monthly mortgage payment is
    $645.71.

21. Strategy
    To find the quarterly mortgage
    payment, use the equation
    $PMT = PV \div a_{\overline{n}|i}$.

    $PV = 19,000,000$, $i\% = \dfrac{10\%}{4} = 2.5\%$,
    $n = 4 \cdot 15 = 60$.

    Solution
    $PMT = PV \div a_{\overline{n}|i}$
    $\quad = 19,000,000 \div 30.908656$
    $\quad \approx 614,714.53$

    The quarterly mortgage payment is
    $614,714.53.

22. Strategy
    To find the quarterly mortgage
    payment, use the equation
    $PMT = PV \div a_{\overline{n}|i}$.

    $PV = 11,500,000$, $i\% = \dfrac{10\%}{4} = 2.5\%$,
    $n = 4 \cdot 30 = 120$.

    Solution
    $PMT = PV \div a_{\overline{n}|i}$
    $\quad = 11,500,000 \div 37.933687$
    $\quad \approx 303,160.62$

    The quarterly mortgage payment is
    $303,160.62.

23. Strategy
    To find the quarterly mortgage
    payment, use the equation
    $PMT = PV \div a_{\overline{n}|i}$.

    $PV = 77,000$, $i\% = \dfrac{12\%}{4} = 3\%$,
    $n = 4 \cdot 15 = 60$.

    Solution
    $PMT = PV \div a_{\overline{n}|i}$
    $\quad = 77,000 \div 27.675564 \approx 2782.24$

    The quarterly mortgage payment is
    $2782.24.

24. Strategy
    To find the quarterly mortgage
    payment, use the equation
    $PMT = PV \div a_{\overline{n}|i}$.

    $PV = 400,000$, $i\% = \dfrac{8\%}{4} = 2\%$,
    $n = 4 \cdot 15 = 60$.

    Solution
    $PMT = PV \div a_{\overline{n}|i}$
    $\quad = 400,000 \div 34.760887 \approx 11,507.19$

    The quarterly mortgage payment is
    $11,507.19.

25. Strategy
    To find the total amount of interest
    paid over the life of a loan:
    • Use the equation $PMT = PV \div a_{\overline{n}|i}$ to
      find the monthly payment.
      $PV = 68,000$, $i\% = \frac{9\%}{12} = 0.75\%$,
      $n = 12 \cdot 20 = 240$.
    • Find the total amount paid over the
      life of the loan by multiplying the
      monthly mortgage payment by the
      number of payments.
    • Subtract the amount of the mortgage
      from the total amount paid over the
      life of the loan.

    Solution
    $PMT = PV \div a_{\overline{n}|i}$
    $= 68,000 \div 111.144954 \approx 611.81$

    Total paid $= PMT \times n$
    $= 611.81(240) = 146,834.40$

    Interest paid
    $= 146,834.40 - 68,000 = 78,834.40$

    The total amount of interest paid is
    \$78,834.40.

26. Strategy
    To find the total amount of interest
    paid over the life of a loan:
    • Use the equation $PMT = PV \div a_{\overline{n}|i}$ to
      find the monthly payment.
      $PV = 105,000$, $i\% = \frac{9\%}{12} = 0.75\%$,
      $n = 12 \cdot 30 = 360$.
    • Find the total amount paid over the
      life of the loan by multiplying the
      monthly mortgage payment by the
      number of payments.
    • Subtract the amount of the mortgage
      from the total amount paid over the
      life of the loan.

    Solution
    $PMT = PV \div a_{\overline{n}|i}$
    $= 105,000 \div 124.281866 \approx 844.85$

    Total paid $= PMT \times n$
    $= 844.85(360) = 304,146$

    Interest paid
    $= 304,146 - 105,000 = 199,146$

    The total amount of interest paid is
    \$199,146.

Business Case Study

1. Down payment $= 0.20(67,000) = 13,400$
   Points $= 0.025(67,000 - 13,400) = 0.025(53,600) = 1340$
   Closing costs $= 325$

   \$13,400 + \$1340 + \$325 = \$15,065

   Savings account: \$18,000 - \$3000 = \$15,000
   Checking account: \$450 - \$300 = \$150
   \$15,000 + \$150 = \$15,150

   \$15,150 is greater than \$15,065.
   Yes, you are willing to take this much money out of your accounts.

2. Monthly mortgage payment $= PV \div a_{\overline{n}|i} = 53,600 \div 124.281866 = 431.28$
   Property tax $= 1152 \div 12 = 96$
   Maintenance $= 60$
   Insurance $= 96 \div 12 = 8$
   Utilities $= [8750(0.07)] \div 12 = 612.50 \div 12 \approx 51.04$

   Total of the monthly payments $= 431.28 + 96 + 60 + 8 + 51.04 = 646.32$

3. Monthly take-home pay - monthly expenses $= \$2239.69 - \$646.32 = \$1593.37$

4. $646.32 \div 2239.69 \approx 28.9\%$

5. Answers will vary.

Review/Test, pages 385–386

1. Strategy
   To find the average daily balance:
   • Find the total amount owed each day of the month.
   • Divide the total amount owed each day of the month by the number of days in the billing period.

   Solution

Date	Payments or Purchases	Daily Balance	Number of Days	Days x Amount
May 5-16		455	12	5,460
May 17-19	233	688	3	2,064
May 20-June 4	-200	488	16	7,808
	Total owed each day of the month			15,332

   There are 31 days in the billing period.
   Average daily balance = 15,332 ÷ 31 ≈ 494.58

   The average daily balance was $494.58.

2. Strategy
   To find the finance charge:
   • Find the total amount owed each day of the month.
   • Find the average daily balance.
   • Multiply the average daily balance by the interest rate per month.

   Solution

Date	Payments or Purchases	Daily Balance	Number of Days	Days x Amount
June 10-17		820	8	6,560
June 18-21	-250	570	4	2,280
June 22-July 9	122	692	18	12,456
	Total owed each day of the month			21,296

   Average daily balance = 21,296 ÷ 30 = 709.87
   Finance charge = 709.87 x 0.015 ≈ 10.65

   The finance charge is $10.65.

3. Strategy
   To find the monthly payment:
   • Find the amount financed.
   • Find the finance charge.
   • Find the total of the installment payments.
   • Divide the total of the installment payments by the number of monthly payments.
   To find the annual percentage rate:
   • Find the finance charge per $100.
   • Use the APR table. The term is 18 months.

   Solution
   Amount financed = cash price − down payment = 2600 − 600 = 2000

   Finance charge = amount financed x interest rate x time = 2000 x 0.10 x $\frac{18}{12}$ = 300

   Total of installment payments = amount financed + finance charges
   $$= 2000 + 300 = 2300$$

   Monthly payment = $\frac{2300}{18} \approx 127.78$

   The monthly payment is $127.78.

   Finance charge per $100 = $\frac{300}{2000}$ x 100 = 15.

   The APR is 18.25%.

4. Strategy
   To find the annual percentage rate:
   • Find the amount financed.
   • Find the finance charge.
   • Find the finance charge per $100.
   • Use the APR table. The term is 6 months.

   Solution
   Amount financed
   = cash price − down payment
   = 380 − 50 = 330

   Finance charge
   = amount financed x interest rate x time
   = 330 x 0.08 x $\frac{6}{12}$ = 13.20

   Finance charge per $100
   = $\frac{13.20}{330}$ x 100 = 4.

   The APR is 13.50%.

5. Strategy
   To find the monthly payment:
   • Find the amount financed.
   • Use the equation PMT = PV + $a\,\overline{_{n}|}\,_{i}$.

     PV = amount financed,
     i% = $\frac{9\%}{12}$ = 0.75%, n = 18.

   Solution
   Amount financed = 1650 − 250 = 1400
   PMT = PV + $a\,\overline{_{n}|}\,_{i}$
   $$= 1400 + 16.799181 \approx 83.44$$

   The monthly payment is $83.44.

6. Strategy
   (a) To find the monthly payment, use the equation $PMT = PV \div a_{\overline{n}|i}$.

   PV = amount financed,
   $i = \frac{12\%}{12} = 1\%$, $n = 15$.

   (b) To find the amount of interest paid the first month, use the simple interest formula, $I = Prt$.

   Solution
   Amount financed
   $= 1160 - 200 = 960$

   $PMT = PV \div a_{\overline{n}|i}$
   $= 960 \div 13.865053 \approx 69.24$

   The monthly payment is $69.24.

   Interest paid $= 960 \times 0.12 \times \frac{1}{12} = 9.60$

   The interest paid the first month is $9.60.

7. Strategy
   To find the loan payoff:
   • Use the equation $PMT = PV \div a_{\overline{n}|i}$ to find the monthly payment.
   $PV = 20,000$, $i\% = \frac{12\%}{12} = 1\%$, $n = 9$.
   • Use the equation $PV = PMT \cdot a_{\overline{n}|i}$
   $n = 9 - 4 = 5$.

   Solution
   $PMT = PV \div a_{\overline{n}|i}$
   $= 20,000 \div 8.566018 \approx 2334.81$

   $PV = PMT \cdot a_{\overline{n}|i}$
   $= 2334.81(4.853431) \approx 11,331.84$

   The loan payoff is $11,331.84.

8. Strategy
   (a) To find the amount of the loan payoff:
      • Use the equation $PMT = PV \div a_{\overline{n}|i}$ to find the monthly payment.

      $PV = 25,000$, $i\% = \frac{9\%}{12} = \frac{3}{4}\%$, $n = 9$.
      • Use the equation $PV = PMT \cdot a_{\overline{n}|i}$, $n = 9 - 6 = 3$.

   (b) To find the unearned finance charge:
      • Find the total of the remaining payments by multiplying the monthly payment by the number of remaining payments.
      • Subtract the loan payoff from the total of the remaining payments.

   Solution
   $PMT = PV \div a_{\overline{n}|i} = 25,000 \div 8.671576 \approx 2882.98$
   $PV = PMT \cdot a_{\overline{n}|i} = 2882.98(2.955556) \approx 8520.81$.

   The loan payoff is $8520.81.
   Total of remaining payments $= 2882.98(3) = 8648.94$
   Unearned finance charge $= 8648.94 - 8520.81 = 128.13$
   The unearned finance charge is $128.13.

9. Strategy
    To find the charge for points, solve
    the basic percent equation for
    percent.

    Solution
    Part = base x rate
        = 125,000 x 0.0175 = 2187.50

    The charge for points is $2187.50.

10. Strategy
    To find the total closing costs:
    • Find the amount paid for points by
      solving the basic percent equation
      for part.
    • Add the amount paid for points to
      the amounts paid for the other
      closing costs.

    Solution
    Part = base x rate
        = 75,000 x 0.02 = 1500

    Closing costs
        = 1500 + 40 + 235 + 156
        = 1931

    The total closing costs are $1931.

11. Strategy
    To find the monthly mortgage payment,
    use the equation $PMT = PV + a_{\overline{n}|i}$.

    $PV = 135,000$, $i\% = \dfrac{9\%}{12} = 0.75\%$,
    $n = 12 \cdot 30 = 360$.

    Solution
    $PMT = PV + a_{\overline{n}|i}$
        $= 135,000 + 124.281866 \approx 1086.24$

    The monthly mortgage payment is
    $1086.24.

12. Strategy
    To find the total amount of interest
    paid over the life of a loan:
    • Use the equation $PMT = PV + a_{\overline{n}|i}$ to
      find the monthly payment.
      $PV = 105,000$, $i\% = \dfrac{8\%}{12} = \dfrac{2}{3}\%$,
      $n = 12 \cdot 20 = 240$.
    • Find the total amount paid over the
      life of the loan by multiplying the
      monthly mortgage payment by the
      number of payments.
    • Subtract the amount of the mortgage
      from the total amount paid over the
      life of the loan.

    Solution
    $PMT = PV + a_{\overline{n}|i}$
        $= 105,000 + 119.554288 \approx 878.26$

    Total paid = PMT x n
             = 878.26(240) = 210,782.40

    Interest paid
        = 210,782.40 - 105,000
        = 105,782.40

    The total amount of interest paid is
    $105,782.40.

CHAPTER 13
Inventory

Section 13.1, pages 393–398

1. Strategy
   To find the value of the inventory, add the costs of the items remaining in inventory.

   Solution
   3 units from Feb. 2 purchase @ 217   =   651
   1 unit from Feb. 23 purchase @ 224   =   224
   2 units from March 14 purchase @ 221   =   442
                                             1317

   The value of the inventory is $1317.

2. Strategy
   To find the value of the inventory, add the costs of the items remaining in inventory.

   Solution
   2 units from Sept. 5 purchase @ 488   =   976
   4 units from Sept. 30 purchase @ 479   = 1916
   1 unit from Oct. 15 purchase @ 483   =   483
                                             3375

   The value of the inventory is $3375.

3. Strategy
   To find the value of the inventory, add the costs of the items remaining in inventory.

   Solution
   4 units from May 3 purchase @ 513   = 2052
   6 units from May 23 purchase @ 533   = 3198
   8 units from June 16 purchase @ 521   = 4168
                                             9418

   The value of the inventory is $9418.

4. Strategy
   To find the value of the inventory, add the costs of the items remaining in inventory.

   Solution
   1 unit from beginning inventory @ 268   =   268
   2 units from May 14 purchase @ 284   =   568
   2 units from May 24 purchase @ 272   =   544
                                           1380

   The value of the inventory was $1380.

5. Strategy
   To find the value of the inventory, add the costs of the items remaining in inventory.

   Solution
   4 units from July 18 purchase @ 590   = 2360
   4 units from July 30 purchase @ 560   = 2240
                                           4600

   The value of the inventory was $4600.

6. Strategy
   To find the value of the inventory, add the costs of the items remaining in inventory.

   Solution
   1 unit from beginning inventory @ 3250   =   3,250
   2 units from March 8 purchase @ 3145   =   6,290
   1 unit from March 20 purchase @ 3295   =   3,295
   5 units from March 28 purchase @ 3275   = 16,375
                                           29,210

   The value of the inventory was $29,210.

7. Strategy
   To find the value of the inventory, add the costs of the items remaining in inventory.

   Solution
   1 unit from beginning inventory @ 315   =   315
   2 units from June 10 purchase @ 305   =   610
   4 units from June 20 purchase @ 320   = 1280
                                           2205

   The value of the inventory was $2205.

8. Strategy
   To find the value of the inventory, add the costs of the items remaining in inventory.

   Solution
   2 units from beginning inventory @ 679 = 1358
   1 unit from May 6 purchase @ 695   =   695
   3 units from May 15 purchase @ 670   = 2010
   3 units from May 24 purchase @ 680   = 2040
                                           6103

   The value of the inventory was $6103.

9. Strategy
    To find the value of the inventory, add the costs of the items remaining in
    inventory.

    Solution
    ```
    2 units from beginning inventory @ 175  =   350
    1 unit from July 3 purchase @ 189       =   189
    7 units from July 16 purchase @ 165     =  1155
    10 units from July 25 purchase @ 179    =  1790
                                              ─────
                                               3484
    ```

    The value of the inventory was $3484.

10. Strategy
    To find the average cost of the boxes of cards:
    • Find the total number of boxes purchased.
    • Find the total cost of the boxes purchased.
    • Divide the total cost by the total number purchased.

    Solution
    Total units purchased = 250 + 400 = 650
    Total cost = 250(3.80) + 400(3.92) = 950 + 1568 = 2518
    Average cost = $\frac{2518}{650} \approx 3.87$

    The average cost was $3.87.

11. Strategy
    To find the average cost of the vases:
    • Find the total number of vases purchased.
    • Find the total cost of the vases purchased.
    • Divide the total cost by the total number purchased.

    Solution
    Total units purchased = 300 + 500 = 800
    Total cost = 300(2.25) + 500(2.40) = 675 + 1200 = 1875
    Average cost = $\frac{1875}{800} \approx 2.34$

    The average cost was $2.34.

12. Total cost = 15(62) = $930   13. Total cost = 30(59) = $1770

14. Total cost = 20(61) = $1220

15. Total cost of purchases = 930 + 1770 + 1220 = $3920

16. Average cost = $\frac{\text{total cost}}{\text{total units}} = \frac{3920}{15+30+20} = \frac{3920}{65} \approx \$60.31$

17. Value of inventory = (average cost)(units in inventory) = 60.31(17) = $1025.27

18. Total cost = 100(12.80) = $1280   19. Total cost = 75(13.20) = $990

20. Total cost = 200(12.75) = $2550

21. Total cost of purchases = 1280 + 990 + 2550 = $4820

22. Average cost = $\frac{\text{total cost}}{\text{total units}} = \frac{4820}{100+75+200} = \frac{4820}{375} \approx \$12.85$

23. Value of inventory = (average cost)(units in inventory) = 12.85(56) = $719.60

24. Total cost = 7(22.45) = $157.15   25. Total cost = 22(21.50) = $473.00

26. Total cost = 40(21.25) = $850.00

27. Total cost of purchases = 157.15 + 473.00 + 850.00 = $1480.15

28. Average cost = $\dfrac{\text{total cost}}{\text{total units}} = \dfrac{1480.15}{7+22+40} = \dfrac{1480.15}{69} \approx$ $21.45

29. Value of inventory = (average cost)(units in inventory) = 21.45(32) = $686.40

30. Total cost = 200(175) = $35,000   31. Number in inventory = 40 + 200 = 240

32. Number in inventory = 240 - 125 = 115   33. Number in inventory = 115 - 55 = 60

34. Total cost = 100(182) = $18,200   35. Number in inventory = 60 + 100 = 160

36. Number in inventory = 160 - 80 = 80   37. Total cost = 150(184) = $27,600

38. Number in inventory = 80 + 150 = 230   39. Number in inventory = 230 - 65 = 165

40. Average cost = $\dfrac{\text{total cost}}{\text{total units}} = \dfrac{6800 + 35,000 + 18,200 + 27,600}{490} \approx$ $178.78

    Value of inventory = (average cost)(units in inventory) = $178.78(165) = $29,498.70

41. Total cost = 150(518) = $77,700   42. Number in inventory = 60 + 150 = 210

43. Number in inventory = 210 - 90 = 120   44. Number in inventory = 120 - 85 = 35

45. Total cost = 200(525) = $105,000   46. Number in inventory = 35 + 200 = 235

47. Number in inventory = 235 - 120 = 115   48. Total cost = 125(509) = $63,625

49. Number in inventory = 115 + 125 = 240

50. Average cost = $\dfrac{\text{total cost}}{\text{total units}} = \dfrac{29,340 + 77,700 + 105,000 + 63,625}{60 + 150 + 200 + 125} = \dfrac{275,665}{535} \approx$ $515.26

    Value of inventory = (average cost)(units in inventory) = $515.26(240) = $123,662.40

Section 13.2, pages 401–404

1. Strategy
   To find the value of the inventory:
   • Determine which units remain in
     inventory.
   • Add the values of these units.

   Solution
   660 units @ 2.65 per unit are in
   inventory.
   660(2.65) = 1749

   The value of the inventory is $1749.

2. Strategy
   To find the value of the inventory:
   • Determine which units remain in
     inventory.
   • Add the values of these units.

   Solution
   1350 units @ 1.15 per unit are in
   inventory.
   1350(1.15) = 1552.50

   The value of the inventory is
   $1552.50.

3. Strategy
   To find the value of the inventory:
   • Determine which units remain in
     inventory.
   • Add the values of these units.

   Solution
   75 units @ 25 per unit
   50 units @ 24 per unit
   150 - (75 + 50) = 150 - 125
     = 25 units @ 21 per unit

   75(25) = 1875
   50(24) = 1200
   25(21) = $\underline{\quad 525}$
           3600

   The value of the inventory is $3600.

4. Strategy
   To find the value of the inventory:
   • Determine which units remain in
     inventory.
   • Add the values of these units.

   Solution
   160 units @ 14 per unit
   250 - 160 = 90 units @ 12 per unit

   160(14) = 2240
    90(12) = $\underline{1080}$
             3320

   The value of the inventory is $3320.

5. Strategy
   To find the value of the inventory:
   • Determine which units remain in
     inventory.
   • Add the values of these units.

   Solution
   125 units from July purchase
   135 - 125 = 10 units from June
   purchase

   125(66.40) = 8300
    10(65.80) = $\underline{\quad 658}$
                8958

   The value of the inventory is $8958.

6. Strategy
   To find the value of the inventory:
   • Determine which units remain in
     inventory.
   • Add the values of these units.

   Solution
   157 units from August purchase
   157(15.95) = 2504.15

   The value of the inventory is
   $2504.15.

7. Strategy
   To find the value of the inventory:
   • Determine which units remain in
     inventory.
   • Add the values of these units.

   Solution
   400 units @ 4.15 per unit
   520 - 400 = 120 units @ 3.95 per unit

   400(4.15) = 1660
   120(3.95) = 474
                ────
                2134

   The value of the inventory is $2134.

8. Strategy
   To find the value of the inventory:
   • Determine which units remain in
     inventory.
   • Add the values of these units.

   Solution
   3000 units @ 1.85 per unit
   4200 - 3000 = 1200 units @ 1.75 per
   unit

   3000(1.85) = 5550
   1200(1.75) = 2100
                ────
                7650

   The value of the inventory is $7650.

9. Strategy
   To find the value of the inventory:
   • Determine which units remain in
     inventory.
   • Add the values of these units.

   Solution
   60 units @ 44 per unit
   72 - 60 = 12 units @ 48 per unit

   60(44) = 2640
   12(48) = 576
            ────
            3216

   The value of the inventory is $3216.

10. Strategy
    To find the value of the inventory:
    • Determine which units remain in
      inventory.
    • Add the values of these units.

    Solution
    250 units @ 65 per unit
    480 - 250 = 230 units @ 62 per unit

    250(65) = 16,250
    230(62) = 14,260
              ──────
              30,510

    The value of the inventory is $30,510.

11. Strategy
    To find the value of the inventory:
    • Determine which units remain in
      inventory.
    • Add the values of these units.

    Solution
    30 units from September purchase
    75 - 30 = 45 units from October
    purchase

    30(62.40) = 1872.00
    45(61.75) = 2778.75
                ───────
                4650.75

    The value of the inventory is
    $4650.75.

12. Strategy
    To find the value of the inventory:
    • Determine which units remain in
      inventory.
    • Add the values of these units.

    Solution
    50 units from March purchase
    55 - 50 = 5 units from April purchase

    50(18.40) = 920.00
     5(17.90) =   89.50
                 ───────
                 1009.50

    The value of the inventory is
    $1009.50.

13. Number in inventory = 40

14. Number in inventory = 40 - 18 = 22

15. Number in inventory = 22 + 50 = 72

16. Number in inventory = 72 - 22 = 50

17. Number in inventory = 50 - 32 = 18

18. Number in inventory = 18 + 30 = 48

19. Ending value of inventory = 30(51.00) + 18(49.50) = 1530 + 891 = $2421

20. Number in inventory = 27 + 20 = 47

21. Number in inventory = 47 - 12 = 35

22. Number in inventory = 35 + 40 = 75   23. Number in inventory = 75 - 17 = 58

24. Number in inventory = 58 - 33 = 25   25. Number in inventory = 25 + 60 = 85

26. Number in inventory = 85 - 27 = 58   27. Number in inventory = 58 - 21 = 37

28. Number in inventory = 37 + 25 = 62

29. Ending value of inventory = 25(22.60) + 37(21.85) = 565.00 + 808.45 = $1373.45

30. Number in inventory = 15   31. Number in inventory = 15 + 25 = 40

32. Number in inventory = 40 - 17 = 23   33. Number in inventory = 23 - 13 = 10

34. Number in inventory = 10 + 12 = 22   35. Number in inventory = 22 - 9 = 13

36. Ending value of inventory = 13(32) = $416

37. Number in inventory = 27 + 75 = 102   38. Number in inventory = 102 - 42 = 60

39. Number in inventory = 60 - 27 = 33   40. Number in inventory = 33 + 50 = 83

41. Number in inventory = 83 + 20 = 103   42. Number in inventory = 103 - 32 = 71

43. Number in inventory = 71 - 9 = 62

44. Ending value of inventory = 27(1.32) + 35(1.22) = 35.64 + 42.70 = $78.34

Section 13.3, pages 407–408

1. Strategy
   To find the average inventory, add the beginning and ending inventories and divide the sum by 2.

   Solution
   Average inventory =
   (beginning inventory + ending inventory) ÷ 2 =
   (58,600 + 49,300) ÷ 2 =
   107,900 ÷ 2 = 53,950

   The average inventory was $53,950.

2. Strategy
   To find the average inventory, add the beginning and ending inventories and divide the sum by 2.

   Solution
   Average inventory =
   (beginning inventory + ending inventory) ÷ 2 =
   (112,500 + 98,400) ÷ 2 =
   210,900 ÷ 2 = 105,450

   The average inventory was $105,450.

3. Strategy
   To find the average inventory, add the beginning and ending inventories and divide the sum by 2.

   Solution
   Average inventory =
   (beginning inventory + ending inventory) ÷ 2 =
   (39,200 + 41,600) ÷ 2 =
   80,800 ÷ 2 = 40,400

   The average inventory was $40,400.

4. Strategy
   To find the average inventory, add the beginning and ending inventories and divide the sum by 2.

   Solution
   Average inventory =
   (beginning inventory + ending inventory) ÷ 2 =
   (17,250 + 19,480) ÷ 2 =
   36,730 ÷ 2 = 18,365

   The average inventory was $18,365.

5. Strategy
   To calculate the rate of turnover at cost, divide the cost of goods sold by the average inventory.

   Solution

   $$\text{Inventory turnover at cost} = \frac{\text{cost of goods sold}}{\text{average inventory}} = \frac{156,000}{38,000} \approx 4.1$$

   The rate of turnover at cost is 4.1.

6. Strategy
   To calculate the rate of turnover at cost, divide the cost of goods sold by the average inventory.

   Solution

   $$\text{Inventory turnover at cost} = \frac{\text{cost of goods sold}}{\text{average inventory}} = \frac{284,000}{15,500} \approx 18.3$$

   The rate of turnover at cost is 18.3.

7. Strategy
   To find the inventory turnover at retail price, divide the net sales by the average inventory based on retail price.

   Solution

   $$\text{Inventory turnover at retail price} = \frac{\text{net sales}}{\text{average inventory based on retail price}}$$
   $$= \frac{204,000}{23,800} \approx 8.6$$

   The inventory turnover at retail price is 8.6.

8. Strategy
   To find the inventory turnover at retail price, divide the net sales by the average inventory based on retail price.

   Solution

   $$\text{Inventory turnover at retail price} = \frac{\text{net sales}}{\text{average inventory based on retail price}}$$
   $$= \frac{454,000}{76,900} \approx 5.9$$

   The inventory turnover at retail price is 5.9.

9. Strategy
   To find the inventory turnover at cost:
   • Calculate the average inventory.
   • Divide the cost of goods sold by the average inventory.

   Solution
   Average inventory = (beginning inventory + ending inventory) ÷ 2
   $$= (42,000 + 39,200) \div 2 = 81,200 \div 2 = 40,600$$
   $$\text{Inventory turnover at cost} = \frac{\text{cost of goods sold}}{\text{average inventory}} = \frac{629,000}{40,600} \approx 15.5$$

   The inventory turnover at cost was 15.5.

10. Strategy
    To find the inventory turnover at cost:
    • Calculate the average inventory.
    • Divide the cost of goods sold by the average inventory.

    Solution
    Average inventory = (beginning inventory + ending inventory) ÷ 2
    $$= (56,500 + 49,200) ÷ 2 = 105,700 ÷ 2 = 52,850$$
    Inventory turnover at cost = $\dfrac{\text{cost of goods sold}}{\text{average inventory}} = \dfrac{785,000}{52,850} ≈ 14.9$

    The inventory turnover at cost was 14.9.

11. Strategy
    To find the inventory turnover at retail price:
    • Calculate the average inventory.
    • Divide the net sales by the average inventory.

    Solution
    Average inventory = (beginning inventory + ending inventory) ÷ 2
    $$= (63,400 + 68,200) ÷ 2 = 131,600 ÷ 2 = 65,800$$
    Inventory turnover at retail price = $\dfrac{\text{net sales}}{\text{average inventory}} = \dfrac{392,000}{65,800} ≈ 6.0$

    The inventory turnover at retail price was 6.0.

12. Strategy
    To find the inventory turnover at retail price:
    • Calculate the average inventory.
    • Divide the net sales by the average inventory.

    Solution
    Average inventory = (beginning inventory + ending inventory) ÷ 2
    $$= (98,700 + 86,100) ÷ 2 = 184,800 ÷ 2 = 92,400$$
    Inventory turnover at retail price = $\dfrac{\text{net sales}}{\text{average inventory}} = \dfrac{476,000}{92,400} ≈ 5.2$

    The inventory turnover at retail price was 5.2.

13. Strategy
    To find the rate of turnover at cost:
    • Calculate the average inventory.
    • Divide the cost of goods sold by the average inventory.

    Solution
    Average inventory = (beginning inventory + ending inventory) ÷ 2
    $$= (87,400 + 93,200) ÷ 2 = 180,600 ÷ 2 = 90,300$$
    Inventory turnover at cost = $\dfrac{\text{cost of goods sold}}{\text{average inventory}} = \dfrac{861,000}{90,300} ≈ 9.5$

    The rate of turnover at cost was 9.5.

14. Strategy
    To find the rate of turnover at cost:
    • Calculate the average inventory.
    • Divide the cost of goods sold by the average inventory.

    Solution
    Average inventory = (beginning inventory + ending inventory) ÷ 2
                      = (43,900 + 36,700) ÷ 2 = 80,600 ÷ 2 = 40,300

    $$\text{Inventory turnover at cost} = \frac{\text{cost of goods sold}}{\text{average inventory}} = \frac{419,000}{40,300} \approx 10.4$$

    The rate of turnover at cost was 10.4.

15. Strategy
    To determine if the inventory turnover has increased or decreased:
    • Calculate the inventory turnover for last year.
    • Calculate the inventory turnover for this year.
    • Compare the two rates.
    To determine by how much, subtract the smaller rate from the larger rate.

    Solution
    Last year:
    Average inventory = (beginning inventory + ending inventory) ÷ 2
                      = (60,000 + 90,000) ÷ 2 = 150,000 ÷ 2 = 75,000

    $$\text{Inventory turnover at cost} = \frac{\text{cost of goods sold}}{\text{average inventory}} = \frac{255,000}{75,000} \approx 3.4$$

    This year:
    Average inventory = (beginning inventory + ending inventory) ÷ 2
                      = (90,000 + 50,000) ÷ 2 = 140,000 ÷ 2 = 70,000

    $$\text{Inventory turnover at cost} = \frac{\text{cost of goods sold}}{\text{average inventory}} = \frac{224,000}{70,000} \approx 3.2$$

    3.2 is less than 3.4.

    The company's inventory has decreased.

    3.4 - 3.2 = 0.2

    The inventory turnover has decreased by 0.2.

16. Strategy
    To determine if the inventory turnover has increased or decreased:
    • Calculate the inventory turnover for last year.
    • Calculate the inventory turnover for this year.
    • Compare the two rates.
    To determine by how much, subtract the smaller rate from the larger rate.

    Solution
    Last year:
    Average inventory = (beginning inventory + ending inventory) ÷ 2
                      = (62,000 + 57,000) ÷ 2 = 119,000 ÷ 2 = 59,500

    $$\text{Inventory turnover at retail price} = \frac{\text{net sales}}{\text{average inventory}} = \frac{511,700}{59,500} \approx 8.6$$

    This year:
    Average inventory = (beginning inventory + ending inventory) ÷ 2
                      = (57,000 + 65,000) ÷ 2 = 122,000 ÷ 2 = 61,000

    $$\text{Inventory turnover at retail price} = \frac{\text{net sales}}{\text{average inventory}} = \frac{542,900}{61,000} \approx 8.9$$

    8.9 is greater than 8.6.

    The company's inventory has increased.

    8.9 - 8.6 = 0.3

    The inventory turnover has increased by 0.3.

Business Case Study

1. Average inventory based on cost = ($40,000 + $41,000) ÷ 2 = $81,000 ÷ 2 = $40,500

2. Beginning inventory based on selling price = $40,000 + 0.35($40,000) = $54,000
   Ending inventory based on selling price = $41,000 + 0.35($41,000) = $55,350

   Average inventory based on selling price = ($54,000 + $55,350) ÷ 2 = $109,350 ÷ 2 = $54,675

3. Net sales = gross sales - (sales returns and allowances + sales discounts)
              = $465,000 - ($9000 + $5000)
              = $465,000 - $14,000
              = $451,000

4. Cost of goods available for sale = beginning inventory + purchases
      = $40,000 + ($342,000 - $7000) = $375,000

5. Cost of goods sold = cost of goods available for sale - ending inventory
      = $375,000 - $41,000 = $334,000

6. Inventory turnover at cost = cost of goods sold ÷ average inventory based on cost
      = $334,000 ÷ $40,500 ≈ 8.247

7. Inventory turnover at selling price = net sales ÷ average inventory based on selling
   price = $451,000 ÷ $54,675 ≈ 8.249

8. The company sells and replaces its merchandise inventory approximately 8 times per year.
365 days ÷ 8.249 ≈ 44 days
The company sells and replaces its merchandise inventory approximately every 44 days.

9. The average inventory turnover of approximately 8.2 is not far from the average inventory turnover of 9 for similar business. Therefore, drastic steps do not appear to be necessary. Management must consider the risks of lowering average inventory, which include losing sales due to the failure of maintaining an adequate stock of items to serve customer demands and not taking advantage of quantity discounts or sales items sold by the suppliers.

10. The cost of the last goods purchased is generally higher than the cost of goods purchased earlier. Therefore, the value of inventory by the LIFO method results in a lower valuation of inventory and a lower value assigned to the cost of goods available for sale, while assigning a higher value to the cost of goods sold.

Review/Test, pages 413–414

1. Strategy
   To find the value of the inventory, add the costs of the items remaining in inventory.

   Solution
   1 unit from April 5 purchase @ 722 = 722
   1 unit from April 16 purchase @ 728 = 728
   4 units from April 24 purchase @ 719 = 2876
   ————
   4326

   The value of the inventory was $4326.

2. Strategy
   To find the value of the inventory:
   • Calculate the total cost of each purchase.
   • Find the average cost by dividing the total cost by the total units purchased.
   • Multiply the average cost by the number of units in inventory.

   Solution
   May 1 purchase: Total cost = 5(189) = 945
   June 3 purchase: Total cost = 12(182) = 2184
   July 6 purchase: Total cost = 16(184) = 2944

   $$\text{Average cost} = \frac{\text{total cost}}{\text{total units}} = \frac{945 + 2184 + 2944}{5 + 12 + 16} = \frac{6073}{33} \approx 184.03$$

   Value of inventory = (average cost)(units in inventory) = 184.03(8) = 1472.24

   The value of the inventory was $1472.24.

3. Strategy
   To find the value of the inventory:
   • Determine which units remain in
   inventory.
   • Add the values of these units.

   Solution
   60 units from June purchase
   67 - 60 = 7 from the May purchase
   60(170) = 10,200
   7(172) = 1,204
            ‾‾‾‾‾‾
            11,404

   The value of the inventory was
   $11,404.

4. Strategy
   To find the value of the inventory:
   • Determine which units remain in
   inventory.
   • Add the values of these units.

   Solution
   80 units from November purchase
   95 - 80 = 15 from the December purchase
   80(7.40) = 592.00
   15(7.50) = 112.50
              ‾‾‾‾‾‾
              704.50

   The value of the inventory was
   $704.50.

5. Strategy
   To find the value of the inventory by the specific identification method, add the
   costs of the items remaining in inventory.

   Solution
   1 unit from beginning inventory @ 765   = 765
   2 units from September 6 purchase @ 755 = 1510
   3 units from September 22 purchase @ 770 = 2310
                                              ‾‾‾‾
                                              4585

   The value of the inventory was $4585.

6. Strategy
   To find the value of the inventory by the average cost method:
   • Calculate the total cost of each purchase.
   • Find the **average** cost by dividing the total cost by the total units purchased.
   • Determine the number of units remaining in inventory.
   • Multiply the average cost by the number of units in inventory.

   Solution
   Beginning inventory: Total cost = 4(765) = 3060
   September 6 purchase: Total cost = 6(755) = 4530
   September 15 purchase: Total cost = 4(760) = 3040
   September 22 purchase: Total cost = 5(770) = 3850

   $$\text{Average cost} = \frac{\text{total cost}}{\text{total units}} = \frac{3060 + 4530 + 3040 + 3850}{4 + 6 + 4 + 5} = \frac{14,480}{19} \approx 762.11$$

   Units remaining in inventory:
   1 from beginning inventory, 2 from September 6 purchase, 3 from September 22
   purchase = 6 units

   Value of inventory = (average cost)(units in inventory) = 762.11(6) = 4572.66

   The value of the inventory was $4572.66.

7. Strategy
   To find the value of the inventory by the FIFO method:
   • Determine the number of units remaining in inventory.
   • Determine which units remain in inventory.
   • Add the values of these units.

   Solution
   Units remaining in inventory:
   1 from beginning inventory, 2 from September 6 purchase, 3 from September 22
   purchase = 6 units
   5 units from September 22 purchase
   6 - 5 = 1 from September 15 purchase

   5(770) = 3850
   1(760) = 760
            ‾‾‾‾
            4610

   The value of the inventory was $4610.

8. Strategy
   To find the value of the inventory by the LIFO method:
   • Determine the number of units remaining in inventory.
   • Determine which units remain in inventory.
   • Add the values of these units.

   Solution
   Units remaining in inventory:
   1 from beginning inventory, 2 from September 6 purchase, 3 from September 22
   purchase = 6 units
   4 units from the beginning inventory
   6 - 4 = 2 from the September 6 purchase

   4(765) = 3060
   2(755) = 1510
            ‾‾‾‾
            4570

   The value of the inventory was $4570.

9. Strategy
   To find the rate of turnover at retail price:
   • Calculate the average inventory.
   • Divide the net sales by the average inventory.

   Solution
   Average inventory = (beginning inventory + ending inventory) ÷ 2
   $$= (115,000 + 94,000) \div 2 = 209,000 \div 2 = 104,500$$

   $$\text{Inventory turnover at retail price} = \frac{\text{net sales}}{\text{average inventory based on retail price}}$$
   $$= \frac{897,000}{104,500} \approx 8.6$$

   The inventory turnover at retail price is 8.6.

10. Strategy
    To find the rate of turnover at cost:
    • Calculate the average inventory.
    • Divide the cost of goods sold by the average inventory.

    Solution
    Average inventory = (beginning inventory + ending inventory) ÷ 2
                      = (58,200 + 53,900) ÷ 2 = 112,100 ÷ 2 = 56,050

    Inventory turnover at cost = $\frac{\text{cost of goods sold}}{\text{average inventory}} = \frac{643,000}{56,050} \approx 11.5$

    The rate of turnover at cost was 11.5.

CHAPTER 14
Depreciation

Section 14.1, pages 421–424

1. Strategy
   To find the total depreciation:
   • Subtract the salvage value from the total cost.
   To find the annual depreciation:
   • Divide the total depreciation by the useful life.

   Solution
   Total cost = 45,000 + 500 + 4000
              = 49,000
   Total depreciation = 49,500 − 6000
                      = 43,500
   Annual depreciation = 43,500 ÷ 8
                       ≈ 5438

   (a) The total depreciation is $43,500.
   (b) The annual depreciation is $5428.

2. Strategy
   To find the total depreciation:
   • Subtract the salvage value from the total cost.
   To find the annual depreciation:
   • Divide the total depreciation by the useful life.

   Solution
   Total cost = 13,500 + 950 + 2000
              = 16,450
   Total depreciation = 16,450 − 2500
                      = 13,950
   Annual depreciation = 13,950 ÷ 10
                       = 1395

   (a) The total depreciation is $13,950.
   (b) The annual depreciation is $1395.

3. Strategy
   To find the three-year accumulated depreciation:
   • Find the total depreciation by subtracting the salvage value from the cost.
   • Find the annual depreciation by dividing the total depreciation by the useful life.
   • Multiply the annual depreciation by 3.

   Solution
   Total depreciation = 32,000 − 8000
                      = 24,000
   Annual depreciation = 24,000 ÷ 5
                       = 4800
   Three-year accumulated depreciation
    = 4800 x 3 = 14,400

   The three-year accumulated depreciation is $14,400.

4. Strategy
   To find the four-year accumulated depreciation:
   • Find the annual depreciation by dividing the total depreciation by the useful life.
   • Multiply the annual depreciation by 4.

   Solution

   Annual depreciation $= \dfrac{18,000 - 2000}{6}$
   ≈ 2666.67
   Accumulated depreciation = 2667 x 4
                            = 10,666.68

   The four-year accumulated depreciation is $10,667.

5. Strategy
   To find the book value after six
   years:
   • Find the annual depreciation by
     dividing the total depreciation by
     the useful life.
   • Find the accumulated depreciation
     by multiplying the annual
     depreciation by 6.
   • Subtract the accumulated
     depreciation from the cost.

   Solution

   Total depreciation = $\frac{32,500 - 7500}{10}$

          = 2500

   Accumulated depreciation = 2500 x 6

           = 15,000

   Book value = 32,500 - 15,000 = 17,500

   The book value after six years is
   $17,500.

6. Strategy
   To find the book value after nine
   years:
   • Find the annual depreciation by
     dividing the total depreciation by
     the useful life.
   • Find the accumulated depreciation
     by multiplying the annual
     depreciation by 9.
   • Subtract the accumulated
     depreciation from the cost.

   Solution

   Total depreciation = $\frac{54,000 - 3000}{15}$

          = 3400

   Accumulated depreciation = 3400 x 9

           = 30,600

   Book value = 54,000 - 30,600 = 23,400

   The book value after nine years is
   $23,400.

7. Strategy
   To find the book value after two years:
   • Find the annual depreciation by dividing the total depreciation by the useful
     life.
   • Find the accumulated depreciation by multiplying the annual depreciation by 2.
   • Subtract the accumulated depreciation from the cost.

   Solution

   Total depreciation = $\frac{18,000 - 2000}{6} \approx 2667$

   Accumulated depreciation = 2667 x 2 = 5334
   Book value = 18,000 - 5334 = 12,666

   The book value after six years is $12,666.

8-20. Strategy
   To prepare the depreciation schedule:
   • Find the annual depreciation by dividing the total depreciation by the useful
     life.
   • Find the accumulated depreciation for each year.
   • Find the book value for each year by subtracting the accumulated depreciation
     for each year from the cost.

   Solution

8. Annual depreciation = $\frac{42,000 - 6000}{6}$ = $6000

9. Depreciation Year 1 = 6000 x 1 = $6000
10. Book value Year 1 = 42,000 - 6000 = $36,000

11. Depreciation Year 2 = 6000 x 2 = $12,000
12. Book value Year 2 = 42,000 - 12,000 = $30,000

13. Depreciation Year 3 = 6000 x 3 = $18,000
14. Book value Year 3 = 42,000 - 18,000 = $24,000

15. Depreciation Year 4 = 6000 x 4 = $24,000
16. Book value Year 4 = 42,000 - 24,000 = $18,000

17. Depreciation Year 5 = 6000 x 5 = \$30,000
18. Book value Year 5 = 42,000 - 30,000 = \$12,000

19. Depreciation Year 6 = 6000 x 6 = \$36,000
20. Book value Year 6 = 42,000 - 36,000 = \$6000

DEPRECIATION SCHEDULE

Year	Depreciation	Accumulated depreciation	Book value
1	6000	6,000	36,000
2	6000	12,000	30,000
3	6000	18,000	24,000
4	6000	24,000	18,000
5	6000	30,000	12,000
6	6000	36,000	6,000

21-31. Strategy
     To prepare the depreciation schedule:
     • Find the annual depreciation by dividing the total depreciation by the useful life.
     • Find the accumulated depreciation for each year.
     • Find the book value for each year by subtracting the accumulated depreciation for each year from the cost.

     Solution
21. Annual depreciation = $\frac{18,000 - 2000}{5}$ = \$3200

22. Depreciation Year 1 = 3200 x 1 = \$3200
23. Book value Year 1 = 18,000 - 3200 = \$14,800

24. Depreciation Year 2 = 3200 x 2 = \$6400
25. Book value Year 2 = 18,000 - 6400 = \$11,600

26. Depreciation Year 3 = 3200 x 3 = \$9600
27. Book value Year 3 = 18,000 - 9600 = \$8400

28. Depreciation Year 4 = 3200 x 4 = \$12,800
29. Book value Year 4 = 18,000 - 12,800 = \$5200

30. Depreciation Year 5 = 3200 x 5 = \$16,000
31. Book value Year 5 = 18,000 - 16,000 = \$2000

DEPRECIATION SCHEDULE

Year	Depreciation	Accumulated depreciation	Book value
1	3200	3,200	14,800
2	3200	6,400	11,600
3	3200	9,600	8,400
4	3200	12,800	5,200
5	3200	16,000	2,000

32-43. Strategy
  For each item:
  • Subtract the salvage value from the cost to find the total depreciation.
  • Divide the total depreciation by the useful life to find the depreciation per
   unit, per mile, or per hour.

  Solution

32. Total depreciation = 10,000 - 2000 = $8000

33. Depreciation per unit = $\frac{8000}{100,000}$ = $.08

34. Total depreciation = 60,000 - 5000 = $55,000

35. Depreciation per unit = $\frac{55,000}{900,000}$ ≈ $.061

36. Total depreciation = 45,000 - 3000 = $42,000

37. Depreciation per mile = $\frac{42,000}{100,000}$ = $.42

38. Total depreciation = 18,000 - 3000 = $15,000

39. Depreciation per mile = $\frac{15,000}{60,000}$ = $.25

40. Total depreciation = 90,000 - 10,000 = $80,000

41. Depreciation per hour = $\frac{80,000}{30,000}$ ≈ $2.67

42. Total depreciation = 35,000 - 5000 = $30,000

43. Depreciation per hour = $\frac{30,000}{24,000}$ = $1.25

44. Strategy
 (a) To find the depreciation per unit:
  • Divide the total depreciation by
   the number of units.
 (b) To find the accumulated depreciation after 800,000 units:
  • Multiply the depreciation per
   unit by 800,000.

 Solution
 (a) Depreciation per unit
  = $\frac{40,000 - 5000}{2,000,000}$ = 0.0175
 (b) Accumulated depreciation
  = 800,000 x 0.0175 = 14,000

 (a) Depreciation per unit is $.0175.
 (b) The accumulated depreciation after
  800,000 units is $14,000.

45. Strategy
 (a) To find the depreciation per hour
  of production:
  • Divide the total depreciation by
   the number of hours.
 (b) To find the accumulated
  depreciation after 6000 hours of
  operation:
  • Multiply the depreciation per
   hour by 6000.

 Solution
 (a) Depreciation per hour
  = $\frac{36,000 - 3000}{15,000}$ = 2.20
 (b) Accumulated depreciation
  = 6000 x 2.20 = 13,200

 (a) Depreciation per hour is $2.20.
 (b) The accumulated depreciation after
  6000 hours is $13,200.

46. Strategy
    (a) To find the depreciation per hour
        of production:
        • Divide the total depreciation by
          the number of hours.
    (b) To find the book value after
        15,000 hours of operation:
        • Find the total depreciation by
          multiplying the depreciation per
          hour by 15,000.
        • Find the book value by subtract-
          ing the total depreciation from
          the cost.

    Solution
    (a) Depreciation per hour
        $= \frac{45,000 - 5000}{25,000} = 1.60$
    (b) Total depreciation = 15,000 x 1.60
                           = 24,000
        Book value = 45,000 - 24,000
                   = 21,000

    (a) The depreciation per hour is
        $1.60.
    (b) The book value after 15,000 hours
        is $21,000.

47. Strategy
    (a) To find the depreciation per unit:
        • Divide the total depreciation by
          the number of units.
    (b) To find the book value after
        500,000 units of production:
        • Find the total depreciation by
          multiplying the depreciation per
          unit by 500,000.
        • Find the book value by subtract-
          ing the total depreciation from
          the cost.

    Solution
    (a) Depreciation per unit
        $= \frac{24,000 - 4000}{800,000} = 0.025$
    (b) Total depreciation
        = 500,000 x 0.025 = 12,500
        Book value = 24,000 - 12,500
                   = 11,500

    (a) The depreciation per unit is
        $.025.
    (b) The book value after 500,000 units
        of production is $11,500.

48. Strategy
    (a) To find the depreciation per mile:
        • Divide the total depreciation by the number of miles.
    (b) To find the first year's depreciation:
        • Multiply the depreciation per mile by the number of miles driven.

    Solution
    (a) Depreciation per mile = $\frac{14,200 - 1500}{100,000} = 0.127$
    (b) First year's depreciation = 0.127 x 22,000 = 2794

    (a) The depreciation per mile is $.127.
    (b) The first year's depreciation is $2794.

49. Strategy
    (a) To find the first year's depreciation:
        • Find the depreciation per unit by dividing the total depreciation by 120,000
          units.
        • Find the first year's depreciation by multiplying 20,000 units by the
          depreciation per unit.
    (b) To find the second year's depreciation, multiply 28,000 units by the
        depreciation per unit.

    Solution
    (a) Depreciation per unit = $\frac{35,000 - 5000}{120,000} = 0.25$
        First year's depreciation = 20,000 x 0.25 = 5000
    (b) Second year's depreciation = 28,000 x 0.25 = 7000

    (a) The first year's depreciation is $5000.
    (b) The second year's depreciation is $7000.

50-61. Strategy

To prepare the depreciation schedule:
- Find the depreciation per unit by dividing the total depreciation by the number of units.
- Find the annual depreciation by multiplying the depreciation per unit times the number of units produced for that year.
- Find the accumulated depreciation for each year by adding the annual depreciation to the previous year's accumulated depreciation.
- Find the book value for each year by subtracting the accumulated depreciation for each year from the cost.

Solution

$$\text{Annual depreciation} = \frac{55,000 - 5000}{80,000} = 0.625$$

50. Depreciation Year 1 = 12,000 x 0.625 = $7500
51. First year's accumulated depreciation = $7500
52. Book value Year 1 = 55,000 - 7500 = $47,500

53. Depreciation Year 2 = 20,000 x 0.0625 = $12,500
54. Two years' accumulated depreciation = 7500 + 12,500 = $20,000
55. Book value Year 2 = 55,000 - 20,000 = $35,000

56. Depreciation Year 3 = 25,000 x 0.0625 = $15,625
57. Three years' accumulated depreciation = 20,000 + 15,625 = $35,625
58. Book value Year 3 = 55,000 - 35,625 = $19,375

59. Depreciation Year 4 = 23,000 x 0.0625 = $14,375
60. Four years' accumulated depreciation = 35,625 + 14,375 = $50,000
61. Book value Year 4 = 55,000 - 50,000 = $5000

DEPRECIATION SCHEDULE

Year	Units	Annual depreciation	Accumulated depreciation	Book value
1	12,000	7,500	7,500	47,500
2	20,000	12,500	20,000	35,000
3	25,000	15,625	35,625	19,375
4	23,000	14,375	50,000	5,000

62-70. Strategy
To prepare the depreciation schedule:
• Find the depreciation per mile by dividing the total depreciation by the useful life in miles.
• Find the annual depreciation by multiplying the depreciation per unit times the miles driven that year.
• Find the accumulated depreciation for each year by adding the annual depreciation to the previous year's accumulated depreciation.
• Find the book value for each year by subtracting the accumulated depreciation for each year from the cost.

Solution

Depreciation per mile = $\dfrac{28,000 - 4000}{120,000}$ = 0.20

62. Depreciation Year 1 = 42,000 x 0.20 = $8400
63. First year's accumulated depreciation = $8400
64. Book value Year 1 = 28,000 - 8400 = $19,600

65. Depreciation Year 2 = 51,000 x 0.20 = $10,200
66. Second year's accumulated depreciation = 8400 + 10,200 = $18,600
67. Book value Year 2 = 28,000 - 18,600 = $9400

68. Depreciation Year 3 = 27,000 x 0.20 = $5400
69. Third year's accumulated depreciation = 18,600 + 5400 = $24,000
70. Book value Year 3 = 28,000 - 24,000 = $4000

DEPRECIATION SCHEDULE

Year	Miles	Annual depreciation	Accumulated depreciation	Book value
1	42,000	8,400	8,400	19,600
2	51,000	10,200	18,600	9,400
3	27,000	5,400	24,000	4,000

Section 14.2, pages 427–428

1. Strategy
To find the double-declining rate of depreciation:
• Find the straight-line rate of depreciation over eight years.
• Multiply the straight-line rate of depreciation by 2.

Solution
Straight-line rate of depreciation over eight years is 1/8 or 12.5%.
Double-declining rate of depreciation = 2 x 12.5% = 25%

The double-declining rate of depreciation is 25%.

2. Strategy
To find the double-declining rate of depreciation:
• Find the straight-line rate of depreciation over five years.
• Multiply the straight-line rate of depreciation by 2.

Solution
Straight-line rate of depreciation over eight years is 1/5 or 20%.
Double-declining rate of depreciation = 2 x 20% = 40%

The double-declining rate of depreciation is 40%.

3. Strategy
    (a) To find the first year's
        depreciation:
        • Find the double-declining rate
          of depreciation.
        • Multiply the cost by the
          double-declining rate of
          depreciation.
    (b) To find the book value at the end
        of the first year:
        • Subtract the first year's
          depreciation from the cost.

    Solution
    (a) Straight-line depreciation over
        six years is 1/6.
        Double-declining rate of
        depreciation = 2 x 1/6 = 1/3.
        First year's depreciation
        = 1/3 x 32,000 ≈ 10,667
    (b) Book value = 32,000 - 10,667
                   = 21,333

    (a) The first year's depreciation is
        $10,667.
    (b) The book value at the end of the
        first year is $21,333.

4. Strategy
    (a) To find the first year's
        depreciation:
        • Find the double-declining rate
          of depreciation.
        • Multiply the cost by the
          double-declining rate of
          depreciation.
    (b) To find the book value at the end
        of the first year:
        • Subtract the first year's
          depreciation from the cost.

    Solution
    (a) Straight-line depreciation over
        fifteen years is 1/15.
        Double-declining rate of
        depreciation = 2 x 1/15 = 2/15.
        First year's depreciation
        = 2/15 x 35,000 ≈ 4667
    (b) Book value = 35,000 - 4667
                   = 30,333

    (a) The first year's depreciation is
        $4667.
    (b) The book value at the end of the
        first year is $30,333.

5. Strategy
    To find the book value at the end of
    two years:
    • Find the double-declining rate of
      depreciation.
    • Find the annual depreciation for
      each year.
    • Find the book value at the end of
      each year.

    Solution
    Double-declining rate of depreciation
    = 2 x 1/8 = 1/4 = 25%
    Depreciation Year 1 = 0.25 x 80,000
                        = 20,000
    Book value Year 1 = 80,000 - 20,000
                      = 60,000
    Depreciation Year 2 = 0.25 x 60,000
                        = 15,000
    Book value Year 2 = 60,000 - 15,000
                      = 45,000

    The book value at the end of two years
    is $45,000.

6. Strategy
    To find the book value at the end of
    two years:
    • Find the double-declining rate of
      depreciation.
    • Find the annual depreciation for
      each year.
    • Find the book value at the end of
      each year.

    Solution
    Double-declining rate of depreciation
    = 2 x 1/15 = 2/15
    Depreciation Year 1 = 2/15 x 240,000
                        = 32,000
    Book value Year 1 = 240,000 - 32,000
                      = 208,000
    Depreciation Year 2 = 2/15 x 208,000
                        = 27,733
    Book value Year 2 = 208,000 - 27,733
                      = 180,267

    The book value at the end of two years
    is $180,267.

7. Strategy
    To find the book value at the end of two years:
    • Find the double-declining rate of depreciation.
    • Find the annual depreciation for each year.
    • Find the book value at the end of each year.

    Solution
    Double-declining rate of depreciation = 2 x 1/10 = 1/5 = 20%
    Depreciation Year 1 = 0.20 x 90,000 = 18,000
    Book value Year 1 = 90,000 - 18,000 = 72,000
    Depreciation Year 2 = 0.20 x 72,000 = 14,400
    Book value Year 2 = 72,000 - 14,400 = 57,600

    The book value at the end of two years is $57,600.

8. Strategy
    To find the book value at the end of two years:
    • Find the double-declining rate of depreciation.
    • Find the annual depreciation for each year.
    • Find the book value at the end of each year.

    Solution
    Double-declining rate of depreciation = 2 x 1/8 = 1/4 = 25%
    Depreciation Year 1 = 0.25 x 62,000 = 15,500
    Book value Year 1 = 62,000 - 15,500 = 46,500
    Depreciation Year 2 = 0.25 x 46,500 = 11,625
    Book value Year 2 = 46,500 - 11,625 = 34,875

    The book value at the end of two years is $34,875.

9-21. Strategy
    To prepare the depreciation schedule:
    • Find the rate of depreciation.
    • Find the annual depreciation and the book value for Years 1, 2, 3, and 4, or
      until the annual depreciation exceeds the salvage value.
    • Find the accumulated depreciation for each year by adding the annual depreciation
      to the previous year's accumulated depreciation.

    Solution

9. Double-declining balance rate = 2 x 1/4 = 1/2 = 50%

10. Depreciation Year 1 = 0.50 x 12,500 = $6250
11. Accumulated depreciation Year 1 = $6250
12. Book value Year 1 = 12,500 - 6250 = $6250

13. Depreciation Year 2 = 0.50 x 6250 = $3125
14. Accumulated depreciation Year 2 = 3125 + 6250 = $9375
15. Book value Year 2 = 6250 - 3125 = $3125

16. Depreciation Year 3 = 0.50 x 3125 ≈ $1563
17. Accumulated depreciation Year 3 = 1563 + 9375 ≈ $10,938
18. Book value Year 3 = 3125 - 1563 = $1562

Depreciation Year 4 = 0.50 x 1562 ≈ $781
This would exceed the salvage value.
19. Depreciation Year 4 = 1562 - 1500 = $62
20. Accumulated depreciation = 62 + 10,938 = $11,000
21. Book value Year 4 = 1562 - 62 = $1500

DEPRECIATION SCHEDULE

Year	Depreciation rate	Depreciation	Accumulated depreciation	Book value
1	50%	6250	6,250	6250
2	50%	3125	9,375	3125
3	50%	1563	10,938	1562
4	50%	62	11,000	1500

22-37. Strategy
To prepare the depreciation schedule:
- Find the rate of depreciation.
- Find the annual depreciation and the book value for Years 1, 2, 3, 4, and 5, or until the annual depreciation exceeds the salvage value.
- Find the accumulated depreciation for each year by adding the annual depreciation to the previous year's accumulated depreciation.

Solution

22. Double-declining balance rate = 2 x 1/5 = 40%

23. Depreciation Year 1 = 0.40 x 80,000 = $32,000
24. Accumulated depreciation Year 1 = $32,000
25. Book value Year 1 = 80,000 - 32,000 = $48,000

26. Depreciation Year 2 = 0.40 x 48,000 = $19,200
27. Accumulated depreciation Year 2 = 19,200 + 32,000 = $51,200
28. Book value Year 2 = 48,000 - 19,200 = $28,800

29. Depreciation Year 3 = 0.40 x 28,800 = $11,520
30. Accumulated depreciation Year 3 - 11,520 + 51,200 = $62,720
31. Book value Year 3 = 28,800 - 11,520 = $17,280

32. Depreciation Year 4 = 0.40 x 17,280 = $6912
33. Accumulated depreciation = 6912 + 62,720 = $69,632
34. Book value Year 4 = 17,280 - 6912 = $10,368

Depreciation Year 5 = 0.40 x 10,368 = $4147.20
This would exceed the salvage value.
35. Depreciation Year 5 = 10,368 - 8000 = $2368
36. Accumulated depreciation = 2368 + 69,632 = $72,000
37. Book value Year 5 = 10,368 - 2368 = $8,000

DEPRECIATION SCHEDULE

Year	Depreciation rate	Depreciation	Accumulated depreciation	Book value
1	40%	32,000	32,000	48,000
2	40%	19,200	51,200	28,800
3	40%	11,520	62,720	17,280
4	40%	6,912	69,632	10,368
5	40%	2,368	72,000	8,000

Section 14.3, pages 431–432

1. Strategy
   (a) Find the sum of the digits by substituting 8 in the formula $\frac{n(n+1)}{2}$.
   (b) Find the fraction of the first year's depreciation by forming the ratio of the years of depreciation remaining (8) to the sum of the digits.

   Solution
   Sum of the digits = $\frac{8(8+1)}{2}$ = 36
   Fraction of first year's depreciation is 8/36.

   (a) The sum of the digits is 36.
   (b) The fraction of the first year's depreciation is 8/36.

2. Strategy
   (a) Find the sum of the digits by substituting 3 in the formula $\frac{n(n+1)}{2}$.
   (b) Find the fraction of the first year's depreciation by forming the ratio of the years of depreciation remaining (3) to the sum of the digits.

   Solution
   Sum of the digits = $\frac{3(3+1)}{2}$ = 6
   Fraction of first year's depreciation is 3/6.

   (a) The sum of the digits is 6.
   (b) The fraction of the first year's depreciation is 3/6.

3. Strategy
   To find the book value at the end of two years:
   • Find the sum of the digits (n = 5).
   • Add the first two ratios to find the ratio for two years of accumulated depreciation.
   • Multiply the ratio for the accumulated depreciation by the total depreciation.
   • Subtract the accumulated depreciation from the total cost.

   Solution
   Sum of the digits = $\frac{5(5+1)}{2}$ = 15

   5/15 of the depreciation is taken the first year.
   4/15 of the depreciation is taken the second year.
   Ratio of two year's accumulated depreciation = 4/15 + 5/15 = 9/15
   Accumulated depreciation (two years) = (9/15)(20,000 − 4000) = 9600
   Book value = 20,000 − 9600 = 10,400

   The book value at the end of two years is $10,400.

4. Strategy
   To find the book value at the end of four years:
   • Find the sum of the digits (n = 10).
   • Add the first four ratios to find the ratio for four years of accumulated depreciation.
   • Multiply the ratio for the accumulated depreciation by the total depreciation.
   • Subtract the accumulated depreciation from the total cost.

   Solution

   Sum of the digits = $\frac{10(10 + 1)}{2}$ = 55

   10/55 of the depreciation is taken the first year.
   9/55 of the depreciation is taken the second year.
   8/55 of the depreciation is taken the third year.
   7/55 of the depreciation is taken the fourth year.
   Ratio of four year's accumulated depreciation = 10/55 + 9/55 + 8/55 + 7/55 = 34/55
   Accumulated depreciation (four years) = (34/55)(12,000 - 2000) ≈ 6182
   Book value = 12,000 - 6182 = 5818

   The book value at the end of four years is $5818.

5. Strategy
   To find the accumulated depreciation:
   • Find the sum of the digits (n = 8).
   • Add the first five ratios to find the ratio for five years of accumulated depreciation.
   • Multiply the ratio for the accumulated depreciation by the total depreciation.

   Solution

   Sum of the digits = $\frac{8(8 + 1)}{2}$ = 36

   8/36 of the depreciation is taken the first year.
   7/36 of the depreciation is taken the second year.
   6/36 of the depreciation is taken the third year.
   5/36 of the depreciation is taken the fourth year.
   4/36 of the depreciation is taken the fifth year.
   Sum of the first five ratios = 8/36 + 7/36 + 6/36 + 5/36 + 4/36 = 30/36
   Accumulated depreciation = (30/36)(5000 - 500) = 3750

   The accumulated depreciation after five years is $3750.

6. Strategy
   To find the accumulated depreciation:
   • Find the sum of the digits (n = 6).
   • Add the first three ratios to find the ratio for three years of accumulated depreciation.
   • Multiply the ratio for the accumulated depreciation by the total depreciation.

   Solution

   Sum of the digits = $\frac{6(6 + 1)}{2}$ = 21

   6/21 of the depreciation is taken the first year.
   5/21 of the depreciation is taken the second year.
   4/21 of the depreciation is taken the third year.
   Sum of the first five ratios = 6/21 + 5/21 + 4/21 = 15/21
   Accumulated depreciation Year 3 = (15/21)(9000 - 900) ≈ 5786

   The accumulated depreciation is $5786.

7. Strategy
    To find the book value at the end of three years:
    • Find the sum of the digits (n = 5).
    • Add the first three ratios to find the ratio for three years of accumulated depreciation.
    • Multiply the ratio for the accumulated depreciation by the total depreciation.
    • Subtract the accumulated depreciation from the total cost.

    Solution
    Sum of the digits $= \dfrac{5(5 + 1)}{2} = 15$

    5/15 of the depreciation is taken the first year.
    4/15 of the depreciation is taken the second year.
    3/15 of the depreciation is taken the third year.
    Sum of the first five ratios = 5/15 + 4/15 + 3/15 = 12/15
    Accumulated depreciation Year 3 = (12/15)(32,000 - 5000) = 21,600
    Book value Year 3 = 32,000 - 21,600 = 10,400

    The book value after three years is $10,400.

8. Strategy
    To find the book value at the end of four years:
    • Find the sum of the digits (n = 6).
    • Add the first four ratios to find the ratio for four years of accumulated depreciation.
    • Multiply the ratio for the accumulated depreciation by the total depreciation.
    • Subtract the accumulated depreciation from the total cost.

    Solution
    Sum of the digits $= \dfrac{6(6 + 1)}{2} = 21$

    6/21 of the depreciation is taken the first year.
    5/21 of the depreciation is taken the second year.
    4/21 of the depreciation is taken the third year.
    3/21 of the depreciation is taken the fourth year.
    Sum of the first five ratios = 6/21 + 5/21 + 4/21 + 3/21 = 18/21
    Accumulated depreciation Year 4 = (18/21)(11,000 - 2500) ≈ 7286
    Book value Year 4 = 11,000 - 7286 = 3714

    The book value after three years is $3714.

9. Strategy
    To find the book value at the end of five years:
    • Find the sum of the digits (n = 15).
    • Add the first five ratios to find the ratio for five years of accumulated depreciation.
    • Multiply the ratio for the accumulated depreciation by the total depreciation.
    • Subtract the accumulated depreciation from the total cost.

    Solution
    Sum of the digits $= \dfrac{15(15 + 1)}{2} = 120$

    15/120 of the depreciation is taken the first year.
    14/120 of the depreciation is taken the second year.
    13/120 of the depreciation is taken the third year.
    12/120 of the depreciation is taken the fourth year.
    11/120 of the depreciation is taken the fifth year.
    Sum of the first five ratios = 15/120 + 14/120 + 13/120 + 12/120 + 11/120 = 65/120
    Accumulated depreciation Year 5 = (65/120)(150,000 - 10,000) ≈ 75,833
    Book value Year 5 = 150,000 - 75,833 = 74,167

    The book value after three years is $74,167.

10. Strategy

To find the book value at the end of six years:
- Find the sum of the digits (n = 15).
- Add the first six ratios to find the ratio for six years of accumulated depreciation.
- Multiply the ratio for the accumulated depreciation by the total depreciation.
- Subtract the accumulated depreciation from the total cost.

Solution

Sum of the digits $= \frac{15(15 + 1)}{2} = 120$

15/120 of the depreciation is taken the first year.
14/120 of the depreciation is taken the second year.
13/120 of the depreciation is taken the third year.
12/120 of the depreciation is taken the fourth year.
11/120 of the depreciation is taken the fifth year.
10/120 of the depreciation is taken the sixth year.
Sum of the first five ratios = 15/120 + 14/120 + 13/120 + 12/120 + 11/120 + 10/120
$\qquad\qquad\qquad\qquad = 75/120$
Accumulated depreciation Year 6 = (75/120)(220,000 − 20,000) = 125,000
Book value Year 5 = 220,000 − 125,000 = 95,000

The book value after three years is $95,000.

11-30. Strategy

To prepare the depreciation schedule:
- Find the sum of the digits (n = 5).
- Find the depreciation ratio for each year.
- Find the yearly depreciation by multiplying the yearly depreciation ratio by the total depreciation.
- Find the accumulated depreciation by adding the yearly depreciation to the accumulated depreciation of the previous years.
- Find the book value by subtracting the accumulated depreciation for the total cost.

Solution

Sum of the digits $= \frac{5(5 + 1)}{2} = 15$

Total depreciation = 120,000 − 8000 = 112,000

11. Depreciation ratio Year 1 = 5/15
12. Depreciation Year 1 = (5/15)(112,000) ≈ $37,333
13. Accumulated depreciation Year 1 = $37,333
14. Book value Year 1 = 120,000 − 37,333 = $82,667

15. Depreciation ratio Year 2 = 4/15
16. Depreciation Year 2 = (4/15)(112,000) ≈ $29,867
17. Accumulated depreciation Year 2 = 37,333 + 29,867 = $67,200
18. Book value Year 2 = 120,000 − 67,200 = $52,800

19. Depreciation ratio Year 3 = 3/15
20. Depreciation Year 3 = (3/15)(112,000) = $22,400
21. Accumulated depreciation Year 3 = 67,200 + 22,400 = $89,600
22. Book value Year 3 = 120,000 − 89,600 = $30,400

23. Depreciation ratio Year 4 = 2/15
24. Depreciation Year 4 = (2/15)(112,000) ≈ $14,933
25. Accumulated depreciation Year 4 = 89,600 + 14,933 = $104,533
26. Book value Year 4 = 120,000 − 104,533 = $15,467

27. Depreciation ratio Year 5 = 1/15
28. Depreciation Year 5 = (1/15)(112,000) ≈ $7467
29. Accumulated depreciation Year 5 = 104,533 + 7467 = $112,000
30. Book value Year 5 = 120,000 - 112,000 = $8000

DEPRECIATION SCHEDULE

Year	Ratio	Yearly depreciation	Accumulated depreciation	Book value
1	5/15	37,333	37,333	82,667
2	4/15	29,867	67,200	52,800
3	3/15	22,400	89,600	30,400
4	2/15	14,933	104,533	15,467
5	1/15	7,467	112,000	8,000

Section 14.4, pages 437–440

1-18. Strategy
   • Find the depreciation period by using the chart on page 433.
   • Find the first year's depreciation by using the depreciation schedule on page 433.
   • Find the first year's depreciation by multiplying the first year's depreciation times the cost.

   Solution

1. Depreciation period for a bus is 10 years.
2. First year's depreciation for a bus is 8%.
3. First year's depreciation = 0.08 x 55,000 = $4400

4. Depreciation for a heavy truck is 5 years.
5. First year's depreciation for a heavy truck is 15%.
6. First year's depreciation = 0.15 x 80,000 = $12,000

7. Depreciation period for a hand drill is 3 years.
8. First year's depreciation for a hand drill is 25%.
9. First year's depreciation = 0.25 x 145 = $36.25

10. Depreciation period for a car is 3 years.
11. First year's depreciation for a car is 25%.
12. First year's depreciation = 0.25 x 12,400 = $3100

13. Depreciation period for a mobile home is 10 years.
14. First year's depreciation for a mobile home is 8%.
15. First year's depreciation = 0.08 x 35,000 = $2800

16. Depreciation period for a copy machine is 5 years.
17. First year's depreciation for a copy machine is 15%.
18. First year's depreciation = 0.15 x 2700 = $405

19. Strategy
    To find the third year's depreciation:
    • Use the tables on page 433 to find the depreciation period and the applicable percent.
    • Multiply the cost by the percent.

    Solution
    Depreciation period for office equipment: 5 years
    Applicable percent for the third year: 21%
    Depreciation Year 3 = 0.21(9500)
    $\qquad\qquad\qquad$ = 1995

    The third-year depreciation is $1995.

20. Strategy
    To find the sixth year's depreciation:
    • Use the tables on page 433 to find the depreciation period and the applicable percent.
    • Multiply the cost by the percent.

    Solution
    Depreciation period for office furniture: 10 years
    Applicable percent for the sixth year: 10%
    Depreciation Year 6 = 0.10(16,000)
    $\qquad\qquad\qquad$ = 1600

    The third-year depreciation is $1600.

21. Strategy
    To find the accumulated depreciation after four years:
    • Add the allowable percents for the Years 1, 2, 3, and 4.
    • Multiply the sum by the cost.

    Solution
    12 + 10 + 9 + 8 = 39
    Accumulated depreciation
    $\quad$ = 0.39 x 145,000 = 56,550

    The accumulated depreciation after four years is $56,550.

22. Strategy
    To find the accumulated depreciation after three years:
    • Add the allowable percents for the Years 1, 2, and 3.
    • Multiply the sum by the cost.

    Solution
    15 + 22 + 21 = 58
    Accumulated depreciation
    $\quad$ = 0.58 x 86,000 = 49,880

    The accumulated depreciation after three years is $49,880.

23. Strategy
    To find the book value after three years:
    • Use the table on page 433 to find the depreciation period for office equipment.
    • Add the allowable percents for Years 1, 2, and 3.
    • Find the accumulated depreciation by multiplying the sum of the percents by the cost.
    • Subtract the accumulated depreciation from the cost.

    Solution
    The depreciation period for office equipment is 5 years.
    Sum of allowable percents = 15% + 22% + 21% = 58%
    Accumulated depreciation Year 3 = 0.58 x 6500 = 3770
    Book value Year 3 = 6500 - 3770 = 2730

    The book value after three years is $2730.

24. Strategy
    To find the book value after five years:
    • Use the table on page 433 to find the depreciation period for office furniture.
    • Add the allowable percents for Years 1, 2, 3, 4, and 5.
    • Find the accumulated depreciation by multiplying the sum of the percents by the cost.
    • Subtract the accumulated depreciation from the cost.

    Solution
    The depreciation period for office furniture is 10 years.
    Sum of allowable percents = 8% + 14% + 12% + 10% + 10% = 54%
    Accumulated depreciation Year 5 = 0.54 x 12,500 = 6750
    Book value Year 5 = 12,500 - 6750 = 5750

    The book value after five years is $5750.

25. Strategy
    To find the book value after six years:
    • Use the table on page 433 to find the depreciation period for a bus.
    • Add the allowable percents for Years 1, 2, 3, 4, 5, and 6.
    • Find the accumulated depreciation by multiplying the sum of the percents by the
      cost.
    • Subtract the accumulated depreciation from the cost.

    Solution
    The depreciation period for a bus is 10 years.
    Sum of allowable percents = 8% + 14% + 12% + 10% + 10% + 10% = 64%
    Accumulated depreciation Year 6 = 0.64 x 52,000 = 33,280
    Book value Year 6 = 52,000 - 33,280 = 18,720

    The book value after six years is $18,720.

26. Strategy
    To find the book value after four years:
    • Use the table on page 433 to find the depreciation period for bottling equipment.
    • Add the allowable percents for Years 1, 2, 3, and 4.
    • Find the accumulated depreciation by multiplying the sum of the percents by the
      cost.
    • Subtract the accumulated depreciation from the cost.

    Solution
    The depreciation period for bottling equipment is 5 years.
    Sum of allowable percents = 15% + 22% + 21% + 21% = 79%
    Accumulated depreciation Year 4 = 0.79 x 17,500 = 13,825
    Book value Year 4 = 17,500 - 13,825 = 3675

    The book value after four years is $3675.

27-46. Strategy
    To complete the depreciation schedule:
    • Use the table on page 433 to find the depreciation period for a computer.
    • Find the annual depreciation by multiplying the allowable percent times the
      cost.
    • Find the accumulated depreciation for each year by adding the annual
      depreciation to the previous year's accumulated depreciation.
    • Find the book value for each year by subtracting the accumulated depreciation
      for each year from the cost.

    Solution
    The depreciation for a computer is five years.

27. Allowable percent Year 1 = 15%
28. Depreciation Year 1 = 0.15 x 42,000 = $6300
29. Accumulated depreciation Year 1 = $6300
30. Book value Year 1 = 42,000 - 6300 = $35,700

31. Allowable percent Year 2 = 22%
32. Depreciation Year 2 = 0.22 x 42,000 = $9240
33. Accumulated depreciation Year 2 = 9240 + 6300 = $15,540
34. Book value Year 2 = 42,000 - 15,540 = $26,460

35. Allowable percent Year 3 = 21%
36. Depreciation Year 3 = 0.21 x 42,000 = $8820
37. Accumulated depreciation Year 3 = 8820 + 15,540 = $24,360
38. Book value Year 3 = 42,000 - 24,360 = $17,640

39. Allowable percent Year 4 = 21%
40. Depreciation Year 4 = 0.21 x 42,000 = $8820
41. Accumulated depreciation Year 4 = 8820 + 24,360 = $33,180
42. Book value Year 4 = 42,000 - 33,180 = $8820

43. Allowable percent Year 5 = 21%
44. Depreciation Year 5 = 0.21 x 42,000 = $8820
45. Accumulated depreciation Year 5 = 8820 + 33,180 = $42,000
46. Book value Year 5 = 42,000 - 42,000 = $0

DEPRECIATION SCHEDULE

Year	Percent depreciation	Yearly depreciation	Accumulated depreciation	Book value
1	15%	6300	6,300	35,700
2	22%	9240	15,540	26,460
3	21%	8820	24,360	17,640
4	21%	8820	33,180	8,820
5	21%	8820	42,000	0

47. Depreciation period = 5 years
48. First year's depreciation rate = 20.00%
49. First year's depreciation = cost x applicable percent = 84,000(0.20) = $16,800

50. Depreciation period = 5 years
51. First year's depreciation rate = 20.00%
52. First year's depreciation = cost x applicable percent = 120,000(0.20) = $24,000

53. Depreciation period = 7 years
54. First year's depreciation rate = 14.29%
55. First year's depreciation = cost x applicable percent = 38,000(0.1429) = $5430

56. Depreciation period = 5 years
57. First year's depreciation rate = 20.00%
58. First year's depreciation = cost x applicable percent = 1500(0.20) = $300

59. Strategy
To find the sixth year's depreciation, multiply the cost by the applicable percent (7.37%).

Solution
35,000(0.0737) ≈ 2580

The sixth year's depreciation is $2580.

60. Strategy
To find the fourth year's depreciation, multiply the cost by the applicable percent (11.52%).

Solution
15,400(0.1152) ≈ 1774

The fourth year's depreciation is $1774.

61. Strategy
To find the accumulated depreciation after three years.
• Add the applicable percents for Years 1, 2, and 3.
• Multiply the sum by the cost.

Solution
0.2000 + 0.3200 + 0.1920 = 0.7120
7500(0.7120) = 5340

The accumulated depreciation after three years is $5340.

62. Strategy
To find the accumulated depreciation after five years.
• Add the applicable percents for Years 1, 2, 3, 4, and 5.
• Multiply the sum by the cost.

Solution
0.1429 + 0.2450 + 0.1749 + 0.1250 + 0.0892 = 0.7770
9450(0.7770) ≈ 7343

The accumulated depreciation after five years is $7343.

63. Strategy
    To find the accumulated depreciation
    after four years:
    • Add the applicable percents for
      Years 1, 2, 3, and 4.
    • Multiply the sum by the cost.

    Solution
    0.2000 + 0.3200 + 0.1920 + 0.1152
     = 0.8272
    35,000(0.8272) = 28,952

    The accumulated depreciation after
    four years is $28,ᵒ52.

64. Strategy
    To find the book value after two
    years:
    • Add the applicable percents for
      Years 1 and 2.
    • Multiply the sum by the cost to
      find the accumulated depreciation.
    • Subtract the accumulated
      depreciation from the cost.

    Solution
    0.3333 + 0.4445 = 0.7778

    Accumulated depreciation
     = 19,500(0.7778) ≈ 15,167

    Book value
     = cost - accumulated depreciation
     = 19,500 - 15,167 = 4333

    The book value after two years is
    $4333.

65. Strategy
    To find the book value after seven
    years:
    • Add the applicable percents for the
      first seven years.
    • Multiply the sum by the cost to
      find the accumulated depreciation.
    • Subtract the accumulated
      depreciation from the cost.

    Solution
    0.1000 + 0.1800 + 0.1440 + 0.1152
     + 0.0922 + 0.0737 + 0.0655 = 0.7706

    Accumulated depreciation
     = 37,600(0.7706) ≈ 28,975

    Book value
     = cost - accumulated depreciation
     = 37,600 - 28,975 = 8625

    The book value after seven years is
    $8625.

66. Strategy
    To find the book value after three
    years:
    • Add the applicable percents for
      Years 1, 2, and 3.
    • Multiply the sum by the cost to
      find the accumulated depreciation.
    • Subtract the accumulated
      depreciation from the cost.

    Solution
    0.2000 + 0.3200 + 0.1920 = 0.7120

    Accumulated depreciation
     = 315,000(0.7120) = 224,280

    Book value
     = cost - accumulated depreciation
     = 315,000 - 224,280 = 90,720

    The book value after three years is
    $90,720.

67. Strategy
    To find the book value after five years:
    • Add the applicable percents for the first five years.
    • Multiply the sum by the cost to find the accumulated depreciation.
    • Subtract the accumulated depreciation from the cost.

    Solution
    0.1000 + 0.1800 + 0.1440 + 0.1152
         + 0.0922 = 0.6314

    Accumulated depreciation
     = 62,000(0.6314) ≈ 39,147

    Book value
     = cost - accumulated depreciation
     = 62,000 - 39,147 = 22,853

    The book value after five years is $22,853.

68. Percent depreciation = 33.33%

69. Annual depreciation
    = 9000(0.3333) = $3000

70. Accumulated depreciation = $3000

71. Book value
    = cost - accumulated depreciation
    = 9000 - 3000 = $6000

72. Percent depreciation = 44.45%

73. Annual depreciation
    = 9000(0.4445) ≈ $4000

74. Accumulated depreciation
    = 3000 + 4000 = $7000

75. Book value
    = cost - accumulated depreciation
    = 9000 - 7000 = $2000

76. Percent depreciation = 14.81%

77. Annual depreciation
    = 9000(0.1481) ≈ $1333

78. Accumulated depreciation
    = 7000 + 1333 = $8333

79. Book value
    = cost - accumulated depreciation
    = 9000 - 8333 = $667

80. Percent depreciation = 7.41%

81. Annual depreciation
    = 9000(0.0741) ≈ $667

82. Accumulated depreciation
    = 8333 + 667 = $9000

83. Book value
    = cost - accumulated depreciation
    = 9000 - 9000 = $0

Business Case Study

1. Straight-line method of depreciation

Year	Rate of Depreciation	Annual Depreciation	Accumulated Depreciation	Book Value
Beginning of Year 1	--	--	--	$12,500
End of Year 1	20%	$2000	$ 2,000	$10,500
End of Year 2	20%	$2000	$ 4,000	$ 8,500
End of Year 3	20%	$2000	$ 6,000	$ 6,500
End of Year 4	20%	$2000	$ 8,000	$ 4,500
End of Year 5	20%	$2000	$10,000	$ 2,500
				(salvage value)

Double-declining balance method of depreciation:

Year	Rate of Depreciation	Annual Depreciation	Accumulated Depreciation	Book Value
New				$12,500
End of Year 1	40%	$5000	$ 5,000	$ 7,500
End of Year 2	40%	$3000	$ 8,000	$ 4,500
End of Year 3	40%	$1800	$ 9,800	$ 2,700
End of Year 4	Max. allowance	$ 200	$10,000	$ 2,500
End of Year 5		$ 0	$10,000	$ 2,500

Sum-of-the-years'-digits method of depreciation:

Year	Rate of Depreciation	Annual Depreciation	Accumulated Depreciation	Book Value
New				$12,500
End of Year 1	5/15	$3333	$ 3,333	$ 9,167
End of Year 2	4/15	$2667	$ 6,000	$ 6,500
End of Year 3	3/15	$2000	$ 8,000	$ 4,500
End of Year 4	2/15	$1333	$ 9,333	$ 3,167
End of Year 5	1/15	$ 667	$10,000	$ 2,500
				(salvage value)

The MACRS method of depreciation:

Year	Rate of Depreciation	Annual Depreciation	Accumulated Depreciation	Book Value
New				$12,500
Year 1	20.00%	$2500	$ 2,500	$10,000
Year 2	32.00%	$4000	$ 6,500	$ 6,000
Year 3	19.20%	$2400	$ 8,900	$ 3,600
Year 4	11.52%	$1440	$10,340	$ 2,160
Year 5	11.52%	$1440	$11,780	$ 720
Year 6	5.76%	$ 720	$12,500	$ 0

2. For the straight-line method of depreciation:
     The sum of the rates of depreciation is 100%.
     The sum of the annual depreciations is $10,000.
     The accumulated depreciation for the last year of the copier's useful life is
       $10,000.
     The book value at the end of the last year is $2500.

   For the double-declining balance method of depreciation:
     The sum of the rates of depreciation is 120%.
       (The salvage value is not subtracted from the cost before calculation of the
       annual depreciation of Year 1. But since the book value cannot fall below
       the salvage value, the 40% rate of depreciation is used only until the book
       value of the asset would fall below the salvage value.)
     The sum of the annual depreciations is $10,000.
     The accumulated depreciation for the last year of the copier's useful life is
       $10,000.
     The book value at the end of the last year is $2500.

   For the sum-of-the-years'-digits method of depreciation:
     The sum of the rates of depreciation is 15/15, which equals 1 or 100%.
     The sum of the annual depreciations is $10,000.
     The accumulated depreciation for the last year of the copier's useful life is
       $10,000.
     The book value at the end of the last year is $2500.

   For the MACRS method of depreciation:
     The sum of the rates of depreciation is 100%.
     The sum of the annual depreciations is $12,500. (The salvage value of the asset
       is disregarded.)
     The accumulated depreciation for the last year of the copier's useful life is
       $12,500. (The salvage value of the asset is disregarded.)
     The book value at the end of the last year is $0. (The salvage value of the
       asset is disregarded.)

3. The annual depreciation for the first year is smallest for the straight-line method
     of depreciation.
   The annual depreciation for the first year is largest for the double-declining
     balance method of depreciation.
   The annual depreciation for the fifth year is smallest for the double-declining
     balance method of depreciation.
   The annual depreciation for the fifth year is largest for the straight-line method
     of depreciation.

4. A constant rate of depreciation of 25% should have been used if the asset was traded
   in after four years.

5. Straight-line method:

Sales Revenue	$30,000
Operating Expenses Before Depreciation	− 12,500
Operating Profit Before Depreciation	= 17,500
Depreciation	− 2,000
Operating Profit	= 15,500

   Double-declining balance method:

Sales Revenue	$30,000
Operating Expenses Before Depreciation	− 12,500
Operating Profit Before Depreciation	= 17,500
Depreciation	− 5,000
Operating Profit	= 15,500

Sum-of-the-years'-digits method:

Sales Revenue	$30,000
Operating Expenses Before Depreciation	- 12,500
Operating Profit Before Depreciation	= 17,500
Depreciation	- 3,333
Operating Profit	= 14,167

MACRS method:

Sales Revenue	$30,000
Operating Expenses Before Depreciation	- 12,500
Operating Profit Before Depreciation	= 17,500
Depreciation	- 2,500
Operating Profit	= 15,000

Operating profit the first year is highest under the straight-line method of depreciation.

Operating profit the first year is lowest under the double-declining balance method of depreciation.

Answers may vary. For example:

A higher operating profit may reflect more favorably on the company when applying for a loan.

A lower operating profit will result in the company paying less in taxes.

Higher depreciation in the early years of an asset's life will offset expenses incurred in maintenance and repair of equipment in later years.

It may be preferable to have greater depreciation in the early years because of the rapid technological changes in our world today. Assets may become obsolete more rapidly and have to be replaced within a shorter period of time than would have been necessary years ago.

6. Tax savings Year 1 = 0.15(depreciation Year 1) = 0.15($2500) = $375
   Tax savings Year 2 = 0.15(depreciation Year 2) = 0.15($4000) = $600
   Tax savings Year 3 = 0.15(depreciation Year 3) = 0.15($2400) = $360
   Tax savings Year 4 = 0.15(depreciation Year 4) = 0.15($1440) = $216
   Tax savings Year 5 = 0.15(depreciation Year 5) = 0.15($1440) = $216
   Tax savings Year 6 = 0.15(depreciation Year 6) = 0.15($720) = $108

   Total of the tax savings over the useful life of the copier
   = $375 + $600 + $360 + $216 + $216 + $108 = $1875

Review/Test, pages 445–446

1. Strategy
   To find the depreciation per unit:
   • Find the total depreciation by subtracting the salvage value from the cost.
   • Divide the total depreciation by the total number of units of production.

   Solution
   Total depreciation = 36,000 − 4000
   $\qquad\qquad\qquad\quad$ = 32,000
   Depreciation per unit = $\frac{32,000}{800,000}$ = 0.04

   The depreciation per unit is $.04.

2. Strategy
   To find the first-year depreciation:
   • Find the depreciation per mile.
   • Multiply the depreciation per mile by the number of miles driven the first year.

   Solution
   Depreciation per mile
   $= \dfrac{\text{cost} - \text{salvage value}}{\text{total miles of useful life}}$
   $= \dfrac{9800 - 2000}{120,000} = \dfrac{7800}{120,000} = 0.065$

   First-year depreciation
   = 0.065(26,000) = 1690

   The first-year depreciation is $1690.

3. Strategy
   To find the total depreciation, subtract the salvage value from the cost.
   To find the annual depreciation, divide the total depreciation by the useful life.

   Solution
   Total depreciation = 4200 − 200 = 4000
   Annual depreciation = $\frac{4000}{5}$ = 800

   The annual depreciation is $800.
   The total depreciation is $4000.

4. Strategy
   To find the book value after five years:
   • Find the annual depreciation by dividing the total depreciation by the useful life.
   • Find the accumulated depreciation by multiplying the annual depreciation by 5.
   • Subtract the accumulated depreciation from the cost.

   Solution
   Annual depreciation = $\dfrac{45,000 - 5000}{8}$
   $\qquad\qquad\qquad\qquad = \dfrac{40,000}{8} = 5000$

   Accumulated depreciation
   = 5000(5) = 25,000
   Book value = 45,000 − 25,000 = 20,000

   The book value after five years is $20,000.

5. Strategy
   To find the depreciation rate, double the rate of straight-line depreciation.
   To find the first year's depreciation, multiply the cost by the depreciation rate.

   Solution
   Straight-line rate = $16\frac{2}{3}\%$

   Double-declining balance rate = $2\left(16\frac{2}{3}\%\right) = 33\frac{1}{3}\%$
   The declining-balance rate is 33.33%.
   Depreciation Year 1 = $22,000\left(\frac{1}{3}\right) \approx 7333$
   The first year's depreciation is $7333.

6. Strategy
    To determine the book value at the end of the third year:
    • Find the rate of depreciation.
    • Find the annual depreciation and the book value at the end of the first year.
    • Find the annual depreciation and the book value at the end of the second year.
    • Find the annual depreciation and the book value at the end of the third year.

    Solution
    Straight-line depreciation = 20%
    Double-declining balance rate = 40%
    Depreciation Year 1 = 10,000(0.4) = 4000
    Book value Year 1 = 10,000 - 4000 = 6000
    Depreciation Year 2 = 6000(0.4) = 2400
    Book value Year 2 = 6000 - 2400 = 3600
    Depreciation Year 3 = 3600(0.4) = 1440
    Book value Year 3 = 3600 - 1440 = 2160

    The book value at the end of the third year is $2160.

7. Strategy
    To find the first year's depreciation:
    • Find the sum of the digits (n=10).
    • Find the total depreciation.
    • Multiply the first year's ratio by the total depreciation.

    Solution
    Sum of the digits = $\frac{10(10 + 1)}{2}$ = 55

    Total depreciation = 48,000 - 8000 = 40,000

    $\frac{10}{55}$ of the depreciation is taken the first year.

    First-year depreciation = $\frac{10}{55}$(40,000) ≈ 7273

    The first year's depreciation is $7273.

8. Strategy
    To find the book value at the end of the third year:
    • Find the sum of the digits (n=6).
    • Find the total depreciation.
    • Find the accumulated depreciation after three years.
    • Subtract the accumulated depreciation from the total depreciation.

    Solution
    Sum of the digits = $\frac{6(6 + 1)}{2}$ = 21

    Total depreciation = 15,000 - 3000 = 12,000

    $\frac{6}{21}$ of the depreciation is taken in the first year.

    $\frac{5}{21}$ of the depreciation is taken in the second year.

    $\frac{4}{21}$ of the depreciation is taken in the third year.

    Sum of the first three ratios = $\frac{6}{21} + \frac{5}{21} + \frac{4}{21} = \frac{15}{21}$

    Accumulated depreciation Year 3 = $\frac{15}{21}$(12,000) ≈ 8671

    Book value Year 3 = 15,000 - 8571 = 6429
    The book value at the end of the third year is $6429.

9. Strategy
    To find the accumulated depreciation after five years:
    • Find the depreciation for each of the first five years.
    • Add the annual depreciations.

    Solution

Year	Cost	x	Percent	=	Depreciation
1	18,000	x	0.08	=	1440
2	18,000	x	0.14	=	2520
3	18,000	x	0.12	=	2160
4	18,000	x	0.10	=	1800
5	18,000	x	0.10	=	1800
			Total	=	9720

    The accumulated depreciation after five years is $9720.

10. Percent depreciation = 33.33%

11. Annual depreciation = 8420(0.3333) ≈ $2806

12. Accumulated depreciation = $2806

13. Book value = cost - accumulated depreciation = 8420 - 2806 = $5614

14. Percent depreciation = 44.45%

15. Annual depreciation = 8420(0.4445) ≈ $3743

16. Accumulated depreciation = 2806 + 3743 = $6549

17. Book value = cost - accumulated depreciation = 8420 - 6549 = $1871

18. Percent depreciation = 14.81%

19. Annual depreciation = 8420(0.1481) ≈ 1247

20. Accumulated depreciation = 6549 + 1247 = $7796

21. Book value = cost - accumulated depreciation = 8420 - 7796 = $624

22. Percent depreciation = 7.41%

23. Annual depreciation = 8420(0.0741) ≈ $624

24. Accumulated depreciation = 7796 + 624 = $8420

25. Book value = cost - accumulated depreciation = 8420 - 8420 = $0

CHAPTER 15
Taxes and Insurance

Section 15.1, pages 455–458

1. State sales tax = 820(0.035) = $28.70
   City sales tax = 820(0.01) = $ 8.20
   Total sales tax = 28.70 + 8.20 = $36.90

2. Total cost = 820.00 + 36.90 = $856.90

3. State sales tax = 79.50(0.05) = $3.98
   City sales tax = 79.50(0.0125) = $1.00
   Total sales tax = 3.98 + 1.00 = $4.98

4. Total cost = 79.50 + 4.98 = $84.48

5. State sales tax = 122.45(0.06) = $7.35
   City sales tax = 122.45(0.0175) = $2.15
   Total sales tax = 7.35 + 2.14 = $9.50

6. Total cost = 122.45 + 9.50 = $131.95

7. State sales tax = 27.99(0.045) = $1.26
   City sales tax = 27.99(0.0225) = $ .63
   Total sales tax = 1.26 + .63 = $1.89

8. Total cost = 27.99 + 1.89 = $29.88

9. State sales tax = 455.00(0.055) = $25.03
   City sales tax = 455.00(0.015) = $ 6.83
   Total sales tax = 25.03 + 6.83 = $31.86

10. Total cost = 455.00 + 31.86 = $486.86

11. State sales tax = 55.68(0.04) = $2.23
    City sales tax = 55.68(0.0075) = $ .42
    Total sales tax = 2.23 + .42 = $2.65

12. Total cost = 55.68 + 2.65 = $58.33

13. Strategy
    To find the state sales tax:
    • Find the total retail price of the purchase.
    • Multiply the total retail price by the state sales tax rate.

    Solution
    Total retail price
    = 3(27.80) + 2(24.50) + 79.50
    = 83.40 + 49.00 + 79.50
    = 211.90
    Sales tax = 211.90(0.045)
            ≈ 9.54

    The state sales tax is $9.54.

14. Strategy
    To find the state sales tax:
    • Find the total retail price of the purchase.
    • Multiply the total retail price by the state sales tax rate.

    Solution
    Total retail price
    = 8(19.95) + 2(9.50) + 68.95
    = 159.60 + 19.00 + 68.95
    = 247.55
    Sales tax = 247.55(0.05)
            ≈ 12.38

    The state sales tax is $12.38.

15. Strategy
    To find the total cost:
    • Find the total retail price of the purchase.
    • Find the state sales tax.
    • Find the city sales tax.
    • Add the taxes to the total retail price.

    Solution
    Total retail price = 149 + 69 = 218
    State sales tax = 218(0.06) = 13.08
    City sales tax = 218(0.0125) = 2.73
    Total cost = 218 + 13.08 + 2.73
              = 233.81

    The total cost is $233.81.

16. Strategy
    To find the total cost:
    • Find the total retail price of the purchase.
    • Find the state sales tax.
    • Find the city sales tax.
    • Add the taxes to the total retail price.

    Solution
    Total retail price = 425 + 329 = 754
    State sales tax = 754(0.045) = 33.93
    City sales tax = 754(0.015) = 11.31
    Total cost = 754 + 33.93 + 11.31
              = 799.24

    The total cost is $799.24.

17. Assessed valuation = 0.50(60,000) = $30,000

18. Property tax = 0.0235(30,000) = $705

19. Assessed valuation = 0.30(120,000) = $36,000

20. Property tax = 0.0325(36,000) = $1170

21. Assessed valuation = rate of assessment x fair market value
          45,000   =   0.40   x fair market value
    Fair market value = 45,000 + 0.40 = $112,500

22. Property tax = 0.0265(45,000) = $1192.50

23. Assessed valuation = rate of assessment x fair market value
          75,000   =   0.60   x fair market value
    Fair market value = 75,000 + 0.60 = $125,000

24. Property tax = 0.0210(75,000) = $1575

25. Assessed valuation = 0.20(42,500) = $8500

26. Property tax = $5.20 \left(\frac{8500}{100} \right)$ = $442

27. Assessed valuation = 0.25(52,400) = $13,100

28. Property tax = $4.65 \left(\frac{13,100}{100} \right)$ = $609.15

29. Assessed valuation = rate of assessment x fair market value
          80,000   =   0.40   x fair market value
    Fair market value = 80,000 + 0.40 = $200,000

30. Property tax = $3.25 \left(\frac{80,000}{100} \right)$ = $2600

31. Assessed valuation = rate of assessment x fair market value
          42,000   =   0.60   x fair market value
    Fair market value = 42,000 + 0.60 = $70,000

32. Property tax = $3.55 \left(\frac{42,000}{100} \right)$ = $1491

33. Strategy
    To find the property tax rate, divide
    the budget by the assessed valuation.

    Solution
    $\dfrac{250,000}{12,000,000} = 0.0208 = 2.08\%$

    The property tax rate is 2.08%.

34. Strategy
    To find the property tax rate, divide
    the budget by the assessed valuation.

    Solution
    $\dfrac{2,400,000}{62,300,000} = 0.0385 = 3.85\%$

    The property tax rate is 3.85%.

35. Strategy
    To find the property tax rate:
    • Divide the budget by the assessed
      valuation.
    • Multiply the decimal tax rate by
      100.

    Solution
    $\dfrac{800,000}{32,500,000} = 0.0246$
    $0.0246(100) = 2.46$

    The tax rate per $100 of assessed
    valuation is $2.46.

36. Strategy
    To find the property tax rate:
    • Divide the budget by the assessed
      valuation.
    • Multiply the decimal tax rate by
      100.

    Solution
    $\dfrac{550,000}{8,500,000} = 0.0647$
    $0.0647(100) = 6.47$

    The tax rate per $100 of assessed
    valuation is $6.47.

37. Strategy
    To find the assessed valuation,
    multiply the fair market value by the
    rate of assessment.

    Solution
    $325,000(0.32) = 104,000$

    The assessed valuation is $104,000.

38. Strategy
    To find the assessed valuation,
    multiply the fair market value by the
    rate of assessment.

    Solution
    $425,000(0.25) = 106,250$

    The assessed valuation is $106,250.

39. Strategy
    To find the property tax:
    • Multiply the fair market value by
      the rate of assessment to find the
      assessed valuation.
    • Multiply the assessed valuation by
      the tax rate.

    Solution
    Assessed valuation = $82,000(0.25)$
    $\qquad\qquad\qquad = 20,500$
    Property tax = $20,500(0.0225) = 461.25$

    The property tax is $461.25.

40. Strategy
    To find the property tax:
    • Multiply the fair market value by
      the rate of assessment to find the
      assessed valuation.
    • Multiply the assessed valuation by
      the tax rate.

    Solution
    Assessed valuation = $325,000(0.30)$
    $\qquad\qquad\qquad = 97,500$
    Property tax = $2.25\left(\dfrac{97,500}{100}\right)$
    $\qquad\qquad\quad = 2193.75$

    The property tax is $2193.75.

41. Strategy
    To find the property tax:
    • Multiply the fair market value by the rate of assessment to find the assessed valuation.
    • Divide the assessed valuation by 100 and multiply the quotient by the tax rate per $100.

    Solution
    Assessed valuation = 825,000(0.25)
    $$= 206,250$$
    Property tax $= 3.20 \left(\frac{206,250}{100}\right) = 6600$

    The property tax is $6600.

42. Strategy
    To find the property tax:
    • Find the total of the tax rates for all the agencies.
    • Multiply the assessed valuation by the total tax rate.

    Solution
    1.0125% + 0.0565% + 0.0085% + 0.0244% + 0.0056% + 0.0105% = 1.118%
    60,000(0.01118) = 670.80

    The property tax is $670.80.

43. Strategy
    To find the property tax:
    • Find the total of the tax rates for all the agencies.
    • Multiply the assessed valuation by the total tax rate.

    Solution
    1.0125% + 0.0565% + 0.0085% + 0.0244% + 0.0056% + 0.0105% = 1.118%
    35,000(0.01118) = 391.30

    The property tax is $391.30.

44. Strategy
    To find the property tax:
    • Multiply the fair market value by the rate of assessment to find the assessed valuation.
    • Find the total of the tax rates for all the agencies.
    • Multiply the assessed valuation by the total tax rate.

    Solution
    Assessed valuation = 72,000(0.30)
    $$= 21,600$$
    1.0125% + 0.0565% + 0.0085% + 0.0244% + 0.0056% + 0.0105% = 1.118%
    Property tax = 21,600(0.01118)
    $$= 241.488$$

    The property tax is $241.49.

45. Strategy
    To find the federal income tax, multiply the taxable income by 15%, since the taxable income is less than $50,000.

    Solution
    0.15(37,500) = 5625

    The federal income tax is $5625.

46. Strategy
    To find the federal income tax, multiply the taxable income by 15%, since the taxable income is less than $50,000.

    Solution
    0.15(42,500) = 6300

    The federal income tax is $6300.

47. Strategy
    To find the federal income tax:
    • Find the tax on the first $50,000 of taxable income using a tax rate of 15%.
    • Find the tax on the next $25,000 of taxable income using a tax rate of 25%.
    • Find the tax on the next $25,000 of taxable income using a tax rate of 34%.
    • Find the tax on the income over $100,000 using a tax rate of 39%.
    • Add the taxes to be paid.

    Solution
    0.15(50,000) = 7500
    0.25(25,000) = 6250
    0.34(25,000) = 8500
    0.39(102,750 - 100,000)
     = 0.39(2750) = 1072.50

    7500 + 6250 + 8500 + 1072.50
     = 23,332.50

    The federal income tax is $23,332.50.

48. Strategy
    To find the federal income tax:
    • Find the tax on the first $50,000 of taxable income using a tax rate of 15%.
    • Find the tax on the next $25,000 of taxable income using a tax rate of 25%.
    • Find the tax on the next $25,000 of taxable income using a tax rate of 34%.
    • Find the tax on the income over $100,000 using a tax rate of 39%.
    • Add the taxes to be paid.

    Solution
    0.15(50,000) = 7500
    0.25(25,000) = 6250
    0.34(25,000) = 8500
    0.39(147,000 - 100,000)
     = 0.39(47,000) = 18,330

    7500 + 6250 + 8500 + 18,330
     = 40,580

    The federal income tax is $40,580.

49. Strategy
    To find the federal income tax:
    • Find the taxable income.
    • Multiply the taxable income by 15%.

    Solution
    Taxable income = 67,500 - 22,400
                   = 45,100
    Tax = 0.15(45,100) = 6765

    The federal income tax is $6765.

50. Strategy
    To find the federal income tax:
    • Find the taxable income.
    • Multiply the taxable income by 15%.

    Solution
    Taxable income = 88,450 - 42,350
                   = 46,100
    Tax = 0.15(46,100) = 6915

    The federal income tax is $6915.

51. Strategy
    To find the federal income tax:
    • Find the taxable income.
    • Find the tax on the first $50,000
      of taxable income using a tax rate
      of 15%.
    • Find the tax on the income over
      $50,000 using a tax rate of 25%.
    • Add the taxes to be paid.

    Solution
    Taxable income = 88,500 - 33,560
    $\qquad\qquad\quad$ = 54,940
    Tax = 0.15(50,000) = 7500
    Tax = 0.25(54,940 - 50,000)
    $\qquad$ = 0.25(4940) = 1235
    Total tax = 7500 + 1235 = 8735

    The federal income tax is $8735.

52. Strategy
    To find the federal income tax:
    • Find the taxable income.
    • Find the tax on the first $50,000
      of taxable income using a tax rate
      of 15%.
    • Find the tax on the next $25,000 of
      taxable income using a tax rate of
      25%.
    • Find the tax on the next $25,000 of
      taxable income using a tax rate of
      34%.
    • Find the tax on the income over
      $100,000 using a tax rate of 39%.
    • Add the taxes to be paid.

    Solution
    236,780 - 134,500 = 102,280
    0.15(50,000) = 7500
    0.25(25,000) = 6250
    0.34(25,000) = 8500
    0.39(102,280 - 100,000)
    $\quad$ = 0.39(2280) = 889.20

    7500 + 6250 + 8500 + 889.20
    $\quad$ = 23,139.20

    The federal income tax is $23,139.20.

53. Strategy
    To find the percent:
    • Find the federal income tax due.
    • Solve the basic percent equation
      for rate.

    Solution
    0.15(50,000) = 7500
    0.25(72,500 - 50,000) = 0.25(22,500)
    $\qquad\qquad\qquad\qquad\qquad$ = 5625
    Total tax = 7500 + 5625 = 13,125

    $\quad$ Part = base x rate
    13,125 = 72,500 x rate
    $\dfrac{13,125}{72,500}$ = r
    0.181034 = r

    The corporation pays 18.1% of the
    taxable income in income tax.

54. Strategy
    To find the percent:
    • Find the federal income tax due.
    • Solve the basic percent equation
      for rate.

    Solution
    0.15(50,000) = 7500
    0.25(25,000) = 6250
    0.34(25,000) = 8500
    0.39(325,000 - 100,000)
    $\quad$ = 0.39(225,000) = 87,750
    Total tax = 7500 + 6250 + 8500
    $\qquad\qquad\qquad$ + 87,750 = 110,000

    $\quad$ Part = base x rate
    110,000 = 325,000 x rate
    $\dfrac{110,000}{325,000}$ = r
    $\quad$ 0.338 ≈ r

    The corporation pays 33.8% of the
    taxable income in income taxes.

Section 15.2, pages 465–468

1. Annual premium = $2.67 \left(\dfrac{75,000}{1000} \right)$ = $200.25

2. Quarterly premium = 200.25(0.2575) = $51.56

3. Annual premium = $21.02 \left(\frac{100,000}{1000} \right)$ = \$2102

4. Quarterly premium = 2102(0.2575) = \$541.27

5. Annual premium = $20.52 \left(\frac{30,000}{1000} \right)$ = \$615.60

6. Quarterly premium = 615.60(0.2575) = \$158.52

7. Annual premium = $12.55 \left(\frac{50,000}{1000} \right)$ = \$627.50

8. Quarterly premium = 627.50(0.2575) = \$161.68

9. Annual premium = $39.10 \left(\frac{80,000}{1000} \right)$ = \$3128

10. Quarterly premium = 3128(0.2575) = \$805.46

11. Annual premium = $34.44 \left(\frac{40,000}{1000} \right)$ = \$1377.60

12. Quarterly premium = 1377.60(0.2575) = \$354.73

13. Annual premium = $2.17 \left(\frac{200,000}{1000} \right)$ = \$434

14. Quarterly premium = 434(0.2575) = \$111.76

15. Annual premium = $20.97 \left(\frac{100,000}{1000} \right)$ = \$2097

16. Quarterly premium = 2097(0.2575) = \$539.98

17. Annual premium = $17.40 \left(\frac{150,000}{1000} \right)$ = \$2610

18. Quarterly premium = 2610(0.2575) = \$672.08

19. Annual premium = $35.42 \left(\frac{75,000}{1000} \right)$ = \$2656.50

20. Quarterly premium = 2656.50(0.2575) = \$684.05

21. Strategy
    To find the annual premium:
    • Use Table 15.1 to find the annual
      premium per \$1000.
    • Use the annual premium formula.

    Solution
    Annual premium per \$1000 = 38.72
    Annual premium = $38.72 \left(\frac{20,000}{1000} \right)$
    $\qquad\qquad\qquad = 774.40$

    The annual premium is \$774.40.

22. Strategy
    To find the annual premium:
    • Use Table 15.1 to find the annual
      premium per \$1000.
    • Use the annual premium formula.

    Solution
    Annual premium per \$1000 = 32.66
    Annual premium = $32.66 \left(\frac{50,000}{1000} \right)$
    $\qquad\qquad\qquad = 1633$

    The annual premium is \$1633.

23. Strategy
    To find the annual premium:
    • Use Table 15.1 to find the annual premium per $1000.
    • Use the annual premium formula.

    Solution
    Annual premium per $1000 = 6.93
    Annual premium = $6.93 \left(\frac{100,000}{1000} \right)$
    $\qquad\qquad\qquad = 693$

    The annual premium is $693.

24. Strategy
    To find the annual premium:
    • Use Table 15.1 to find the annual premium per $1000.
    • Use the annual premium formula.

    Solution
    Annual premium per $1000 = 2.11
    Annual premium = $2.11 \left(\frac{25,000}{1000} \right)$
    $\qquad\qquad\qquad = 52.75$

    The annual premium is $52.75.

25. Strategy
    To find the quarterly premium:
    • Use Table 15.1 to find the annual premium per $1000.
    • Calculate the annual premium.
    • Multiply the annual premium by the quarterly factor (0.2575).

    Solution
    Annual premium per $1000 = 28.16
    Annual premium = $28.16 \left(\frac{150,000}{1000} \right)$
    $\qquad\qquad\qquad = 4224$
    Quarterly premium = 4224(0.2575)
    $\qquad\qquad\qquad = 1087.68$

    The quarterly premium is $1087.68.

26. Strategy
    To find the quarterly premium:
    • Use Table 15.1 to find the annual premium per $1000.
    • Calculate the annual premium.
    • Multiply the annual premium by the quarterly factor (0.2575).

    Solution
    Annual premium per $1000 = 42.91
    Annual premium = $42.91 \left(\frac{60,000}{1000} \right)$
    $\qquad\qquad\qquad = 2574.60$
    Quarterly premium = 2574.60(0.2575)
    $\qquad\qquad\qquad = 662.96$

    The quarterly premium is $662.96.

27. Strategy
    To find the monthly premium:
    • Use Table 15.1 to find the annual premium per $1000.
    • Calculate the annual premium.
    • Multiply the annual premium by the monthly factor (0.0875).

    Solution
    Annual premium per $1000 = 10.14
    Annual premium = $10.14 \left(\frac{75,000}{1000} \right)$
    $\qquad\qquad\qquad = 760.50$
    Monthly premium = 760.50(0.0875)
    $\qquad\qquad\qquad = 66.54$

    The monthly premium is $66.54.

28. Strategy
    To find the monthly premium:
    • Use Table 15.1 to find the annual premium per $1000.
    • Calculate the annual premium.
    • Multiply the annual premium by the monthly factor (0.0875).

    Solution
    Annual premium per $1000 = 29.66
    Annual premium = $29.66 \left(\frac{180,000}{1000} \right)$
    $\qquad\qquad\qquad = 5338.80$
    Monthly premium = 5338.80(0.0875)
    $\qquad\qquad\qquad = 467.15$

    The monthly premium is $467.15.

29. Strategy
    To find the semiannual premium:
    - Use Table 15.1 to find the annual premium per $1000.
    - Calculate the annual premium.
    - Multiply the annual premium by the semiannual factor (0.51).

    Solution
    Annual premium per $1000 = 26.16
    Annual premium = $26.16 \left(\frac{75,000}{1000} \right)$
    $\qquad = 1962$
    Semiannual premium = 1962(0.51)
    $\qquad = 1000.62$

    The semiannual premium is $1000.62.

30. Strategy
    To find the semiannual premium:
    - Use Table 15.1 to find the annual premium per $1000.
    - Calculate the annual premium.
    - Multiply the annual premium by the semiannual factor (0.51).

    Solution
    Annual premium per $1000 = 32.20
    Annual premium = $32.20 \left(\frac{50,000}{1000} \right)$
    $\qquad = 1610$
    Semiannual premium = 1610(0.51)
    $\qquad = 821.10$

    The semiannual premium is $821.10.

31. Strategy
    To find how much less the policy would be:
    - Find the annual premium if the policy were issued at age 40.
    - Find the annual premium if the policy were issued at age 25.
    - Find the difference between the annual premiums.

    Solution
    Annual premium, issued at age 40 = $32.44 \left(\frac{50,000}{1000} \right) = 1622$

    Annual premium, issued at age 25 = $22.67 \left(\frac{50,000}{1000} \right) = 1133.50$

    $1622 - 1133.50 = 488.50$

    If the policy had been issued at age 25, the annual premium would be $488.50 less.

32. Strategy
    To find how much less the policy would be:
    - Find the annual premium if the policy were issued at age 35.
    - Find the annual premium if the policy were issued at age 20.
    - Find the difference between the annual premiums.

    Solution
    Annual premium, issued at age 35 = $36.17 \left(\frac{20,000}{1000} \right) = 723.40$

    Annual premium, issued at age 20 = $30.42 \left(\frac{20,000}{1000} \right) = 608.40$

    $723.40 - 608.40 = 115$

    If the policy had been issued at age 20, the annual premium would be $115 less.

33. Strategy
    To find the annual premium:
    - Use Table 15.1 to find the annual premium per $1000.
    - Use the annual premium formula.

    Solution
    Annual premium per $1000 = 17.40
    Annual premium = $17.40 \left(\frac{250,000}{1000} \right)$
    $\qquad = 4350$

    The annual premium is $4350.

34. Strategy
    To find the total annual premium:
    - Find the annual premium for the 35-year-old partner.
    - Find the annual premium for the 55-year-old partner.
    - Add the two annual premiums.

    Solution
    Annual premium for 35-year-old
    $= 3.17 \left(\frac{10,000}{1000} \right) = 31.70$

    Annual premium for 55-year-old
    $= 17.40 \left(\frac{10,000}{1000} \right) = 174.00$

    $31.70 + 174.00 = 205.70$

    The total annual premium is $205.70.

35. $183.60

36. 183.60(1.20) = $220.32

37. $50.50

38. 50.50(1.00) = $50.50

39. $42.60

40. 42.60(1.80) = $76.68

41. $70.30

42. 70.30(1.40) = $98.42

43. $151.00

44. 151.00(1.10) = $166.10

45. $25.90

46. 25.90(1.05) = $27.20

47. $158.00

48. 158.00(2.20) = $347.60

49. $108.50

50. 108.50(1.50) = $162.75

51. $170.00

52. 170.00(1.30) = $221.00

53. $195.80

54. 195.80(1.00) = $195.80

55. $38.40

56. 38.40(1.20) = $46.08

57. **Strategy**
To find the semiannual premium:
- Use the tables to find the base rate for each kind of coverage.
- Add the base rates.
- Multiply the sum by the rating factor.

Solution

Liability	195.80
Property damage	65.00
Medical	25.90
Comprehensive	107.50
Collision	274.00
	668.20

Semiannual premium = 668.20(1.00)
= 668.20

The semiannual premium is $668.20.

58. **Strategy**
To find the semiannual premium:
- Use the tables to find the base rate for each kind of coverage.
- Add the base rates.
- Multiply the sum by the rating factor.

Solution

Liability	158.00
Property damage	70.30
Medical	37.50
Comprehensive	108.50
Collision	286.50
	660.80

Semiannual premium = 660.80(1.00)
= 660.80

The semiannual premium is $660.80.

59. **Strategy**
To find the semiannual premium:
- Use the tables to find the base rate for each kind of coverage.
- Add the base rates.
- Multiply the sum by the rating factor.

Solution

Liability	183.60
Property damage	61.00
Medical	25.90
Uninsured motorist	38.40
Comprehensive	45.00
Collision	151.00
	504.90

Semiannual premium = 504.90(1.00)
= 504.90

The semiannual premium is $504.90.

60. **Strategy**
To find the semiannual premium:
- Use the tables to find the base rate for each kind of coverage.
- Add the base rates.
- Multiply the sum by the rating factor.

Solution

Liability	122.00
Property damage	55.30
Medical	21.70
Uninsured motorist	32.00
Comprehensive	49.50
Collision	158.00
	438.50

Semiannual premium = 438.50(1.00)
= 438.50

The semiannual premium is $438.50.

61. Strategy
    To find the semiannual premium:
    • Use the tables to find the base
      rate for each kind of coverage.
    • Add the base rates.
    • Multiply the sum by the rating
      factor.

    Solution
Liability	195.80
Property damage	70.30
Medical	45.40
Uninsured motorist	42.60
Comprehensive	50.50
Collision	147.50
	552.10

    Semiannual premium = 552.10(1.20)
    $\qquad\qquad\qquad\quad$ = 662.52

    The semiannual premium is $662.52.

62. Strategy
    To find the semiannual premium:
    • Use the tables to find the base
      rate for each kind of coverage.
    • Add the base rates.
    • Multiply the sum by the rating
      factor.

    Solution
Liability	158.00
Property damage	65.00
Medical	37.50
Uninsured motorist	38.40
Comprehensive	112.00
Collision	249.50
	660.40

    Semiannual premium = 660.40(1.20)
    $\qquad\qquad\qquad\quad$ = 792.48

    The semiannual premium is $792.48.

63. Strategy
    To find the semiannual premium:
    • Use the tables to find the base
      rate for each kind of coverage.
    • Add the base rates.
    • Multiply the sum by the rating
      factor.

    Solution
Liability	195.80
Property damage	76.70
Medical	37.50
Uninsured motorist	42.60
Comprehensive	83.50
Collision	246.50
	682.60

    Semiannual premium = 682.60(1.25)
    $\qquad\qquad\qquad\quad$ = 853.25

    The semiannual premium is $853.25.

64. Strategy
    To find the semiannual premium:
    • Use the tables to find the base
      rate for each kind of coverage.
    • Add the base rates.
    • Multiply the sum by the rating
      factor.

    Solution
Liability	138.50
Property damage	61.00
Medical	21.70
Uninsured motorist	32.00
Comprehensive	73.50
Collision	181.00
	507.70

    Semiannual premium = 507.70(1.30)
    $\qquad\qquad\qquad\quad$ = 660.01

    The semiannual premium is $660.01.

Section 15.3, pages 475–478

1. Strategy
   To find the amount of loss paid by the insurance company:
   • Determine whether the coinsurance clause is satisfied.
   • Find the recovery.

   Solution
   0.8(84,000) = 67,200 is greater than 50,000
   The coinsurance clause is not satisfied.

   Recovery = $\dfrac{\text{carried}}{\text{required}}$ x loss = $\dfrac{50,000}{67,200}$ x 30,000 = 22,321.43

   The insurance company will pay $22,321.43 on the loss.

2. Strategy
    To find the amount of loss paid by the insurance company:
    • Determine whether the coinsurance clause is satisfied.
    • Find the recovery.

    Solution
    0.8(120,000) = 96,000 is greater than 75,000
    The coinsurance clause is not satisfied.

    Recovery = $\dfrac{\text{carried}}{\text{required}}$ x loss = $\dfrac{75,000}{96,000}$ x 60,000 = 46,875

    The insurance company will pay $46,875 on the loss.

3. Strategy
    To find the amount of loss paid by the insurance company:
    • Determine whether the coinsurance clause is satisfied.
    • If the coinsurance clause is satisfied, the total loss will be paid.

    Solution
    0.8(125,000) = 100,000 is less than 120,000
    The coinsurance clause is satisfied.

    The total $40,000 loss will be paid.

4. Strategy
    To find the amount of loss paid by the insurance company:
    • Determine whether the coinsurance clause is satisfied.
    • If the coinsurance clause is satisfied, the total loss will be paid.

    Solution
    0.9(155,000) = 139,500 is less than 150,000
    The coinsurance clause is satisfied.

    The total $62,500 loss will be paid.

5. Strategy
    To find the amount of loss paid by the insurance company:
    • Determine whether the coinsurance clauses are satisfied.
    • Find the recovery.
    • Add the amounts paid on the store and on the inventory.

    Solution
    0.8(100,000) = 80,000; 0.8(30,000) = 24,000
    The coinsurance clauses are not satisfied.

    Recovery = $\dfrac{\text{carried}}{\text{required}}$ x loss = $\dfrac{60,000}{80,000}$ x 50,000 = 37,500

    Recovery = $\dfrac{\text{carried}}{\text{required}}$ x loss = $\dfrac{15,000}{24,000}$ x [0.50(30,000)] = $\dfrac{15,000}{24,000}$ x 15,000 = 9375

    37,500 + 9375 = 46,875

    The insurance company will pay $46,875 on the loss.

6. Strategy
   To find the amount of loss paid by the insurance company:
   • Determine whether the coinsurance clauses are satisfied.
   • Find the recovery.
   • Add the amounts paid on the store and on the inventory.

   Solution
   $0.8(80,000) = 64,000$; $0.8(25,000) = 20,000$
   The coinsurance clauses are not satisfied.
   Recovery $= \dfrac{\text{carried}}{\text{required}} \times \text{loss} = \dfrac{50,000}{64,000} \times 50,000 = 39,062.50$
   Recovery $= \dfrac{\text{carried}}{\text{required}} \times \text{loss} = \dfrac{15,000}{20,000} \times [0.50(25,000)] = \dfrac{15,000}{20,000} \times 12,500 = 9375$
   $39,062.50 + 9375 = 48,437.50$

   The insurance company will pay \$48,437.50 on the loss.

7. Strategy
   To find the total recovery from the two insurance companies:
   • Determine whether the coinsurance clause is satisfied by either policy.
   • Find the recovery from Company A.
   • Find the recovery from Company B.
   • Add the two amounts.

   Solution
   $0.8(500,000) = 400,000$
   The coinsurance clause is not satisfied by either policy.
   Recovery $= \dfrac{\text{carried}}{\text{required}} \times \text{loss} = \dfrac{250,000}{400,000} \times 290,000 = 181,250$
   Recovery $= \dfrac{\text{carried}}{\text{required}} \times \text{loss} = \dfrac{150,000}{400,000} \times 290,000 = 108,750$
   $181,250 + 108,750 = 290,000$

   The total recovery from the two insurance companies is \$290,000.

8. Strategy
   To find the total recovery from the two insurance companies:
   • Determine whether the coinsurance clause is satisfied by either policy.
   • Find the recovery from Company A.
   • Find the recovery from Company B.
   • Add the two amounts.

   Solution
   $0.8(450,000) = 360,000$
   The coinsurance clause is not satisfied by either policy.
   Recovery $= \dfrac{\text{carried}}{\text{required}} \times \text{loss} = \dfrac{200,000}{360,000} \times 325,000 = 180,555.56$
   Recovery $= \dfrac{\text{carried}}{\text{required}} \times \text{loss} = \dfrac{125,000}{360,000} \times 325,000 = 112,847.22$
   $180,555.56 + 112,847.22 = 293,402.78$

   The total recovery from the two insurance companies is \$293,402.78.

9. Strategy
   To find the total annual premium:
   - Use Table 15.5 to find the rate per $100 of insurance for the building and the contents.
   - Use the annual premium formula to find the annual premium for the building and for the contents.
   - Add the two premiums.

   Solution
   Building rate: 0.52
   Contents rate: 0.70

   Premium (building) $= 0.52 \left(\frac{55,000}{100} \right)$
   $= 286$

   Premium (contents) $= 0.70 \left(\frac{12,000}{100} \right)$
   $= 84$

   Total premium $= 286 + 84 = 370$

   The total annual premium is $370.

10. Strategy
    To find the total annual premium:
    - Use Table 15.5 to find the rate per $100 of insurance for the building and the contents.
    - Use the annual premium formula to find the annual premium for the building and for the contents.
    - Add the two premiums.

    Solution
    Building rate: 0.36
    Contents rate: 0.46

    Premium (building) $= 0.36 \left(\frac{72,000}{100} \right)$
    $= 259.20$

    Premium (contents) $= 0.46 \left(\frac{15,000}{100} \right)$
    $= 69$

    Total premium $= 259.20 + 69 = 328.20$

    The total annual premium is $328.20.

11. Strategy
    To find the total annual premium:
    - Use Table 15.5 to find the rate per $100 of insurance for the building and the contents.
    - Use the annual premium formula to find the annual premium for the building and for the contents.
    - Add the two premiums.

    Solution
    Building rate: 0.34
    Contents rate: 0.41

    Premium (building) $= 0.34 \left(\frac{42,000}{100} \right)$
    $= 142.80$

    Premium (contents) $= 0.41 \left(\frac{5000}{100} \right)$
    $= 20.50$

    Total premium $= 142.80 + 20.50$
    $= 163.30$

    The total annual premium is $163.30.

12. Strategy
    To find the total annual premium:
    - Use Table 15.5 to find the rate per $100 of insurance for the building and the contents.
    - Use the annual premium formula to find the annual premium for the building and for the contents.
    - Add the two premiums.

    Solution
    Building rate: 0.68
    Contents rate: 0.80

    Premium (building) $= 0.68 \left(\frac{60,000}{100} \right)$
    $= 408$

    Premium (contents) $= 0.80 \left(\frac{10,000}{100} \right)$
    $= 80$

    Total premium $= 408 + 80 = 488$

    The total annual premium is $488.

13. Strategy
    To find the annual premium:
    - Find the amount the building is insured for.
    - Use Table 15.5 to find the rate per $100 of insurance for the building.
    - Use the annual premium formula.

    Solution
    Insurance coverage $= 0.80(162,000)$
    $= 129,600$
    Building rate: 0.45
    Premium $= 0.45 \left(\frac{129,600}{100} \right) = 583.20$

    The annual premium is $583.20.

14. Strategy
    To find the annual premium:
    - Find the amount the building is insured for.
    - Use Table 15.5 to find the rate per $100 of insurance for the building.
    - Use the annual premium formula.

    Solution
    Insurance coverage $= 0.90(98,000)$
    $= 88,200$
    Building rate: 0.36
    Premium $= 0.36 \left(\frac{88,200}{100} \right) = 317.52$

    The annual premium is $317.52.

15. Strategy
    To find the premium:
    • Find the amounts the building and the contents are insured for.
    • Use Table 15.5 to find the rate per $100 of insurance for the building and the contents.
    • Use the annual premium formula to find the annual premium for the building and for the contents.
    • Add the two premiums.

    Solution
    Building insurance coverage
    = 0.90(90,000) = 81,000
    Contents insurance coverage
    = 0.90(30,000) = 27,000
    Building rate: 0.51
    Contents rate: 0.62

    Premium (building) = $0.51 \left(\frac{81,000}{100}\right)$
    $\qquad = 413.10$
    Premium (contents) = $0.62 \left(\frac{27,000}{100}\right)$
    $\qquad = 167.40$
    Total premium = 413.10 + 167.40
    $\qquad = 580.50$

    The premium is $580.50.

16. Strategy
    To find the premium:
    • Find the amounts the building and the contents are insured for.
    • Use Table 15.5 to find the rate per $100 of insurance for the building and the contents.
    • Use the annual premium formula to find the annual premium for the building and for the contents.
    • Add the two premiums.

    Solution
    Building insurance coverage
    = 0.80(125,000) = 100,000
    Contents insurance coverage
    = 0.80(40,000) = 32,000
    Building rate: 0.34
    Contents rate: 0.41

    Premium (building) = $0.34 \left(\frac{100,000}{100}\right)$
    $\qquad = 340$
    Premium (contents) = $0.41 \left(\frac{32,000}{100}\right)$
    $\qquad = 131.20$
    Total premium = 340 + 131.20 = 471.20

    The premium is $471.20.

17. Strategy
    To find the monthly premium:
    • Use the tables to find the premium for each type of coverage.
    • Add the premiums.

    Solution
    $250 deductible: 42
    Disability: 5
                     ──
                      47

    The monthly premium is $47.

18. Strategy
    To find the monthly premium:
    • Use the tables to find the premium for each type of coverage.
    • Add the premiums.

    Solution
    $100 deductible: 84
    Disability: 28
                     ───
                     112

    The monthly premium is $112.

19. Strategy
    To find the monthly premium, add the single premium to one-half of the difference between the single premium and the family premium.

    Solution
    71 + 0.5(197 − 71) = 71 + 63 = 134

    The monthly premium is $134.

20. Strategy
    To find the monthly premium, add the single premium to one-half of the difference between the single premium and the family premium.

    Solution
    53 + 0.5(159 − 53) = 53 + 53 = 106

    The monthly premium is $106.

21. Strategy
    To find the monthly premium:
    • Use the tables to find the premium for each type of coverage for each employee.
    • Add the premiums.

    Solution

Age	$100 deductible	Disability	Life	Total
44	197	16	12	225
37	177	7	8	192
56	328	94	41	463
60	395	110	59	564
				1444

    The monthly premium is $1444.

22. Strategy
    To find the monthly premium:
    • Use the tables to find the premium for each type of coverage for each employee.
    • Add the premiums.

    Solution

Age	$250 deductible	Disability	Life	Total
44	177	16	12	205
23	135	5	6	146
45	196	30	17	243
				594

    The monthly premium is $594.

23. Strategy
    To find the monthly premium:
    • Use the tables to find the premium for each type of coverage for each employee.
    • Add the premiums.

    Solution

Age	$250 deductible	Disability	Life	Total
34	159	7	8	174
44	177	16	12	205
28	135	5	6	146
				525

    The monthly premium is $525.

24. Strategy
    To find the monthly premium:
    • Use the tables to find the premium for each type of coverage for each employee.
    • Add the premiums.

    Solution

Age	$100 deductible	Disability	Life	Total
22	150	5	6	161
29	150	5	6	161
45	218	30	17	265
				587

    The monthly premium is $587.

25. Strategy
    To find the monthly premium:
    • Add the single premium to one-half of the difference between the single premium
      and the family premium for each type of coverage for each employee.
    • Add the premiums.

    Solution

Age	Deductible	Disability	Life
33	41 + 0.5(124 − 41) = 82.50	7	6 + 0.5(8 − 6) = 7.00
26	33 + 0.5(105 − 33) = 69.00	5	5 + 0.5(6 − 5) = 5.50
38	41 + 0.5(124 − 41) = 82.50	7	6 + 0.5(8 − 6) = 7.00
	234.00	19	19.50

    234.00 + 19 + 19.50 = 272.50

    The monthly premium is $272.50.

26. Strategy
    To find the monthly premium:
    • Add the single premium to one-half of the difference between the single premium
      and the family premium for each type of coverage for each employee.
    • Add the premiums.

    Solution

Age	Deductible	Disability	Life
36	53 + 0.5(159 − 53) = 106	19	6 + 0.5(8 − 6) = 7.00
38	53 + 0.5(159 − 53) = 106	19	6 + 0.5(8 − 6) = 7.00
54	105 + 0.5(246 − 105) = 175.50	36	21 + 0.5(26 − 21) = 23.50
	387.50	74	37.50

    387.50 + 74 + 37.50 = 499

    The monthly premium is $499.

27. Strategy
    To find the annual premium:
    • Use Table 15.9 to find the annual
      premium for each employee.
    • Add the premiums.

    Solution
    Full-time carpenters: 2(640) = 1280
    Part-time carpenters: 3(213) = 639
    Part-time interior
            decorators: 2(166) = 332
                                  2251

    The annual premium is $2251.

28. Strategy
    To find the annual premium:
    • Use Table 15.9 to find the annual
      premium for each employee.
    • Add the premiums.

    Solution
    Full-time electrician: 1(692) = 692
    Part-time electricians: 2(231) = 462
    Part-time concrete
            workers: 3(602) = 1806
                              2960

    The annual premium is $2960.

29. Strategy
    To find the annual premium:
    • Use Table 15.9 to find the annual premium for each employee.
    • Add the premiums.

    Solution
    Full-time carpenters: 3(541) = 1623
    Part-time carpenters: 4(180) = 720
    Full-time electricians: 2(468) = 936
    Part-time interior
              decorator: 1(146) = 146
                                      ────
                                      3425

    The annual premium is $3425.

30. Strategy
    To find the annual premium:
    • Use Table 15.9 to find the annual premium for each employee.
    • Add the premiums.

    Solution
    Full-time concrete
               workers: 2(1292) = 2584
    Part-time concrete
               workers: 3(431) = 1293
    Full-time electricians: 3(553) = 1659
    Part-time electrician: 1(184) = 184
                                     ────
                                     5720

    The annual premium is $5720.

Business Case Study

Case 1

1. Market value after five years = 200,000(1.469328) ≈ 293,866

   The market value of the business today is approximately $293,866.

2. 0.80($293,866) = $235,092.80
   $235,092.80 is greater than $160,000.
   The coinsurance clause is not satisfied.

   Recovery $= \dfrac{\text{carried}}{\text{required}} = \dfrac{160,000}{235,092.80} \approx 0.68$

   The insurance company would cover approximately 68% of the loss.

3. Estimated market value - insurance payment = 293,866 - 160,000 = 133,866

   The difference is $133,866.

4. Today's prices for reconstruction of the building and replacement of the equipment need to be determined. These costs should be added to the market value of the real estate on which the business is located. The insurance coverage must be changed to cover 80% of the total.

Case 2

1. The following records should be kept: income statements, balance sheets, payroll registers, and tax forms.

2. Financial records should be kept in a safe place at a location away from the office, for example, in a safe deposit box in a bank. Then, if the office is damaged by such mishaps as fire or flood, the records will not be destroyed.

Buying or Leasing a Copier

Case 3

1.

Year of Ownership	Percent Depreciation	Amount of Depreciation	Tax Savings
1	20.00	359	54
2	32.00	574	86
3	19.20	345	52
4	11.52	207	31
5	11.52	207	31
6	5.76	103	15

2. Note that the MACRS assumes that the asset has been owned for half the year during the first year of ownership and during the last year of ownership. Therefore, for each present value calculation of tax savings, the number of months for the compounding factor is 6, 18, 30, 42, 54, and 66. Not all of these values are in the Compound Interest Table. The Calculator Procedures for Chapter 10 can be used to calculate these figures.

        PV (Tax Savings Year 1) =   51.63
        PV (Tax Savings Year 2) =   75.18
        PV (Tax Savings Year 3) =   41.56
        PV (Tax Savings Year 4) =   22.65
        PV (Tax Savings Year 5) =   20.71
        PV (Tax Savings Year 6) =   9.16
        Total   202.89

    PV (Purchase Price) = 1795
    PV (Maintenance Agreement) = 763.15
    $202.89 + $1795 + $763.15 = $2761.04

3. PV (lease payments) = $PMT \cdot a_{\overline{n}|i}(1 + i)$ = \$38.77[48.173374(1.0075)] = \$1881.69

4. $1881.69 is less than $2761.04.
   The company should lease the copier.

Review/Test, pages 483–484

1. Strategy
   To find the total cost:
   • Find the total cost of the TV and the VCR.
   • Find the state and city sales taxes.
   • Add the taxes to the total cost of the TV and VCR.

   Solution
   425 + 329 = 754
   State sales tax = 754(0.04) = 30.16
   City sales tax = 754(0.0075) ≈ 5.66
   754 + 30.16 + 5.66 = 789.82

   The total cost is $789.82.

2. Strategy
   To find the property tax rate, divide the budget by the assessed valuation.

   Solution
   Property tax rate = $\dfrac{1{,}285{,}000}{88{,}000{,}000}$ = 0.0146

   The property tax rate is 1.46%.

3. Strategy
To find the property tax, divide the assessed valuation by 100 and multiply the quotient by the tax rate.

Solution
Property tax = $2.35 \times \dfrac{550,000}{100} = 12,925$

The property tax is $12,925.

5. Strategy
To find the property tax:
• Find the assessed valuation by multiplying the fair market value by the rate of assessment.
• Multiply the assessed valuation by the tax rate.

Solution
Assessed valuation = 122,000(0.28)
                   = 34,160
Property tax = 0.032(34,160) = 1093.12

The property tax is $1093.12.

4. Strategy
To find the assessed valuation, multiply the fair market value by the rate of assessment.

Solution
Assessed valuation = 185,000(0.35)
                   = 64,750

The assessed valuation is $64,750.

6. Strategy
To find the federal income tax:
• Find the taxable income.
• Find the tax on the first $50,000 of taxable income using a tax rate of 15%.
• Find the tax on the next $25,000 of taxable income using a tax rate of 25%.
• Find the tax on the next $25,000 of taxable income using a tax rate of 34%.
• Find the tax on the taxable income over $100,000 using a tax rate of 39%.
• Add the taxes to be paid.

Solution
345,000 − 216,450 = 128,550
0.15(50,000) = 7500
0.25(25,000) = 6250
0.34(25,000) = 8500
0.39(128,550 − 100,000) = 0.39(28,550)
                        = 11,134.50
7500 + 6250 + 8500 + 11,134.50
 = 33,384.50

The federal income tax is $33,384.50.

7. Strategy
To find the annual premium:
• Use Table 15.1 to find the annual premium per $1000.
• Use the annual premium formula.

Solution
Annual premium per $1000 = 38.72
Annual premium = $38.72 \left(\dfrac{75,000}{1000} \right)$
               = 2904

The annual premium is $2904.

8. Strategy
To find the monthly premium:
• Use Table 15.1 to find the annual premium per $1000.
• Calculate the annual premium.
• Multiply the annual premium by the monthly factor (0.0875).

Solution
Annual premium per $1000 = 15.27
Annual premium = $15.27 \left(\dfrac{100,000}{1000} \right)$
               = 1527
Monthly premium = 1525(0.0875)
                ≈ 133.61

The monthly premium is $133.61.

9. Strategy
   To find how much less the annual
   premium would be:
   • Find the annual premium for the
     policy issued at age 45.
   • Find the annual premium for the
     policy issued at age 30.
   • Find the difference between the two
     annual premiums.

   Solution
   Age 45:
   Annual premium per $1000 = 37.65
   Annual premium = $37.65 \left(\frac{75,000}{1000}\right)$
   $\qquad\qquad\qquad = 2823.75$
   Age 30:
   Annual premium per $1000 = 25.41
   Annual premium = $25.41 \left(\frac{75,000}{1000}\right)$
   $\qquad\qquad\qquad = 1905.75$
   2823.75 - 1905.75 = 918

   The annual premium would be $918 less
   if the policy had been issued at age
   30.

10. Strategy
    To find the semiannual premium:
    • Use the tables to find the base
      rate for each kind of coverage.
    • Add the base rates.
    • Multiply the sum by the rating
      factor.

    Solution
    Liability   183.60
    Property damage   70.30
    Medical   25.90
    Comprehensive   104.00
    Collision   237.00
                        ──────
                        620.80

    Semiannual premium = 620.80(1.20)
    $\qquad\qquad\qquad\qquad = 744.96$

    The semiannual premium is $744.96.

11. Strategy
    To find the amount of loss paid by the
    insurance company:
    • Determine whether the coinsurance
      clause is satisfied.
    • Find the recovery.

    Solution
    0.8(130,000) = 104,000
    104,000 is greater than 100,000.
    The coinsurance clause is not
    satisfied.
    Recovery = $\dfrac{\text{carried}}{\text{required}}$ x loss
    $\qquad\quad = \dfrac{100,000}{104,000}$ x 52,000 = 50,000

    The insurance company will pay $50,000
    on the loss.

12. Strategy
    To find the annual premium:
    • Use Table 15.5 to find the rate per
      $100 of insurance for the building
      and the contents.
    • Use the annual premium formula to
      find the premium for the building
      and the contents.
    • Add the two premiums.

    Solution

    Building rate: 0.51
    Contents: 0.62
    Premium (Building) = $0.51 \left(\frac{140,000}{100}\right)$
    $\qquad\qquad\qquad\qquad = 714$
    Premium (Contents) = $0.62 \left(\frac{45,000}{100}\right)$
    $\qquad\qquad\qquad\qquad = 279$
    Total premium = 714 + 279 = 993

    The total annual premium is $993.

250   *Chapter 15*

13. Strategy
    To find the monthly premium:
    • Use the tables to find the premium
      for each type of coverage for each
      employee.
    • Add the premiums.

    Solution

	Age	Premium
$250 deductible:	23	135
	37	159
	42	177
Disability:	23	15
	37	19
	42	23
Life:	23	6
	37	8
	42	12
		554

    The monthly premium is $554.

14. Strategy
    To find the annual premium:
    • Use Table 15.9 to find the annual
      premium for each employee.
    • Add the premiums.

    Solution
    Full-time carpenters: 3(541) = 1623
    Part-time electricians: 2(156) = 312
    ────
                                     1935

    The annual premium is $1935.

CHAPTER 16
International Business

Section 16.1, pages 491–494

1. Strategy
   To determine whether the balance of trade was favorable or unfavorable, determine whether the value of the exports or the imports is greater.

   Solution
   Since the value of the exports ($127 billion) is greater than the value of the imports ($116 billion), Canada had a favorable balance of trade.

2. Strategy
   To find Canada's balance of trade, subtract the smaller number (116 billion) from the larger number (127 billion).

   Solution
   127 billion - 116 billion = 11 billion

   Canada's balance of trade in 1990 was $11 billion.

3. Strategy
   To determine whether the balance of trade was favorable or unfavorable, determine whether the value of the exports or the imports is greater.

   Solution
   Since the value of the exports ($287 billion) is greater than the value of the imports ($235 billion), Japan had a favorable balance of trade.

4. Strategy
   To find Japan's balance of trade, subtract the smaller number (235 billion) from the larger number (287 billion).

   Solution
   287 billion - 235 billion = 52 billion

   Canada's balance of trade in 1990 was $52 billion.

5. Strategy
   To determine whether the balance of trade was favorable or unfavorable, determine whether the value of the exports or the imports is greater.

   Solution
   Since the value of the imports ($2,227 million) is greater than the value of the exports ($1,054 million), Kenya had an unfavorable balance of trade.

6. Strategy
   To find Kenya's balance of trade, subtract the smaller number (1,054 million) from the larger number (2,227 million). Since the balance of trade is unfavorable, use a negative sign.

   Solution
   2,227 million - 1,054 million = 1,173 million

   Kenya's balance of trade in 1990 was -$1,173 million.

7. Strategy
   To determine whether the balance of trade was favorable or unfavorable, determine whether the value of the exports or the imports is greater.

   Solution
   Since the value of the imports ($25,072 million) is greater than the value of the exports ($16,348 million), Portugal had an unfavorable balance of trade.

8. Strategy
   To find Portugal's balance of trade, subtract the smaller number (16,348 million) from the larger number (25,072 million). Since the balance of trade is unfavorable, use a negative sign.

   Solution
   25,072 million - 16,348 million = 8,724 million

   Portugal's balance of trade in 1990 was -$8,724 million.

9. Strategy
   (a) To determine whether the balance of trade was favorable or unfavorable, determine whether the value of the exports or imports is greater.
   (b) To find Trinidad's balance of trade, subtract the smaller number (1,222 million) from the larger number (2,049 million). If the balance of trade is unfavorable, use a negative sign.

   Solution
   Since the value of the exports is greater than the value of the imports, Trinidad had a favorable balance of trade.
   2,049 million - 1,222 million = 827 million

   Trinidad's balance of trade in 1990 was $827 million.

10. Strategy
    (a) To determine whether the balance of trade was favorable or unfavorable, determine whether the value of the exports or imports is greater.
    (b) To find Indonesia's balance of trade, subtract the smaller number (21,837 million) from the larger number (25,675 million). If the balance of trade is unfavorable, use a negative sign.

    Solution
    Since the value of the exports is greater than the value of the imports, Indonesia had a favorable balance of trade.
    25,675 million - 21,837 million = 3,838 million

    Indonesia's balance of trade in 1990 was $3,838 million.

11. Strategy
    (a) To determine whether the balance of trade was favorable or unfavorable, determine whether the value of the exports or imports is greater.
    (b) To find Switzerland's balance of trade, subtract the smaller number (63,884 million) from the larger number (69,869 million). If the balance of trade is unfavorable, use a negative sign.

    Solution
    Since the value of the imports is greater than the value of the exports, Switzerland had an unfavorable balance of trade.
    69,869 million - 63,884 million = 5,985 million

    Switzerland's balance of trade in 1990 was -$5,985 million.

12. Strategy
    (a) To determine whether the balance of trade was favorable or unfavorable, determine whether the value of the exports or imports is greater.
    (b) To find New Zealand's balance of trade, subtract the smaller number (9,435 million) from the larger number (9,489 million). If the balance of trade is unfavorable, use a negative sign.

    Solution
    Since the value of the imports is greater than the value of the exports, New Zealand had an unfavorable balance of trade.
    9,489 million - 9,435 million = 54 million

    New Zealand's balance of trade in 1990 was -$54 million.

13. Strategy
    (a) To determine whether the United States had a trade deficit, determine whether the value of the exports or imports is greater.
    (b) To find the balance of trade for the United States, subtract the smaller number (393.9 billion) from the larger number (516.6 billion). If the balance of trade is unfavorable, use a negative sign.

    Solution
    Since the value of the imports is greater than the value of the exports, the United States had a trade deficit.
    516.6 billion - 393.9 billion = 122.7 billion

    In 1990, the balance of trade for the United States was -$122.7 billion.

14. Strategy
    (a) To determine whether the United Kingdom had a trade deficit, determine whether the value of the exports or imports is greater.
    (b) To find the balance of trade for the United Kingdom, subtract the smaller number (186.0 billion) from the larger number (224.9 billion). If the balance of trade is unfavorable, use a negative sign.

    Solution
    Since the value of the imports is greater than the value of the exports, the United Kingdom had a trade deficit.
    224.9 billion - 186.0 billion = 38.9 billion

    In 1990, the balance of trade for the United Kingdom was -$38.9 billion.

15. Strategy
     To find Peru's balance of trade in 1990:
     • Determine whether the balance of trade was favorable or unfavorable.
     • Subtract the smaller number (2,455 million) from the larger number (3,274
       million). If the balance of trade is unfavorable, use a negative sign.

     Solution
     Since the value of the exports is greater than the value of the imports, Peru had a
     favorable balance of trade.
     3,274 million - 2,455 million = 819 million

     Peru's balance of trade in 1990 was $819 million.

16. Strategy
     To find Denmark's balance of trade in 1990:
     • Determine whether the balance of trade was favorable or unfavorable.
     • Subtract the smaller number (31,766 million) from the larger number (35,112
       million). If the balance of trade is unfavorable, use a negative sign.

     Solution
     Since the value of the exports is greater than the value of the imports, Denmark had
     a favorable balance of trade.
     35,112 million - 31,766 million = 3,346 million

     Denmark's balance of trade in 1990 was $3,346 million.

17. Strategy
     To find Austria's balance of trade in 1990:
     • Determine whether the balance of trade was favorable or unfavorable.
     • Subtract the smaller number (41.9 billion) from the larger number (50.0 billion).
       If the balance of trade is unfavorable, use a negative sign.

     Solution
     Since the value of the imports is greater than the value of the exports, Austria had
     an unfavorable balance of trade.
     50.0 billion - 41.9 billion = 8.1 billion

     Austria's balance of trade in 1990 was -$81.1 billion.

18. Strategy
     To find Italy's balance of trade in 1990:
     • Determine whether the balance of trade was favorable or unfavorable.
     • Subtract the smaller number (168.7 billion) from the larger number (180.1
       billion). If the balance of trade is unfavorable, use a negative sign.

     Solution
     Since the value of the imports is greater than the value of the exports, Italy had
     an unfavorable balance of trade.
     180.1 billion - 168.7 billion = 8.1 billion

     Italy's balance of trade in 1990 was -$11.4 billion.

19. Strategy
     To find the duty paid, multiply the
     specific duty (3.7¢ = $.037) by the
     number of dozen pairs of gloves
     imported.

     Solution
     50 x 0.037 = 1.85

     The duty paid is $1.85.

20. Strategy
     To find the duty paid, multiply the
     specific duty (30¢ = $.30) by the
     number of fishing reels imported.

     Solution
     200 x 0.30 = 60

     The duty paid is $60.

21. Strategy
    To find the duty paid, multiply the specific duty (21.5¢ = $.215) by the number of square meters of woven carpet imported.

    Solution
    750 x 0.215 = 161.25

    The duty paid is $161.25.

22. Strategy
    To find the duty paid, multiply the specific duty (0.77¢ = $.0077) by the number of liters of cane molasses imported.

    Solution
    800 x 0.0077 = 6.16

    The duty paid is $6.16.

23. Strategy
    To find the duty paid, multiply the value of the shipment ($1250) by the ad valorem percent (5% = 0.05).

    Solution
    1250 x 0.05 = 62.50

    The duty paid is $62.50.

24. Strategy
    To find the duty paid, multiply the value of the shipment ($4750) by the ad valorem percent (3.5% = 0.035).

    Solution
    4750 x 0.035 = 166.25

    The duty paid is $166.25.

25. Strategy
    To find the duty paid, multiply the value of the shipment ($280) by the ad valorem percent (4.9% = 0.049).

    Solution
    280 x 0.049 = 13.72

    The duty paid is $13.72.

26. Strategy
    To find the duty paid, multiply the value of the shipment ($1490) by the ad valorem percent (3.7% = 0.037).

    Solution
    1490 x 0.037 = 55.13

    The duty paid is $55.13.

27. Strategy
    (a) To find the ad valorem duty paid per parachute, multiply the value of each parachute ($100) by the ad valorem percent (6% = 0.06).
    (b) To find the ad valorem duty paid on the entire shipment, multiply the ad valorem duty paid per parachute by the number of parachutes (200).

    Solution
    (a) 100 x 0.06 = 6

    The ad valorem duty paid per parachute is $6.

    (b) 200 x 6 = 1200

    The ad valorem duty paid on the entire shipment is $1200.

28. Strategy
    (a) To find the ad valorem duty paid per inflatable raft, multiply the value of each inflatable raft ($50) by the ad valorem percent (3.8% = 0.038).
    (b) To find the ad valorem duty paid on the entire shipment, multiply the ad valorem duty paid per inflatable raft by the number of inflatable rafts (150).

    Solution
    (a) 50 x 0.038 = 1.9

    The ad valorem duty paid per raft is $1.90.

    (b) 150 x 1.90 = 285

    The ad valorem duty paid on the entire shipment is $285.

29. Strategy
    To find the ad valorem duty paid:
    * Multiply the value of each paint roller ($1.10) by the ad valorem percent (7.5% = 0.075) to find the ad valorem duty paid per roller.
    * Multiply the ad valorem duty paid per roller by the number of rollers (500) to find the ad valorem duty paid on the entire shipment.

    Solution
    0.075 x 1.10 = 0.0825
    0.0825 x 500 = 41.25

    The ad valorem duty paid by the company for the shipment is $41.25.

30. Strategy
    To find the ad valorem duty paid:
    * Multiply the value of each refrigerator ($225) by the ad valorem percent (2.9% = 0.029) to find the ad valorem duty paid per refrigerator.
    * Multiply the ad valorem duty paid per refrigerator by the number of refrigerators (350) to find the ad valorem duty paid on the entire shipment.

    Solution
    0.029 x 225 = 6.525
    6.525 x 350 = 2283.75

    The ad valorem duty paid by the company for the shipment is $2283.75.

31. Strategy
    (a) To find the specific duty paid on the jewelry boxes, multiply the specific duty (2.2¢ = $.022) by the number of kilograms of jewelry boxes imported (40).
    (b) To find the ad valorem duty paid on the jewelry boxes, multiply the value of the shipment ($1200) by the ad valorem percent (2.9% = 0.029).
    (c) To find the total import duties paid on the shipment, add the specific duty and the ad valorem duty.

    Solution
    40 x 0.022 = 0.88

    The specific duty paid on the jewelry boxes is $.88.

    1200 x 0.029 = 34.8

    The ad valorem duty paid on the jewelry boxes is $34.80.

    0.88 + 34.8 = 35.68

    The total import duties paid are $35.68.

32. Strategy
    (a) To find the specific duty paid on the imported gloves, multiply the specific
        duty (33.1¢ = $.331) by the number of kilograms of gloves imported (10).
    (b) To find the ad valorem duty paid on the gloves, multiply the value of the
        shipment ($850) by the ad valorem percent (7.4% = 0.074).
    (c) To find the total import duties paid on the shipment, add the specific duty and
        the ad valorem duty.

    Solution
    10 x 0.0331 = 3.31

    The specific duty paid on the gloves is $3.31.

    850 x 0.074 = 62.90

    The ad valorem duty paid on the gloves is $62.90.

    3.31 + 62.90 = 66.21

    The total import duties paid are $66.21.

33. Strategy
    To find the duty paid:
    • Multiply the specific duty (8.8¢ = $.088) by the number of kilograms of plastic
      safety headgear (130) to find the specific duty.
    • Multiply the value of the shipment ($5600) by the ad valorem percent (3.4% =
      0.034) to find the ad valorem duty.
    • Add the specific duty and the ad valorem duty.

    Solution
    130 x 0.088 = 1144
    5600 x 0.034 = 190.4
    11.44 + 190.4 = 201.84

    The duty paid is $201.84.

34. Strategy
    To find the duty paid:
    • Multiply the specific duty (1.1¢ = $.011) by the number of kilograms of soap
      (350) to find the specific duty.
    • Multiply the value of the shipment ($280) by the ad valorem percent (3.6% =
      0.036) to find the ad valorem duty.
    • Add the specific duty and the ad valorem duty.

    Solution
    350 x 0.011 = 3.85
    280 x 0.036 = 10.08
    3.85 + 10.08 = 13.93

    The duty paid is $13.93.

35. Strategy
    (a) To find the specific duty paid for the order, multiply the specific duty
        (0.8¢ = $.008) by the number of refills imported (500).
    (b) To find the ad valorem duty paid for the order:
        • Multiply the value of each refill ($.12) by the ad valorem percent
          (5.4% = 0.054) to find the ad valorem duty paid per refill.
        • Multiply the ad valorem duty paid per refill by the number of refills (500) to
          find the ad valorem duty paid for the entire order.
    (c) To find the total import duties paid on the order, add the specific duty and the
        ad valorem duty.

    Solution
    500 x 0.008 = 4

    The specific duty paid for the order is $4.

    0.12 x 0.054 = 0.00648
    500 x 0.00648 = 3.24

    The ad valorem duty paid for the order is $3.24.

    4 + 3.24 = 7.24

    The total import duties paid are $7.24.

36. Strategy
    (a) To find the specific duty paid for the order, multiply the specific duty
        (0.5¢ = $.005) by the number of pipes imported (30).
    (b) To find the ad valorem duty paid for the order:
        • Multiply the value of each pipe ($2.25) by the ad valorem percent (4% = 0.04)
          to find the ad valorem duty paid per pipe.
        • Multiply the ad valorem duty paid per pipe by the number of pipes (30) to
          find the ad valorem duty paid for the entire order.
    (c) To find the total import duties paid on the order, add the specific duty and the
        ad valorem duty.

    Solution
    30 x 0.005 = 0.15

    The specific duty paid for the order is $.15.

    2.25 x 0.04 = 0.09
    30 x 0.09 = 2.7

    The ad valorem duty paid for the order is $2.70.

    0.15 + 2.70 = 2.85

    The total import duties paid are $2.85.

37. Strategy
    (a) To find the specific duty paid for the order:
        • Multiply the specific duty (68.3¢ = $.683) by the number of kilograms each cape weighs (1.2) to find the specific duty paid per cape.
        • Multiply the specific duty paid per cape by the number of capes (750) to find the specific duty paid on the entire order.
    (b) To find the ad valorem duty paid for the order:
        • Multiply the value of each cape ($28) by the ad valorem percent (20% = 0.2) to find the ad valorem duty paid per cape.
        • Multiply the ad valorem duty paid per cape by the number of capes (750) to find the ad valorem duty paid for the entire order.
    (c) To find the total import duties paid on the order, add the specific duty and the ad valorem duty.

    Solution
    1.2 x 0.683 = 0.8196
    750 x 0.8196 = 614.7

    The specific duty paid on the order is $614.70.

    28 x 0.2 = 5.6
    750 x 5.6 = 4200

    The ad valorem duty paid on the order is $4200.

    614.70 + 4200 = 4814.70

    The total import duties paid are $4814.70.

38. Strategy
    (a) To find the specific duty paid for the order:
        • Multiply the specific duty (11¢ = $.11) by the number of kilograms each bottle weighs (0.4) to find the specific duty paid per bottle.
        • Multiply the specific duty paid per bottle by the number of bottles (250) to find the specific duty paid on the entire order.
    (b) To find the ad valorem duty paid for the order:
        • Multiply the value of each bottle ($.80) by the ad valorem percent (4.5% = 0.045) to find the ad valorem duty paid per bottle.
        • Multiply the ad valorem duty paid per bottle by the number of bottles (250) to find the ad valorem duty paid for the entire order.
    (c) To find the total import duties paid on the order, add the specific duty and the ad valorem duty.

    Solution
    0.4 x 0.11 = 0.044
    250 x 0.044 = 11

    The specific duty paid on the shipment is $11.

    0.8 x 0.045 = 0.036
    250 x 0.036 = 9

    The ad valorem duty paid on the shipment is $9.

    11 + 9 = 20

    The total import duties paid are $20.

39. Strategy
    To find the import duty paid on the shipment:
    • Multiply the specific duty (0.2¢ = $.002) by the number of toothbrushes (1200) to find the specific duty paid on the shipment.
    • Multiply the value of each toothbrush ($.30) by the ad valorem percent (3.4% = 0.034) to find the ad valorem duty paid per toothbrush.
    • Multiply the ad valorem duty paid per toothbrush by the number of toothbrushes (1200) to find the ad valorem duty paid for the entire shipment.
    • Add the specific duty and the ad valorem duty to find the total import duty paid on the shipment.

    Solution
    0.002 x 1200 = 2.4
    0.30 x 0.034 = 0.0102
    1200 x 0.0102 = 12.24
    2.4 + 12.24 = 14.64

    The total import duty paid is $14.64.

40. Strategy
    To find the import duty paid on the shipment:
    • Divide the number of hats (600) by 12 to find the number of dozens of hats.
    • Multiply the specific duty ($1.10) by the number of dozens of hats to find the specific duty paid on the shipment.
    • Multiply the value of each hat ($.95) by the ad valorem percent (1.6% = 0.016) to find the ad valorem duty paid per hat.
    • Multiply the ad valorem duty paid per hat by the number of hats (600) to find the ad valorem duty paid for the entire shipment.
    • Add the specific duty and the ad valorem duty to find the total import duty paid on the shipment.

    Solution
    600 ÷ 12 = 50
    50 x 1.10 = 55
    0.95 x 0.016 = 0.0152
    600 x 0.0152 = 9.12
    55 + 9.12 = 64.12

    The total import duty paid is $64.12.

Section 16.2, pages 499–502

1. peso
2. 1.01
3. 0.99 peso
4. dollar
5. 0.8415
6. $1.1883 Canadian
7. peso
8. 0.04184
9. 23.90 pesos
10. shekel
11. 0.4184
12. 2.3900 shekel
13. won
14. 0.0012671
15. 789.20 won
16. cruzeiro
17. 0.00020
18. 4920.00 cruzeiros

19. Strategy
    To determine whether the value of the U.S. dollar rose or fell relative to the value
    of the German mark, use Columns 4 and 5 to determine whether the exchange rate for
    German marks per U.S. dollar increased or decreased from Monday to Tuesday.

    Solution
    Since the exchange rate for German marks per U.S. dollar decreased from Monday to
    Tuesday (1.4030 to 1.4003), the value of the U.S. dollar fell relative to the German
    mark.

20. Strategy
    To determine whether the value of the U.S. dollar rose or fell relative to the value
    of the Singapore dollar, use Columns 4 and 5 to determine whether the exchange rate
    for Singapore dollars per U.S. dollar increased or decreased from Monday to Tuesday.

    Solution
    Since the exchange rate for Singapore dollars per U.S. dollar decreased from Monday
    to Tuesday (1.6015 to 1.6005), the value of the U.S. dollar fell relative to the
    Singapore dollar.

21. Strategy
    To determine whether the value of the U.S. dollar rose or fell relative to the value
    of the Irish punt, use Columns 4 and 5 to determine whether the exchange rate for
    Irish punts per U.S. dollar increased or decreased from Monday to Tuesday.

    Solution
    Since the exchange rate for Singapore dollars per U.S. dollar increased from Monday
    to Tuesday (0.5292 to 0.5298), the value of the U.S. dollar rose relative to the
    Irish punt.

22. Strategy
    To determine whether the value of the U.S. dollar rose or fell relative to the value
    of the Peruvian new sol, use Columns 4 and 5 to determine whether the exchange rate
    for Peruvian new sols per U.S. dollar increased or decreased from Monday to Tuesday.

    Solution
    Since the exchange rate for Peruvian new sols per U.S. dollar increased from Monday
    to Tuesday (1.25 to 1.29), the value of the U.S. dollar rose relative to the
    Peruvian new sol.

23. Strategy
    TO find the number of U.S. dollars that would be exchanged on Monday, multiply the
    exchange rate in Column 3 by the number of Swedish kronon (10,000).

    Solution
    From Column 3:
    $.1950 U.S. = 1 Swedish krona
    0.1950 x 10,000 = 1950

    $1950 U.S. would be exchanged for 10,000 Swedish kronon on Monday.

24. Strategy
    To find the number of U.S. dollars that would be exchanged on Tuesday, multiply the
    exchange rate in Column 2 by the number of Chinese renminbi (50,000).

    Solution
    From Column 2:
    $184003 U.S. = 1 Chinese renminbi
    0.184003 x 50,000 = 9200.15

    $9200.15 U.S. would be exchanged for 50,000 Chinese renminbi on Tuesday.

25. Strategy
     To find the number of Indian rupees that would be exchanged on Tuesday, multiply the
     exchange rate in Column 4 by the number of U.S. dollars (8000).

     Solution
     From Column 4:
     28.18 Indian rupees = $1 U.S.
     28.18 x 8000 = 225,440

     225,440 Indian rupees would be exchanged for $8000 U.S. on Tuesday.

26. Strategy
     To find the number of Indonesian rupiah that would be exchanged on Monday, multiply
     the exchange rate in Column 5 by the number of U.S. dollars (15,000).

     Solution
     2027.04 Indonesian rupiah = $1 U.S.
     2027.04 x 15,000 = 30,405,600

     30,405,600 Indonesian rupiah would be exchanged for $15,000 U.S. on Monday.

27. Strategy
     To find the number of U.S. dollars that would be exchanged on Monday, multiply the
     exchange rate in Column 3 by the number of Swiss francs (20,000).

     Solution
     From Column 3:
     $.8045 U.S. = 1 Swiss franc
     0.8045 x 20,000 = 16,090

     $16,090 U.S. would be exchanged for 20,000 Swiss francs on Monday.

28. Strategy
     To find the number of U.S. dollars that would be exchanged on Tuesday, multiply the
     exchange rate in Column 2 by the number of New Zealand dollars (42,000).

     Solution
     From Column 2:
     $.5413 U.S. = 1 New Zealand
     0.5413 x 42,000 = 22,734.6

     $22,734.60 U.S. would be exchanged for $42,000 New Zealand on Tuesday.

29. Strategy
     To find the number of Australian dollars that would be exchanged on Tuesday,
     multiply the exchange rate in Column 4 by the number of U.S. dollars (35,000).

     Solution
     From Column 4:
     $1.4065 Australian = $1 U.S.
     1.4065 x 35,000 = 49,227.5

     $49,227.50 Australian would be exchanged for $35,000 U.S. on Tuesday.

30. Strategy
    To find the number of British pounds that would be exchanged on Monday, multiply the
    exchange rate in Column 5 by the number of U.S. dollars (40,000).

    Solution
    From Column 5:
    0.5016 British pounds = $1 U.S.
    0.5016 x 40,000 = 20,064

    20,064 British pounds would be exchanged for $40,000 U.S. on Monday.

31. Strategy
    To find the purchase price in U.S. dollars, multiply the exchange rate in Column 2
    by the purchase price in Colombian pesos (8,000,000).

    Solution
    $.001709 U.S. = 1 Colombian peso
    0.001709 x 8,000,000 = 13,672

    The purchase price is $13,672 U.S.

32. Strategy
    To find the purchase price in U.S. dollars, multiply the exchange rate in Column 2
    by the purchase price in French francs (650,000).

    Solution
    From Column 2:
    $.20929 U.S = 1 French franc
    0.20929 x 650,000 = 136,038.50

    The purchase price is $136,038.50 U.S.

33. Strategy
    To find the purchase price in Netherlands guilders, multiply the exchange rate in
    Column 4 by the purchase price in U.S. dollars (85,000).

    Solution
    From Column 4:
    1.5785 Netherlands guilders = $1 U.S.
    1.5785 x 85,000 = 134,174.50

    The purchase price is 134,172.50 Netherlands guilders.

34. Strategy
    To find the purchase price in Danish kroner, multiply the exchange rate in Column 4
    by the purchase price in U.S. dollars (40,000).

    Solution
    From Column 4:
    5.4192 Danish kroner = $1 U.S.
    5.4192 x 40,000 = 216,768

    The purchase price is 216,768 Danish kroner.

35. Strategy
    To find the price in Italian lira, multiply the exchange rate in Column 4 by the
    price in U.S. dollars (75,000).

    Solution
    From Column 4:
    1069.98 Italian lira = $1 U.S.
    1069.98 x 75,000 = 80,248,500

    The price is 80,248,500 Italian lira.

36. Strategy
    To find the price in Thailand bahts, multiply the exchange rate in Column 4 by the price in U.S. dollars (42,000).

    Solution
    From Column 4:
    25.20 Thailand bahts = $1 U.S.
    25.20 x 42,000 = 1,058,400

    The price is 1,058,400 Thailand bahts.

37. Strategy
    (a) To find the number of Finnish markkas that would be exchanged on Monday, multiply the exchange rate in Column 5 by the number of U.S. dollars (25,000).
    (b) To find the number of Finnish markkas that would be exchanged on Tuesday, multiply the exchange rate in Column 4 by the number of U.S. dollars (25,000).
    (c) To find the difference between the two currency exchanges, subtract the smaller number from the larger number.

    Solution
    From Column 5:
    3.8717 Finnish markkas = $1 U.S.
    3.8717 x 25,000 = 96,792.5

    96,792.50 Finnish markkas would be exchanged for $25,000 U.S. on Monday.

    From Column 4:
    3.8769 Finnish markkas = $1 U.S.
    3.8769 x 25,000 = 96,922.5

    96,922.50 Finnish markkas would be exchanged for $25,000 U.S. on Tuesday.

    96,922.5 - 96,792.5 = 130

    The difference between the two currency exchanges is 130 Finnish markkas.

38. Strategy
    (a) To find the number of Belgian francs that would be exchanged on Monday, multiply the exchange rate in Column 5 by the number of U.S. dollars (12,000).
    (b) To find the number of Belgian francs that would be exchanged on Tuesday, multiply the exchange rate in Column 4 by the number of U.S. dollars (12,000).
    (c) To find the difference between the two currency exchanges, subtract the smaller number from the larger number.

    Solution
    From Column 5:
    28.94 Belgian francs = $1 U.S.
    28.94 x 12,000 = 347,280

    347,280 Belgian francs would be exchanged for $12,000 U.S. on Monday.

    From Column 4:
    28.86 Belgian francs = $1 U.S.
    28.86 x 12,000 = 346,320

    346,320 Belgian francs would be exchanged for $12,000 U.S. on Tuesday.

    347,280 - 346,320 = 960

    The difference between the two currency exchanges is 960 Belgian francs.

39. Strategy
    (a) To find the number of U.S. dollars that would be exchanged on Monday, multiply the exchange rate in Column 3 by the number of Austrian schillings (30,000).
    (b) To find the number of U.S. dollars that would be exchanged on Tuesday, multiply the exchange rate in Column 2 by the number of Austrian schillings (30,000).
    (c) To find the difference between the two currency exchanges, subtract the smaller number from the larger number.

    Solution
    From Column 3:
    0.10130 Austrian schillings = $1 U.S.
    0.0130 x 30,000 = 3039

    $3039 U.S. dollars would be exchanged for 30,000 Austrian schillings on Monday.

    From Column 2:
    0.10149 Austrian schillings = $1 U.S.
    0.10149 x 30,000 = 3044.7

    $3044.70 U.S. would be exchanged for 30,000 Austrian schillings on Tuesday.

    3044.70 - 3039 = 5.7

    The difference between the two currency exchanges is $5.70 U.S.

40. Strategy
    (a) To find the number of U.S. dollars that would be exchanged on Monday, multiply the exchange rate in Column 3 by the number of Polish zloty (8,000,000).
    (b) To find the number of U.S. dollars that would be exchanged on Tuesday, multiply the exchange rate in Column 2 by the number of Polish zloty (8,000,000).
    (c) To find the difference between the two currency exchanges, subtract the smaller number from the larger number.

    Solution
    From Column 3:
    0.00007686 Polish zloty = $1 U.S.
    0.00007686 x 8,000,000 = 614.88

    $614.88 U.S. would be exchanged for 8,000,000 Polish zloty on Monday.

    From Column 2:
    0.00007422 Polish zloty = $1 U.S.
    0.00007422 x 8,000,000 = 593.76

    $593.76 U.S. would be exchanged for 8,000,000 Polish zloty on Tuesday.

    614.88 - 593.76 = 21.12

    The difference between the two currency exchanges is $21.12 U.S.

41. Strategy

    To find the difference between the number of Portuguese escudos that would be exchanged on Monday and the number that would be exchanged on Tuesday:
    - Multiply the exchange rate in Column 5 by the number of U.S. dollars (20,000) to find the number of Portuguese escudos that would be exchanged on Monday.
    - Multiply the exchange rate in Column 4 by the number of U.S. dollars (20,000) to find the number of Portuguese escudos that would be exchanged on Tuesday.
    - Subtract the smaller number from the larger number.

    Solution
    From Column 5:
    123.53 Portuguese escudos = $1 U.S.
    123.53 x 20,000 = 2,470,600

    From Column 4:
    122.74 Portuguese escudos = $1 U.S.
    122.74 x 20,000 = 2,454,800

    2,470,600 - 2,454,800 = 15,800

    The difference between the number of Portuguese escudos that would be exchanged for $20,000 U.S. on Monday and on Tuesday is 15,800 Portuguese escudos.

42. Strategy

    To find the difference between the number of Spanish pesetas that would be exchanged on Monday and the number that would be exchanged on Tuesday:
    - Multiply the exchange rate in Column 5 by the number of U.S. dollars (45,000) to find the number of Spanish pesetas that would be exchanged on Monday.
    - Multiply the exchange rate in Column 4 by the number of U.S. dollars (45,000) to find the number of Spanish pesetas that would be exchanged on Tuesday.
    - Subtract the smaller number from the larger number.

    Solution
    From Column 5:
    90.62 Spanish pesetas = $1 U.S.
    90.62 x 45,000 = 4,077,900

    From Column 4:
    90.95 Spanish pesetas = $1 U.S.
    90.95 x 45,000 = 4,092,750

    4,092,750 - 4,077,900 = 14,850

    The difference between the number of Spanish pesetas that would be exchanged for $45,000 U.S. on Monday and on Tuesday is 14,850 Spanish pesetas.

43. Strategy
     To find the difference between the number of U.S. dollars that would be exchanged on
     Monday and the number that would be exchanged on Tuesday:
     • Multiply the exchange rate in Column 3 by the number of Taiwanese dollars
       (5,000,000) to find the number of U.S. dollars that would be exchanged on Monday.
     • Multiply the exchange rate in Column 2 by the number of Taiwanese dollars
       (5,000,000) to find the number of U.S. dollars that would be exchanged on
       Tuesday.
     • Subtract the smaller number from the larger number.

     Solution
     From Column 3:
     $.040225 U.S. = $1 Taiwanese
     0.040225 x 5,000,000 = 201,125

     From Column 2:
     $.039746 U.S. = $1 Taiwanese
     0.039746 x 5,000,000 = 198,730

     201,125 - 198,730 = 2395

     The difference between the number of U.S. dollars that would be exchanged for
     $5,000,000 Taiwanese on Monday and on Tuesday is $2395 U.S.

44. Strategy
     To find the difference between the number of U.S. dollars that would be exchanged on
     Monday and the number that would be exchanged on Tuesday:
     • Multiply the exchange rate in Column 3 by the number of Turkish lira (9,000,000)
       to find the number of U.S. dollars that would be exchanged on Monday.
     • Multiply the exchange rate in Column 2 by the number of Turkish lira (9,000,000)
       to find the number of U.S. dollars that would be exchanged on Tuesday.
     • Subtract the smaller number from the larger number.

     Solution
     From Column 3:
     $.0001447 U.S. = 1 Turkish lira
     0.0001447 x 9,000,000 = 1302.3

     From Column 2:
     $.0001458 U.S. = 1 Turkish lira
     0.0001458 x 9,000,000 = 1312.2

     1312.2 - 1302.3 = 9.9

     The difference between the number of U.S. dollars that would be exchanged for
     9,000,000 Turkish lira on Monday and on Tuesday is $9.90 U.S.

45. Strategy
To find how many more U.S. dollars would be paid for the order if the exchange rate
for Monday were used rather than the exchange rate for Tuesday:
*   Multiply the exchange rate in Column 3 by the number of Chilean pesos
    (50,000,000) to find the number of U.S. dollars that would be exchanged on
    Monday.
*   Multiply the exchange rate in Column 2 by the number of Chilean pesos
    (50,000,000) to find the number of U.S. dollars that would be exchanged on
    Tuesday.
*   Subtract the number of U.S. dollars that would be exchanged on Tuesday from the
    number of U.S. dollars that would be exchanged on Monday.

Solution
$.002788 U.S. = 1 Chilean peso
0.002788 x 50,000,000 = 139,400

From Column 2:
$.002690 U.S. = 1 Chilean peso
0.002690 x 50,000,000 = 134,500

139,400 - 134,500 = 4900

$4900 U.S. more would be paid for the order if the exchange rate for Monday were
used rather than the exchange rate for Tuesday.

46. Strategy
To find how many more U.S. dollars would be paid for the aluminum if the exchange
rate for Tuesday were used rather than the exchange rate for Monday:
*   Multiply the exchange rate in Column 3 by the number of Norwegian kroner
    (700,000) to find the number of U.S. dollars that would be exchanged on Monday.
*   Multiply the exchange rate in Column 2 by the number of Norwegian kroner
    (700,000) to find the number of U.S. dollars that would be exchanged on Tuesday.
*   Subtract the number of U.S. dollars that would be exchanged on Tuesday from the
    number of U.S. dollars that would be exchanged on Monday.

Solution
From Column 3:
$.1801 U.S. = 1 Norwegian krone
0.1801 x 700,000 = 126,070

From Column 2:
$.1805 U.S. = 1 Norwegian krone
0.1805 x 700,000 = 126,350

126,350 - 126,070 = 280

$280 U.S. more would be paid for the order if the exchange rate for Tuesday were
used rather than the exchange rate for Monday.

Business Case Study

1.

Item	Total Weight	Unit Cost in U.S. $	Total Cost in U.S. $	Import Duties	Freight Charges	Total Cost + Import Duties + Freight Charges	Cost + Duties + Shipping Per Unit	Selling Price Per Unit
Sweaters	75 kg	$ 13.00	$1950.00	$ 666.90	$150	$2766.90	$18.45	$ 27.68
Overcoats	200 kg	59.80	5980.00	1348.40	400	7728.40	77.28	115.92
Capes	60 kg	45.50	2275.00	505.53	120	2900.53	58.01	87.02
Bathrobes	35 kg	14.95	747.50	63.54	70	881.04	17.62	26.43
Suits	90 kg	149.50	7475.00	2089.38	180	9744.38	194.88	292.32
Jackets	100 kg	36.40	3640.00	1038.50	200	4878.50	48.79	73.19
Trousers	40 kg	14.30	1430.00	321.46	80	1831.46	18.31	27.47
Vests	10 kg	12.35	617.50	211.19	20	848.69	16.97	25.46
Sweatshirts	30 kg	9.10	910.00	311.22	60	1281.22	12.81	19.22
T-shirts	27 kg	7.15	1072.50	364.65	54	1491.15	9.94	14.91
Tank tops	15 kg	5.85	585.00	198.90	30	813.90	8.14	12.21
Windbreakers	22 kg	13.00	1300.00	221.00	44	1565.00	15.65	23.48
Terry suits	14 kg	4.55	455.00	102.03	28	585.03	5.85	8.78
Overalls	6 kg	7.80	390.00	84.68	12	486.68	9.73	14.60
Dresses	8 kg	9.10	455.00	99.25	16	570.25	11.41	17.12
Coveralls	18 kg	8.45	845.00	185.78	36	1066.78	10.67	16.01
	750 kg		30,127.50	7812.41	1500			

2. (a) The total weight of the shipment is 750 kg.
   (b) The total cost of the items ordered in U.S. dollars is $30,127.50.
   (c) The total paid in import duties is $7812.41.
   (d) The total paid in freight charges is $1500.

3. Commission = 0.02($30,127.50) = $602.55

4. Total cost = total cost of items + total paid in import duties + total paid in
            freight charges + commission
          = $30,127.50 + $7812.41 + $1500 + $602.55 = $40,042.46

5. Answers will vary. For example:
   Buying domestic products is favorable for the balance of trade. It also strengthens
   domestic industries, thereby increasing employment opportunities for the nation's
   citizens and increasing business tax revenues for the government. It can further
   domestic growth and economic stability.

Review/Test, pages 507–508

1. Strategy
   (a) To determine whether the balance of trade was favorable or unfavorable, determine whether the value of the exports or imports is greater.
   (b) To find Sweden's balance of trade, subtract the smaller number (54,580 million) from the larger number (57,423 million). If the balance of trade is unfavorable, use a negative sign.

   Solution
   Since the value of the exports is greater than the value of the imports, Sweden had a favorable balance of trade.
   57,423 million - 54,580 million = 2,843 million

   Sweden's balance of trade in 1990 was $2,843 million.

2. Strategy
   (a) To determine whether the balance of trade was favorable or unfavorable, determine whether the value of the exports or imports is greater.
   (b) To find France's balance of trade, subtract the smaller number (210.0 billion) from the larger number (233.2 billion). If the balance of trade is unfavorable, use a negative sign.

   Solution
   Since the value of the imports is greater than the value of the exports, France had an unfavorable balance of trade.
   233.2 billion - 210.0 billion = 23.2 billion

   France's balance of trade in 1990 was -$23.2 billion.

3. Strategy
   (a) To determine whether Pakistan had a trade deficit, determine whether the value of the exports or imports is greater.
   (b) To find the balance of trade for Pakistan, subtract the smaller number (5,522 million) from the larger number (7,356 million). If the balance of trade is unfavorable, use a negative sign.

   Solution
   Since the value of the imports is greater than the value of the exports, Pakistan had a trade deficit.
   7,356 million - 5,522 million = 1,834 million

   In 1990, the balance of trade for Pakistan was -$1,834 million.

4. Strategy
   To find the Netherlands' balance of trade in 1990:
   • Determine whether the balance of trade was favorable or unfavorable.
   • Subtract the smaller number (126.2 billion) from the larger number (131.8 billion). If the balance of trade is unfavorable, use a negative sign.

   Solution
   Since the value of the exports is greater than the value of the imports, the Netherlands had a favorable balance of trade.
   131.8 billion - 126.2 billion = 5.6 billion

   The Netherlands' balance of trade in 1990 was $5.6 billion.

5. Strategy
    To find the duty paid, multiply the specific duty (6.6¢ = $.066) by the number of
    liters imported (150).

    Solution
    150 x 0.066 = 9.9

    The duty paid is $9.90.

6. Strategy
    To find the duty paid, multiply the value of the shipment ($12,000) by the ad
    valorem percent (6.9% = 0.069).

    Solution
    12,000 x 0.069 = 828

    The duty paid is $828.

7. Strategy
    To find the ad valorem duty paid:
    • Multiply the value of each bicycle ($84) by the ad valorem percent (11% = 0.11)
      to find the ad valorem duty paid per bicycle.
    • Multiply the ad valorem duty paid per bicycle by the number of bicycles (175) to
      find the ad valorem duty paid on the entire shipment.

    Solution
    0.11 x 84 = 9.24
    9.24 x 175 = 1617

    The ad valorem duty paid by the company for the shipment is $1617.

8. Strategy
    To find the duty paid:
    • Multiply the specific duty (4.4¢ = $.044) by the number of kilograms of adhesives
      (270) to find the specific duty.
    • Multiply the value of the shipment ($13,500) by the ad valorem percent
      (6% = 0.06) to find the ad valorem duty.
    • Add the specific duty and the ad valorem duty.

    Solution
    270 x 0.044 = 11.88
    13,500 x 0.06 = 810
    11.88 + 810 = 821.88

    The duty paid is $821.88.

9. Strategy
    (a) To find the specific duty paid for the order, multiply the specific duty
        (37.5¢ = $.375) by the number of jackets imported (850) by the weight of each
        jacket (1.4).
    (b) To find the ad valorem duty paid for the order:
        • Multiply the value of each jacket ($23) by the ad valorem percent
          (27.5% = 0.275) to find the ad valorem duty paid per jacket.
        • Multiply the ad valorem duty paid per jacket by the number of jackets (850) to
          find the ad valorem duty paid for the entire order.
    (c) To find the total import duties paid on the order, add the specific duty and the
        ad valorem duty.

    Solution
    850 x 0.375 x 1.4 = 446.25

    The specific duty paid for the order is $446.25.

    23 x 0.275 = 6.325
    850 x 6.325 = 5376.25

    The ad valorem duty paid for the order is $5376.25.

    446.25 + 5376.25 = 5822.50

    The total import duties paid are $5822.50.

10. Strategy
    To find the import duty paid on the shipment:
    • Multiply the specific duty (0.3¢ = $.003) by the number of hair brushes (800) to
      find the specific duty paid on the shipment.
    • Multiply the value of each hair brush ($1.65) by the ad valorem percent
      (3.6% = 0.036) to find the ad valorem duty paid per hair brush.
    • Multiply the ad valorem duty paid per hair brush by the number of hair brushes
      (800) to find the ad valorem duty paid for the entire shipment.
    • Add the specific duty and the ad valorem duty to find the total import duty paid
      on the shipment.

    Solution
    0.003 x 800 = 2.4
    1.65 x 0.036 = 0.0594
    800 x 0.0594 = 47.52
    2.4 + 47.52 = 49.92

    The total import duties paid are $49.92.

11. Strategy
    To determine whether the value of the U.S. dollar rose or fell relative to the value
    of the Swedish krona, use Columns 4 and 5 to determine whether the exchange rate for
    Swedish krona per U.S. dollar increased or decreased from Monday to Tuesday.

    Solution
    Since the exchange rate for Swedish krona per U.S. dollar decreased from Monday to
    Tuesday (5.1278 to 5.1217), the value of the U.S. dollar fell relative to the
    Swedish krona.

Copyright © Houghton Mifflin Company. All rights reserved.

12. Strategy
    To find the number of U.S. dollars that would be exchanged on Tuesday, multiply the exchange rate in Column 2 by the number of German marks (12,000).

    Solution
    From Column 2:
    $.7141 U.S. = 1 German mark
    0.7141 x 12,000 = 8569.2

    $8569.20 U.S. would be exchanged for 12,000 German marks on Tuesday.

13. Strategy
    To find the number of Irish punts that would be exchanged on Monday, multiply the exchange rate in Column 5 by the number of U.S. dollars (35,000).

    Solution
    0.5292 Irish punts = $1 U.S.
    0.5292 x 35,000 = 18,522

    18,522 Irish punts would be exchanged for $35,000 U.S. on Monday.

14. Strategy
    To find the purchase price in U.S. dollars, multiply the exchange rate in Column 2 by the purchase price in Philippine pesos (642,000).

    Solution
    $.04184 U.S. = 1 Philippine peso
    0.04184 x 642,000 = 26,861.28

    The purchase price is $26,861.28 U.S.

15. Strategy
    To find the purchase price in Argentinian pesos, multiply the exchange rate in Column 4 by the purchase price in U.S. dollars (178,000).

    Solution
    From Column 4:
    0.99 Argentinian pesos = $1 U.S.
    0.99 x 178,000 = 176,220

    The purchase price is 176,220 Argentinian pesos.

16. Strategy
    To find the difference between the number of Brazilian cruzeiros that would be exchanged on Monday and the number that would be exchanged on Tuesday:
    • Multiply the exchange rate in Column 5 by the number of U.S. dollars (10,000) to find the number of Brazilian cruzeiros that would be exchanged on Monday.
    • Multiply the exchange rate in Column 4 by the number of U.S. dollars (10,000) to find the number of Brazilian cruzeiros that would be exchanged on Tuesday.
    • Subtract the smaller number from the larger number.

    Solution
    From Column 5:
    4699.00 Brazilian cruzeiros = $1 U.S.
    4699.00 x 10,000 = 46,990,000

    From Column 4:
    4920 Brazilian cruzeiros = $1 U.S.
    4920.00 x 10,000 = 49,200,000
    49,200,000 - 46,990,000 = 2,210,000

    The difference between the number of Brazilian cruzeiros that would be exchanged for $10,000 U.S. on Monday and on Tuesday is 2,210,000 Brazilian cruzeiros.

17. Strategy
     To find the difference between the number of U.S. dollars that would be exchanged on
     Monday and the number that would be exchanged on Tuesday:
     • Multiply the exchange rate in Column 3 by the number of Peruvian new sols
       (50,000) to find the number of U.S. dollars that would be exchanged on Monday.
     • Multiply the exchange rate in Column 2 by the number of Peruvian new sols
       (50,000) to find the number of U.S. dollars that would be exchanged on Tuesday.
     • Subtract the smaller number from the larger number.

     Solution
     From Column 3:
     $.8026 U.S. = 1 Peruvian new sol
     0.8026 x 50,000 = 40,130

     From Column 2:
     $.7782 U.S. = 1 Peruvian new sol
     0.7782 x 50,000 = 38,910
     40,130 - 38,910 = 1220

     The difference between the number of U.S. dollars that would be exchanged for 50,000
     Peruvian new sols on Monday and on Tuesday is $1220 U.S.

18. Strategy
     To find how many more U.S. dollars would be paid for the order if the exchange rate
     for Monday were used rather than the exchange rate for Tuesday:
     • Multiply the exchange rate in Column 3 by the number of Israeli shekel (218,000)
       to find the number of U.S. dollars that would be exchanged on Monday.
     • Multiply the exchange rate in Column 2 by the number of shekel (218,000) to find
       the number of U.S. dollars that would be exchanged on Tuesday.
     • Subtract the number of U.S. dollars that would be exchanged on Tuesday from the
       number of U.S. dollars that would be exchanged on Monday.

     Solution
     From Column 3:
     $.4185 U.S. = 1 shekel
     0.4185 x 218,000 = 91,233

     From Column 2:
     $.4184 U.S. = 1 shekel
     0.4184 x 218,000 = 91,211.20
     91,233 - 91.211.20 = 21.80

     $21.80 U.S. more would be paid for the order if the exchange rate for Monday were
     used rather than the exchange rate for Tuesday.

CHAPTER 17
Investments

Section 17.1, pages 519–524

1. $28\frac{1}{8}$

2. $13\frac{1}{2}$

3. (a) 24   (b) $42\frac{5}{8}$

4. (a) $.30   (b) 1.2%

5. Cost = $200\left(24\frac{1}{2}\right) = \$4900$

6. Cost = $500\left(47\frac{7}{8}\right) = \$23,937.50$

7. Dividend = $500(1.56) = \$780$

8. Dividend = $300(1.10) = \$330$

9. Strategy
   To find the selling price, multiply the price per share $\left(37\frac{3}{4}\right)$ by the number of shares (325).

   Solution
   $325\left(37\frac{3}{4}\right) = 12,268.75$

   The selling price is $12,268.75.

10. Strategy
    To find the buying price, multiply the price per share $\left(12\frac{7}{8}\right)$ by the number of shares (250).

    Solution
    $250\left(12\frac{7}{8}\right) = 3218.75$

    The buying price is $3218.75.

11. Strategy
    To find the odd-lot differential fee, multiply the odd-lot differential fee $\left(\$\frac{1}{8}\right)$ by the number of shares in the odd lot (60).

    Solution
    $60\left(\frac{1}{8}\right) = 7.50$

    The odd-lot differential fee is $7.50.

12. Strategy
    To find the odd-lot differential fee, multiply the odd-lot differential fee $\left(\$\frac{1}{4}\right)$ by the number of shares in the odd lot (45).

    Solution
    $45\left(\frac{1}{4}\right) = 11.25$

    The odd-lot differential fee is $11.25.

13. Strategy
    To find the brokerage fee:
    - Multiply the number of shares (1500) by the price per share $\left(28\frac{3}{4}\right)$ to find the selling price of the shares.
    - Multiply the selling price by 2.2%.
    To find the total amount paid for the shares, add the selling price and the brokerage fee.

    Solution
    $1500\left(28\frac{3}{4}\right) = 43,125$
    $43,125(0.022) = 948.75$

    The brokerage fee is $948.75.

    $43,125 + 948.75 = 44,073.75$

    The total amount paid for the shares is $44,073.75.

14. Strategy
    To find the brokerage fee:
    - Multiply the number of shares (800) by the price per share $\left(51\frac{1}{8}\right)$ to find the selling price of the shares.
    - Multiply the selling price by 2.8%.
    To find the total amount paid for the shares, add the selling price and the brokerage fee.

    Solution
    $800\left(51\frac{1}{8}\right) = 40,900$
    $40,900(0.028) = 1145.20$

    The brokerage fee is $1145.20.

    $40,900 + 1145.20 = 42,045.20$

    The total amount paid for the shares is $42,045.20.

15. Strategy
    To find the brokerage fee:
    - Find the brokerage fee for the first $20,000 of stock by multiplying $20,000 by 2.8%.
    - Find the brokerage fee for the purchase of the next $20,000 of stock by multiplying $20,000 by 2.4%.
    - Find the brokerage fee for the remainder of the purchase by multiplying the amount over $40,000 by 2%.
    - Add the three fees.

    Solution
    $20,000(0.028) = 560$
    $20,000(0.024) = 480$
    $(64,000 - 40,000)(0.02) = 24,000(0.02) = 480$
    $560 + 480 + 480 = 1520$

    The brokerage fee is $1520.

16. Strategy
    To find the brokerage fee:
    • Find the brokerage fee for the first $20,000 of stock by multiplying $20,000 by 2.8%.
    • Find the brokerage fee for the purchase of the next $20,000 of stock by multiplying $20,000 by 2.4%.
    • Find the brokerage fee for the remainder of the purchase by multiplying the amount over $40,000 by 2%.
    • Add the three fees.

    Solution
    20,000(0.028) = 560
    20,000(0.024) = 480
    (72,000 − 40,000)(0.02) = 32,000(0.02) = 640
    560 + 480 + 640 = 1680

    The brokerage fee is $1680.

17. Strategy
    To find the total amount paid to the stockbroker:
    • Find the selling price of the shares by multiplying the number of shares (690) by the price per share $\left(52\frac{1}{2}\right)$.
    • Find the brokerage fee by multiplying the selling price by 2.6%.
    • Find the differential fee by multiplying the number of shares in the odd lot (90) by $\frac{1}{8}$.
    • Add the brokerage fee and the differential fee.

    Solution
    $690\left(52\frac{1}{2}\right) = 36,225$
    36,225(0.026) = 941.85
    $90\left(\frac{1}{8}\right) = 11.25$
    941.85 + 11.25 = 953.10

    The total amount paid to the stockbroker is $953.10.

18. Strategy
    To find the total amount paid to the stockbroker:
    • Find the selling price of the shares by multiplying the number of shares (430) by the price per share $\left(16\frac{3}{4}\right)$.
    • Find the brokerage fee by multiplying the selling price by 2.3%.
    • Find the differential fee by multiplying the number of shares in the odd lot (30) by $\frac{1}{4}$.
    • Add the brokerage fee and the differential fee.

    Solution
    $430\left(16\frac{3}{4}\right) = 7020.50$
    7020.50(0.023) ≈ 165.66
    $30\left(\frac{1}{4}\right) = 7.50$
    165.66 + 7.50 = 173.16

    The total amount paid to the stockbroker is $173.16.

19. Strategy

    To find the selling price, multiply the number of shares (370) by the price per share $\left(47\frac{3}{8}\right)$.

    To find the brokerage fee, multiply the selling price by 2%.

    To find the differential fee, multiply the number of shares in the odd lot (70) by $\frac{1}{4}$.

    To find the proceeds, subtract the brokerage fee and the differential fee from the selling price.

    Solution

    $370\left(47\frac{3}{8}\right) = 17,528.75$

    The selling price is $17,528.75.

    $17,528.75(0.02) \approx 350.58$

    The brokerage fee is $350.58.

    $70\left(\frac{1}{4}\right) = 17.50$

    The differential fee is $17.50.

    $17,528.75 - (350.58 + 17.50) = 17,528.75 - 368.08 = 17,160.67$

    The proceeds are $17,160.67.

20. Strategy

    To find the selling price, multiply the number of shares (465) by the price per share $\left(23\frac{1}{8}\right)$.

    To find the brokerage fee, multiply the selling price by 1.8%.

    To find the differential fee, multiply the number of shares in the odd lot (65) by $\frac{1}{8}$.

    To find the proceeds, subtract the brokerage fee and the differential fee from the selling price.

    Solution

    $465\left(23\frac{1}{8}\right) \approx 10,753.13$

    The selling price is $10,753.13.

    $10,753.13(0.018) \approx 193.56.$

    The brokerage fee is $193.56.

    $65\left(\frac{1}{8}\right) \approx 8.13$

    The differential fee is $8.13.

    $10,753.13 - (193.56 + 8.13) = 10,753.13 - 201.69 = 10,551.44$

    The proceeds are $10,551.44.

21. Strategy
    To find the annual dividend, multiply the dividend per share (75) by 7%.

    Solution
    75(0.07) = 5.25

    The annual dividend is $5.25.

22. Strategy
    To find the annual dividend, multiply the dividend per share (50) by 6%.

    Solution
    50(0.06) = 3

    The annual dividend is $3.

23. Strategy
    To find the dividends paid, multiply the number of shares outstanding (20,000) by 8.

    Solution
    20,000(8) = 160,000

    The dividends paid to preferred stockholders were $160,000.

24. Strategy
    To find the dividends paid, multiply the number of shares outstanding (15,000) by 5.

    Solution
    15,000(5) = 75,000

    The dividends paid to preferred stockholders were $75,000.

25. Strategy
    To find the dividends paid:
    • Multiply the par value (100) by 8% to find the dividend per share.
    • Multiply the dividend per share by the number of shares outstanding (32,000).

    Solution
    100(0.08) = 8
    32,000(8) = 256,000

    The dividends paid to the preferred stockholders were $256,000.

26. Strategy
    To find the dividends paid:
    • Multiply the par value (75) by 5% to find the dividend per share.
    • Multiply the dividend per share by the number of shares outstanding (18,000).

    Solution
    75(0.05) = 3.75
    18,000(3.75) = 67,500

    The dividends paid to the preferred stockholders were $67,500.

27. Strategy

    To find the amount owed in dividends:
    - Multiply the par value (100) by 8% to find the dividend per share.
    - Multiply the dividend per share by the number of shares outstanding (40,000) to find the total dividends owed per year.
    - Multiply the total dividends owed per year by 2.

    Solution
    100(0.08) = 8
    40,000(8) = 320,000
    320,000(2) = 640,000

    The company owes $640,000 in dividends to the cumulative preferred stockholders.

28. Strategy

    To find the amount owed in dividends:
    - Multiply the par value (75) by 7% to find the dividend per share.
    - Multiply the dividend per share by the number of shares outstanding (25,000) to find the total dividends owed per year.
    - Multiply the total dividends owed per year by 2.

    Solution
    75(0.07) = 5.25
    25,000(5.25) = 131,250
    131,250(2) = 262,500

    The company owes $262,500 in dividends to the cumulative preferred stockholders.

29. Strategy

    To find the dividends paid to the preferred stockholders, multiply the dividend per share (5) by the number of shares (10,000).
    To find the dividend paid for each share of common stock:
    - Subtract the total amount paid in preferred dividends from the total amount paid in dividends (130,000).
    - Divide the result by the number of outstanding shares of common stock (32,000).

    Solution
    5(10,000) = 50,000

    $50,000 was paid in dividends to the preferred stockholders.

    130,000 - 50,000 = 80,000
    80,000 ÷ 32,000 = 2.50

    The dividend per share of common stock was $2.50.

30. Strategy

    To find the dividends paid to the preferred stockholders, multiply the dividend per share (4) by the number of shares (8000).
    To find the dividend paid for each share of common stock:
    - Subtract the total amount paid in preferred dividends from the total amount paid in dividends (86,000).
    - Divide the result by the number of outstanding shares of common stock (10,000).

    Solution
    4(8000) = 32,000

    $32,000 was paid in dividends to the preferred stockholders.

    86,000 - 32,000 = 54,000
    54,000 ÷ 10,000 = 5.40

    The dividend per share of common stock was $5.40.

31. Strategy
    To find the dividend per share of common stock:
    • Find the dividend per share of preferred stock by multiplying the par value (50) by 7%.
    • Find the total amount paid in preferred dividends by multiplying the dividend per share by the number of shares (12,000).
    • Subtract the total amount paid in preferred dividends from the total amount paid in dividends (234,000).
    • Divide the result by the number of shares of common stock (30,000).

    Solution
    Dividend per share of preferred stock = 50(0.07) = 3.50
    Total preferred dividends = 3.50(12,000) = 42,000
    234,000 - 42,000 = 192,000
    192,000 ÷ 30,000 = 6.40

    The dividend per share of common stock was $6.40.

32. Strategy
    To find the dividend per share of common stock:
    • Find the dividend per share of preferred stock by multiplying the par value (75) by 6%.
    • Find the total amount paid in preferred dividends by multiplying the dividend per share by the number of shares (10,000).
    • Subtract the total amount paid in preferred dividends from the total amount paid in dividends (90,000).
    • Divide the result by the number of shares of common stock (20,000).

    Solution
    Dividend per share of preferred stock = 75(0.06) = 4.50
    Total preferred dividends = 4.50(10,000) = 45,000
    90,000 - 45,000 = 45,000
    45,000 ÷ 20,000 = 2.25

    The dividend per share of common stock was $2.25.

33. Strategy
    To find the dividend paid on each share of preferred stock:
    • Find the dividend per share of preferred stock by multiplying the par value (100) by 8%.
    • Multiply the dividend per share by 2.
    To find the dividend per share of common stock:
    • Find the total preferred dividends paid by multiplying the dividend per share by the number of shares (14,000).
    • Subtract the total amount paid in preferred dividends from the total amount paid in dividends (314,000).
    • Divide the result by the number of shares of common stock (25,000).

    Solution
    Dividend per share of preferred stock = 100(0.08) = 8
    Preferred dividend owed for past two years = 8(2) = 16

    The dividend paid on each share of preferred stock is $16.

    Total preferred dividends = 16(14,000) = 224,000
    314,000 - 224,000 = 90,000
    90,000 ÷ 25,000 = 3.60

    The dividend per share of common stock is $3.60.

34. Strategy
    To find the dividend paid on each share of preferred stock:
    • Find the dividend per share of preferred stock by multiplying the par value (50) by 7%.
    • Multiply the dividend per share by 2.
    To find the dividend per share of common stock:
    • Find the total preferred dividends paid by multiplying the dividend per share by the number of shares (62,000).
    • Subtract the total amount paid in preferred dividends from the total amount paid in dividends (874,000).
    • Divide the result by the number of shares of common stock (50,000).

    Solution
    Dividend per share of preferred stock = 50(0.07) = 3.50
    Preferred dividend owed for past two years = 3.50(2) = 7

    The dividend paid on each share of preferred stock is $7.

    Total preferred dividends = 7(62,000) = 434,000
    874,000 - 434,000 = 440,000
    440,000 ÷ 50,000 = 8.80

    The dividend per share of common stock is $8.80.

35. Strategy
    To find the dividend per share of common stock:
    • Find the dividend per share of preferred stock by multiplying the par value (100) by 5%.
    • Find the dividend owed per share of preferred stock by multiplying the dividend per share by 3.
    • Find the total amount paid in preferred dividends by multiplying the dividend per share by the number of shares (8000).
    • Subtract the total amount paid in preferred dividends from the total amount paid in dividends (150,000).
    • Divide the result by the number of shares of common stock (25,000).

    Solution
    Dividend per share of preferred stock = 100(0.05) = 5
    Preferred dividend owed for past 3 years = 5(3) = 15
    Total preferred dividends = 15(8000) = 120,000
    150,000 - 120,000 = 30,000
    30,000 ÷ 25,000 = 1.20

    The dividend per share of common stock was $1.20.

36. Strategy
    To find the dividend per share of common stock:
    • Find the dividend per share of preferred stock by multiplying the par value (100) by 6%.
    • Find the dividend owed per share of preferred stock by multiplying the dividend per share by 3.
    • Find the total amount paid in preferred dividends by multiplying the dividend per share by the number of shares (9000).
    • Subtract the total amount paid in preferred dividends from the total amount paid in dividends (340,000).
    • Divide the result by the number of shares of common stock (32,000).

    Solution
    Dividend per share of preferred stock = 100(0.06) = 6
    Preferred dividend owed for past 3 years = 6(3) = 18
    Total preferred dividends = 18(9000) = 162,000
    340,000 − 162,000 = 178,000
    178,000 ÷ 32,000 ≈ 5.56

    The dividend per share of common stock is $5.56.

37. Strategy
    To find the current percent yield, use the formula for current percent yield.

    Solution
    Current percent yield $= \frac{1.16}{31.75} \times 100$
    $= 3.7\%$

    The current percent yield is 3.7%.

38. Strategy
    To find the current percent yield, use the formula for current percent yield.

    Solution
    Current percent yield $= \frac{5.23}{95.375} \times 100$
    $= 5.5\%$

    The current percent yield is 5.5%.

39. Strategy
    To find the earnings per share, divide the earnings by the number of shares outstanding.

    Solution
    4,700,000 ÷ 2,000,000 = 2.35

    The earnings per share is $2.35.

40. Strategy
    To find the earnings per share, divide the earnings by the number of shares outstanding.

    Solution
    2,200,000 ÷ 800,000 = 2.75

    The earnings per share is $2.75.

41. Strategy
    To find the price-earnings ratio:
    • Find the annual earnings per share by dividing the earnings by the number of shares outstanding.
    • Use the P/E formula.

    Solution
    Annual earnings per share
    $= \frac{214,000}{60,000} = 3.57$
    $P/E = \frac{23.375}{3.57} = 7$

    The price-earnings ratio is 7.

42. Strategy
    To find the price-earnings ratio:
    • Find the annual earnings per share by dividing the earnings by the number of shares outstanding.
    • Use the P/E formula.

    Solution
    Annual earnings per share
    $= \frac{52,000}{80,000} = 0.65$
    $P/E = \frac{6.375}{0.65} = 10$

    The price-earnings ratio is 10.

43. Current percent yield
    $= \frac{1.75}{23.375} \times 100 = 7.5\%$

44. Earnings per share
    $= \frac{205,000}{75,000} = \$2.73$

45. Price-earnings ratio = $\frac{23.375}{2.73}$ = 9

46. Current price yield
    = $\frac{0.80}{15.50}$ x 100 = 5.2%

47. Earnings per share = $\frac{415,000}{200,000}$ = $2.08

48. Price-earnings ratio = $\frac{15.50}{2.08}$ = 7

49. Current percent yield
    = $\frac{3.15}{62.375}$ x 100 = 5.1%

50. Earnings per share = $\frac{96,000}{25,000}$ = $3.84

51. Price-earnings ratio = $\frac{62.375}{3.84}$ = 16

52. Current price yield
    = $\frac{2.75}{45.875}$ x 100 = 6.0%

53. Earnings per share = $\frac{175,000}{40,000}$ = $4.38

54. Price-earnings ratio = $\frac{45.875}{4.38}$ = 10

55. Current percent yield
    = $\frac{0.55}{5.125}$ x 100 = 10.7%

56. Earnings per share = $\frac{120,000}{100,000}$ = $1.20

57. Price-earnings ratio = $\frac{5.125}{1.20}$ = 4

58. Current percent yield
    = $\frac{4.50}{88.125}$ x 100 = 5.1%

59. Earnings per share = $\frac{3,500,000}{500,000}$ = $7.00

60. Price-earnings ratio = $\frac{88.125}{7.00}$ = 13

61. Current percent yield
    = $\frac{3.75}{72.375}$ x 100 = 5.2%

62. Earnings per share = $\frac{1,900,000}{250,000}$ = $7.60

63. Price-earnings ratio = $\frac{72.375}{7.60}$ = 10

64. Current percent yield
    = $\frac{0.85}{12.50}$ x 100 = 6.8%

65. Earnings per share = $\frac{2,400,000}{1,000,000}$ = $2.40

66. Price-earnings ratio = $\frac{12.50}{2.40}$ = 5

Section 17.2, pages 531–534

1. 2006

2. 1995

3. 7.7%

4. 10.7%

5. 5.5%

6. 9.25%

7. Annual interest = 0.0975(1000)
    = $97.50

8. Annual interest = 0.06875(1000)
    = $68.75

9. Price = 0.87(6000) = $5220

10. Price = 1.025(5000) = $5125

11. Strategy
    To find the annual interest, multiply
    the face value of the bond (1000) by
    the interest rate $\left(7\frac{1}{4} \right)$.

    Solution
    1000(0.0725) = 72.50

    The annual interest is $72.50.

12. Strategy
    To find the annual interest, multiply
    the face value of the bond (1000) by
    the interest rate $\left(6\frac{7}{8} \right)$.

    Solution
    1000(0.06875) = 68.75

    The annual interest is $68.75.

13. Strategy
    To find the annual interest, multiply
    the face value of the bond (9000) by
    the interest rate $\left(8\frac{1}{8} \right)$.

    Solution
    9000(0.08125) = 731.25

    The annual interest is $731.25.

14. Strategy
    To find the annual interest, multiply
    the face value of the bond (5000) by
    the interest rate $\left(7\frac{3}{4} \right)$.

    Solution
    7000(0.0775) = 387.50

    The annual interest is $387.50.

15. Strategy
    To find the current price, multiply
    the face value (1000) by the quoted
    price $\left(91\frac{7}{8}\% = 0.91875 \right)$.

    Solution
    1000(0.91875) = 918.75

    The current price is $918.75.

16. Strategy
    To find the current price, multiply
    the face value (1000) by the quoted
    price $\left(86\frac{5}{8}\% = 0.86625 \right)$.

    Solution
    1000(0.86625) = 866.25

    The current price is $866.25.

17. Strategy
    To find the selling price, multiply
    the face value (14,000) by the quoted
    price $\left(102\frac{3}{8}\% = 1.02375 \right)$.

    Solution
    14,000(1.02375) = 14,332,50

    The selling price is $14,332.50.

18. Strategy
    To find the selling price, multiply
    the face value (10,000) by the quoted
    price $\left(101\frac{1}{2}\% = 1.015 \right)$.

    Solution
    10,000(1.015) = 10,150

    The selling price is $10,150.

19. Strategy
    To find the annual interest, multiply
    the face value of the bond (3000) by
    the interest rate (6.8%).
    To find the current price of the bond,
    multiply the face value by the quoted
    price $\left(91\frac{1}{4}\% = 0.9125 \right)$.

    Solution
    3000(0.068) = 204

    The annual interest is $204.

    3000(0.9125) = 2737.50

    The current price is $2737.50.

20. Strategy
    To find the annual interest, multiply
    the face value of the bond (8000) by
    the interest rate (7.4%).
    To find the current price of the bond,
    multiply the face value by the quoted
    price $\left(82\frac{7}{8}\% = 0.82875 \right)$.

    Solution
    8000(0.074) = 592

    The annual interest is $592.

    8000(0.82875) = 6630

    The current price is $6630.

286   *Chapter 17*

21. Strategy
To find the annual interest, multiply
the face value of the bond (18,000) by
the interest rate (5.9%).
To find the current price of the bond,
multiply the face value by the quoted
price $\left(93\frac{1}{8}\% = 0.93125\right)$.

Solution
18,000(0.059) = 1062

The annual interest is $1062.

18,000(0.93125) = 16,762.50

The current price is $16,762.50.

22. Strategy
To find the annual interest, multiply
the face value of the bond (25,000) by
the interest rate (8.3%).
To find the current price of the bond,
multiply the face value by the quoted
price $\left(101\frac{3}{4}\% = 1.0175\right)$.

Solution
25,000(0.083) = 2075

The annual interest is $2075.

25,000(1.0175) = 25,437.50

The current price is $25,437.50.

23. Strategy
To find the accrued interest, use the
accrued interest formula. P = 6000,
r = 0.059, t = $\frac{54}{360}$

Solution
I = Prt
I = 6000(0.059) $\left(\frac{54}{360}\right)$ = 53.10

The accrued interest is $53.10.

24. Strategy
To find the accrued interest, use the
accrued interest formula. P = 4000,
r = 0.067, t = $\frac{120}{360}$

Solution
I = Prt
I = 4000(0.067) $\left(\frac{120}{360}\right)$ ≈ 89.33

The accrued interest is $89.33.

25. Strategy
To find the proceeds:
• Find the selling price by
multiplying the quoted price as a
percent (97% = 0.97) by the face
value (18,000).
• Add the selling price and the
accrued interest (276).

Solution
Selling price = 18,000(0.97) = 17,460
Proceeds = 17,460 + 276 = 17,736

The proceeds are $17,736.

26. Strategy
To find the proceeds:
• Find the selling price by
multiplying the quoted price as a
percent (92% = 0.92) by the face
value (2000).
• Add the selling price and the
accrued interest (28).

Solution
Selling price = 2000(0.92) = 1840
Proceeds = 1840 + 28 = 1868

The proceeds are $1868.

27. Strategy
To find the accrued interest:
• Find the number of days from
January 1 to May 5.
• Use the accrued interest formula to
find the accrued interest.

Solution
There are 124 days from January 1 to
May 5.
I = Prt
I = 25,000(0.09) $\left(\frac{124}{360}\right)$ = 775

The accrued interest is $775.

28. Strategy
To find the accrued interest:
• Find the number of days from
March 1 to July 22.
• Use the accrued interest formula to
find the accrued interest.

Solution
There are 143 days from March 1 to
July 22.
I = Prt
I = 14,000(0.07) $\left(\frac{143}{360}\right)$ ≈ 389.28

The accrued interest is $389.28.

29. Strategy
    To find the accrued interest:
    - Find the selling price by multiplying the quoted price as a percent $\left(101\frac{3}{4}\% = 1.0175\right)$ by the face value (50,000).
    - Find the number of days from May 1 to July 8.
    - Use the accrued interest formula to find the accrued interest.
    To find the proceeds, add the selling price and the accrued interest.

    Solution
    Selling price = 50,000(1.0175)
    $\qquad\qquad\quad$ = 50,875
    There are 68 days from May 1 to July 8.
    I = Prt
    $I = 50,000(0.063)\left(\frac{68}{360}\right) = 595$

    The accrued interest is $595.

    50,875 + 595 = 51,470

    The proceeds are $51,470.

30. Strategy
    To find the accrued interest:
    - Find the selling price by multiplying the quoted price as a percent $\left(108\frac{1}{2}\% = 1.085\right)$ by the face value (25,000).
    - Find the number of days from July 1 to October 2.
    - Use the accrued interest formula to find the accrued interest.
    To find the proceeds, add the selling price and the accrued interest.

    Solution
    Selling price = 25,000(1.085)
    $\qquad\qquad\quad$ = 27,125
    There are 93 days from July 1 to October 2.
    I = Prt
    $I = 25,000(0.084)\left(\frac{93}{360}\right) = 542.50$

    The accrued interest is $542.50.

    27,125 + 542.50 = 27,667.50

    The proceeds are $27,667.50.

31. Strategy
    To find the proceeds:
    - Find the selling price by multiplying the quoted price as a percent $\left(95\frac{1}{2}\% = 0.955\right)$ by the face value (50,000).
    - Find the number of days from January 1 to May 5.
    - Use the accrued interest formula to find the accrued interest.
    - Add the selling price and the accrued interest.

    Solution
    Selling price = 50,000(0.955) = 47,750
    There are 124 days from January 1 to May 5.

    I = Prt
    $I = 50,000(0.08)\left(\frac{124}{360}\right) \approx 1377.78$
    47,750 + 1377.78 = 49,127.78

    The proceeds are $49,127.78.

32. Strategy
    To find the proceeds:
    - Find the selling price by multiplying the quoted price as a percent $\left(101\frac{1}{4}\% = 1.0125\right)$ by the face value (30,000).
    - Find the number of days from March 1 to June 9.
    - Use the accrued interest formula to find the accrued interest.
    - Add the selling price and the accrued interest.

    Solution
    Selling price = 30,000(1.0125)
    $\qquad\qquad\quad$ = 30,375
    There are 100 days from March 1 to June 9.

    I = Prt
    $I = 30,000(0.09)\left(\frac{100}{360}\right) \approx 750$
    30,375 + 750 = 31,125

    The proceeds are $31,125.

33. Strategy
    To find the annual interest, multiply
    the face value of the bond (8000) by
    the interest rate (6.2%).
    To find the current price of the bond,
    multiply the face value by the quoted
    price $\left(93\frac{1}{2}\% = 0.935\right)$.
    To find the current yield, use the
    formula for current yield.

    Solution
    8000(0.062) = 496

    The annual interest is $496.

    8000(0.935) = 7480

    The current price is $7480.

    Current yield = $\dfrac{\text{annual interest}}{\text{current price}}$ x 100
    $= \dfrac{496}{7840} \times 100 \approx 6.6$

    The current yield is 6.6%.

34. Strategy
    To find the annual interest, multiply
    the face value of the bond (10,000) by
    the interest rate (7.7%).
    To find the current price of the bond,
    multiply the face value by the quoted
    price (98% = 0.98).
    To find the current yield, use the
    formula for current yield.

    Solution
    10,000(0.077) = 770

    The annual interest is $770.

    10,000(0.98) = 9800

    The current price is $9800.

    Current yield = $\dfrac{\text{annual interest}}{\text{current price}}$ x 100
    $= \dfrac{770}{9800} \times 100 \approx 7.9$

    The current yield is 7.9%.

35. Strategy
    To find the current yield:
    • Find the annual interest by
      multiplying the face value of the
      bond by the interest rate.
    • Find the current price of the bond.
    • Use the formula for current yield.

    Solution
    Annual interest = 20,000(0.09) = 1800
    Current price = 20,000(1.0825)
                  = 21,650
    Current yield = $\dfrac{\text{annual interest}}{\text{current price}}$ x 100
    $= \dfrac{1800}{21,650} \times 100 \approx 8.3$

    The current yield is 8.3%.

36. Strategy
    To find the current yield:
    • Find the annual interest by
      multiplying the face value of the
      bond by the interest rate.
    • Find the current price of the bond.
    • Use the formula for current yield.

    Solution
    Annual interest = 12,000(0.102) = 1224
    Current price = 12,000(1.01375)
                  = 12,165
    Current yield = $\dfrac{\text{annual interest}}{\text{current price}}$ x 100
    $= \dfrac{1224}{12,165} \times 100 = 10.1$

    The current yield is 10.1%.

37. Strategy
    To find the current yield:
    * Find the annual interest by multiplying the face value of the bond by the interest rate.
    * Find the current price of the bond.
    * Use the formula for current yield.

    Solution
    Annual interest = 15,000(0.088) = 1320
    Current price = 15,000(0.9225)
    $\qquad\qquad$ = 13,837.50
    Current yield = $\dfrac{\text{annual interest}}{\text{current price}}$ x 100
    $\qquad\qquad$ = $\dfrac{1320}{13,837.50}$ x 100 $\approx$ 9.5

    The current yield is 9.5%.

38. Strategy
    To find the current yield:
    * Find the annual interest by multiplying the face value of the bond by the interest rate.
    * Find the current price of the bond.
    * Use the formula for current yield.

    Solution
    Annual interest = 16,000(0.065) = 1040
    Current price = 16,000(0.8275)
    $\qquad\qquad$ = 13,240
    Current yield = $\dfrac{\text{annual interest}}{\text{current price}}$ x 100
    $\qquad\qquad$ = $\dfrac{1040}{13,240}$ x 100 $\approx$ 7.9

    The current yield is 7.9%.

Section 17.3, pages 537–538

1. $20.37

2. $19.60

3. Sales charge = offer price - NAV = 10.95 - 10.62 = $.33

4. Sales charge = offer price - NAV = 27.91 - 26.93 = $.98

5. Sales charge = 300(11.48 - 10.50) = 300(0.98) = $294

6. Sales charge = 500(8.81 - 8.39) = 500(0.42) = $210

7. (14.03 - 13.61) ÷ 13.61 = 0.42 + 13.61 $\approx$ 0.031 = 3.1%

8. (9.71 - 9.27) ÷ 9.27 = 0.44 + 9.27 $\approx$ 0.047 = 4.7%

9. Number of shares purchased = 5000 ÷ 14.04 $\approx$ 356.125 shares

10. Number of shares purchased = 4000 ÷ 10.82 $\approx$ 369.686 shares

11. Strategy
    To find the management fee, multiply the total assets by 1.25%.

    Solution
    17,452,000(0.0125) = 218,150

    The management fee is $218,150.

12. Strategy
    To find the management fee, multiply the total assets by $\frac{7}{8}$%.

    Solution
    3,450,000(0.00875) = 30,187.50

    The management fee is $30,187.50.

13. Strategy
    To find the net asset value, divide
    the current value of the stocks in the
    mutual fund (3,200,000) by the number
    of shares issued by the fund
    (400,000).

    Solution
    $$NAV = \frac{3,200,000}{400,000} = 8$$

    The net asset value is $8.

14. Strategy
    To find the net asset value, divide
    the current value of the stocks in the
    mutual fund (12,600,000) by the number
    of shares issued by the fund
    (800,000).

    Solution
    $$NAV = \frac{12,600,000}{800,000} = 15.75$$

    The net asset value is $15.75.

15. Strategy
    To find the sales charge, subtract the NAV (22.32) from the offer price (24.09).
    To find the sales charge on the sale of 400 shares, multiply the sales charge by
    400.
    To find what percent of the NAV is the sales charge, solve the basic percent
    equation for the rate.
    To find how many shares can be purchased for $5000, divide 5000 by the offer price.

    Solution
    Sales charge = offer price - NAV = 24.09 - 22.32 = 1.77

    The sales charge is $1.77.

    400(1.77) = 708

    The sales charge on the sale of 400 shares is $708.

    Part = base x rate
    1.77 = 22.32 x rate
    $\frac{1.77}{22.32}$ = rate
    0.079 ≈ rate

    The sales charge is 7.9% of the NAV.

    5000 ÷ 24.09 = 207.555

    207.555 shares can be purchased for $5000.

16. Strategy
    To find the sales charge, subtract the NAV (12.73) from the offer price (13.49).
    To find the sales charge on the sale of 400 shares, multiply the sales charge by 400.
    To find what percent of the NAV is the sales charge, solve the basic percent equation for the rate.
    To find how many shares can be purchased for $7500, divide 7500 by the offer price.

    Solution
    Sales charge = offer price - NAV = 13.49 - 12.73 = 0.76

    The sales charge is $.76.

    400(0.76) = 304

    The sales charge on the sale of 400 shares is $304.

    Part = base x rate
    0.76 = 12.73 x rate
    $\frac{0.76}{12.73}$ = rate
    0.060 ≈ rate

    The sales charge is 6.0% of the NAV.

    7500 ÷ 13.49 = 555.967

    555.967 shares can be purchased for $7500.

Section 17.4, pages 541–542

1. Strategy
   To find the amounts distributed, multiply each percent by the profits.

   Solution
   0.40(85,000) = 34,000
   0.35(85,000) = 29,750
   0.25(85,000) = 21,250

   The amounts distributed are $34,000, $29,750, and $21,250.

2. Strategy
   To find the amounts distributed, multiply each percent by the profits.

   Solution
   0.45(15,000) = 6750
   0.35(15,000) = 5250
   0.20(15,000) = 3000

   The amounts distributed are $6750, $5250, and $3000.

3. Strategy
   To find the annual income received by each partner:
   • Find West's annual salary.
   • Find Miller's annual salary.
   • Find each partner's equal share of the profits by subtracting the total of the two annual salaries from the profits and dividing the result by 2.
   • Add each partner's equal share of the profits to the annual salary.

   Solution
   West's annual salary = 12(2000) = 24,000
   Miller's annual salary = 12(1800) = 21,600

   72,000 - (24,000 + 21,600) = 72,000 - 45,600 = 26,400
   Each partner's equal share of the profits = 26,400 ÷ 2 = 13,200

   West's annual income = 24,000 + 13,200 = 37,200
   Miller's annual income = 21,600 + 13,200 = 34,800

   West's annual income is $37,200, and Miller's annual income is $34,800.

4. Strategy
   To find the annual income received by each partner:
   • Find Grant's annual salary.
   • Find Davis's annual salary.
   • Find each partner's equal share of the profits by subtracting the total of the two annual salaries from the profits and dividing the result by 2.
   • Add each partner's equal share of the profits to the annual salary.

   Solution
   Grant's annual salary = 12(2400) = 28,800
   Davis's annual salary = 12(2800) = 33,600

   72,000 - (28,800 + 33,600) = 72,000 - 62,400 = 9600
   Each partner's equal share of the profits = 9600 ÷ 2 = 4800

   Grant's annual income = 28,800 + 4800 = 33,600
   Davis's annual income = 33,600 + 4800 = 38,400

   Grant's annual income is $33,600, and Davis's annual income is $38,400.

5. Strategy
   To find the amount received by each partner:
   • Find the interest earned on the investment by each partner by multiplying the investment by 10%.
   • Find the remaining profits by subtracting the sum of the three returns on investment from the profits (80,000).
   • Find the sum of Brooks's and Reed's investments.
   • Multiply Brooks's and Reed's share of their investments by the remaining profits.
   • For each general partner, add the return on investment and the share of the remaining profits.

   Solution
   Brooks: 0.10(100,000) = 10,000
   Reed: 0.10(80,000) = 8000
   Nash: 0.10(120,000) = 12,000
   80,000 - (10,000 + 8000 + 12,000) = 80,000 - 30,000 = 50,000
   100,000 + 80,000 = 180,000
   Brooks: $\frac{100,000}{180,000}$ x 50,000 = 27,777.78
   Reed: $\frac{80,000}{180,000}$ x 50,000 = 22,222.22
   Brooks: 27,777.78 + 10,000 = 37,777.78
   Reed: 22,222.22 + 8000 = 30,222.22

   Brooks receives $37,777.78, Reed receives $30,222.22, and Nash receives $12,000.

6. Strategy
    To find the amount received by each partner:
    *   Find the interest earned on the investment by each partner by multiplying the investment by 9%.
    *   Find the remaining profits by subtracting the sum of the three returns on investment from the profits (110,000).
    *   Find the sum of Mason's and Katona's investments.
    *   Multiply Mason's and Katona's share of their investments by the remaining profits.
    *   For each general partner, add the return on investment and the share of the remaining profits.

    Solution
    Mason: 0.09(120,000) = 10,800
    Katona: 0.09(60,000) = 5400
    Costa: 0.09(150,000) = 13,500
    110,000 - (10,800 + 5400 + 13,500) = 110,000 - 29,700 = 80,300
    120,000 + 60,000 = 180,000
    Mason: $\frac{120,000}{180,000}$ x 80,300 = 53,533.33
    Katona: $\frac{60,000}{180,000}$ x 80,300 = 26,766.67
    Mason: 53,533.33 + 10,800 = 64,333.33
    Katona: 26,766.67 + 5400 = 32,166.67

    Mason receives $64,333.33, Katona receives $32,166.67, and Costa receives $13,500.

7. Strategy
    To find the amount received by each partner at the end of the year:
    *   Find the interest earned on the investment by each partner by multiplying the investment by 8%.
    *   Find the remaining profits by subtracting the sum of the three returns on investment from the profits (125,000).
    *   Divide the remaining profits by 3.
    *   For each partner, add the return on investment and the share of the remaining profits and subtract the drawings.

    Solution
    Phillips: 0.08(30,000) = 2400
    Taylor: 0.08(45,000) = 3600
    Shumei: 0.08(55,000) = 4400
    125,000 - (2400 + 3600 + 4400) = 125,000 - 10,400 = 114,600
    114,600 + 3 = 38,200
    Phillips: 2400 + 38,200 - 24,000 = 16,600
    Taylor: 3600 + 38,200 - 28,800 = 13,000
    Shumei: 4400 + 38,200 - 26,000 = 16,600

    Phillips receives $16,600, Taylor receives $13,000, and Shumei receives $16,600.

8. Strategy
   To find the amount received by each partner at the end of the year:
   - Find the interest earned on the investment by each partner by multiplying the investment by 7%.
   - Find the remaining profits by subtracting the sum of the three returns on investment from the profits (117,000).
   - Divide the remaining profits by 3.
   - For each partner, add the return on investment and the share of the remaining profits and subtract the drawings.

   Solution
   Roberts: 0.07(40,000) = 2800
   Boyd: 0.07(50,000) = 3500
   Hall: 0.07(75,000) = 5250
   117,000 - (2800 + 3500 + 5250) = 117,000 - 11,550 = 105,450
   105,450 ÷ 3 = 35,150
   Roberts: 2800 + 35,150 - 27,500 = 10,450
   Boyd: 3500 + 35,150 - 25,000 = 13,650
   Hall: 5250 + 35,150 - 30,000 = 10,400

   Roberts receives $10,450, Boyd receives $13,650, and Hall receives $10,400.

9. Strategy
   To find the amount received by each partner at the end of the year:
   - Find the interest earned on the investment by each limited partner by multiplying the investment by 9.5%.
   - Find the remaining profits by subtracting the sum of the two returns on investment from the profits (180,000).
   - For each general partner, multiply the remaining profit by the percent of the profits received.

   Solution
   Walker: 0.095(120,000) = 11,400
   Chen: 0.095(90,000) = 8550
   180,000 - (11,400 + 8550) = 180,000 - 19,950 = 160,050
   Aluarez: 0.55(160,050) = 88,027.50
   Gordon: 0.45(160,050) = 72,022.50

   Walker receives $11,400, Chen receives $8550, Aluarez receives $88,027.50, and Gordon receives $72,022.50.

10. Strategy
    To find the amount received by each partner at the end of the year:
    - Find the interest earned on the investment by each limited partner by multiplying the investment by 9%.
    - Find the remaining profits by subtracting the sum of the two returns on investment from the profits (90,000).
    - For each general partner, multiply the remaining profit by the percent of the profits received.

    Solution
    Palmer: 0.09(110,000) = 9900
    Wallace: 0.09(80,000) = 7200
    90,000 - (9900 + 7200) = 90,000 - 17,100 = 72,900
    Protski: 0.60(72,900) = 43,740
    Morgan: 0.40(72,900) = 29,160

    Palmer receives $9900, Wallace receives $7200, Protski receives $43,740, and Morgan receives $29,160.

11. Strategy
    To find the amount received by each partner at the end of the year:
    - Find the interest earned on the investment by each limited partner by multiplying the investment by 8.5%.
    - Find the remaining profits by subtracting the sum of the four returns on investment from the profits (140,000).
    - Find each general partner's share of the remaining profits by dividing the remaining profits by 2.
    - For each general partner, add the return on investment and the share of the remaining profits and subtract the drawings.

    Solution
    Rogers: 0.085(50,000) = 4250
    Quinn: 0.085(40,000) = 3400
    Hughes: 0.085(120,000) = 10,200
    Brown: 0.085(90,000) = 7650
    140,000 − (4250 + 3400 + 10,200 + 7650) = 140,000 − 25,500 = 114,500
    114,500 ÷ 2 = 57,250
    Rogers: 4250 + 57,250 − 28,000 = 33,500
    Quinn: 3400 + 57,250 − 35,000 = 25,650

    Rogers receives $33,500, Quinn receives $25,650, Hughes receives $10,200, and Brown receives $7650.

12. Strategy
    To find the amount received by each partner at the end of the year:
    - Find the interest earned on the investment by each limited partner by multiplying the investment by 9.5%.
    - Find the remaining profits by subtracting the sum of the four returns on investment from the profits (136,000).
    - Find each general partner's share of the remaining profits by dividing the remaining profits by 2.
    - For each general partner, add the return on investment and the share of the remaining profits and subtract the drawings.

    Solution
    Ramirez: 0.095(70,000) = 6650
    Dunn: 0.095(80,000) = 7600
    Sullivan: 0.095(150,000) = 14,250
    Ross: 0.085(120,000) = 11,400
    136,000 − (6650 + 7600 + 14,250 + 11,400) = 136,000 − 39,900 = 96,100
    96,100 ÷ 2 = 48,050
    Ramirez: 6650 + 48,050 − 35,000 = 19,700
    Dunn: 7600 + 48,050 − 26,000 = 29,650

    Ramirez receives $19,700, Dunn receives $29,650, Sullivan receives $14,250, and Ross receives $11,400.

Business Case Study

Case 1   Partnerships

1.

	Davis	Burns	Gray
Annual allowance (9% of investment)	$20,700	$13,500	$10,800
Salary allowance	2,800	2,400	2,000
	$23,500	$15,900	$12,800

Total in allowances = $23,500 + $15,900 + $12,800 = $52,200

Gray's bonus: $190,000 - $52,200 - $50,000 = $87,800
$$0.25(\$87,800) = \$21,950$$

Profit - allowances - Gray's bonus = $190,000 - $52,200 - $21,950 = $115,850

Total invested = $230,000 + $150,000 + $120,000 = $500,000

Davis's ratio = $\frac{230,000}{500,000}$ = 46%; 0.46($115,850) = $53,291

Burns's ratio = $\frac{150,000}{500,000}$ = 30%; 0.30($115,850) = $34,755

Gray's ratio = $\frac{120,000}{500,000}$ = 24%; 0.24($115,850) = $27,804

Total annual income:
   Davis: $23,500 + $53,291 = $76,791
   Burns: $15,900 + $34,755 = $50,655
   Gray: $12,800 + $21,950 + $27,804 = $62,554

2.   PMT = PV $\div$ $a_{\overline{n}|i}$ = $120,000 $\div$ 21.889146 $\approx$ $5482.17

$5482.17 x 12 = $65,786.04

The total of the loan payments during the first year was $65,786.04.

PV = PMT$\cdot a_{\overline{n}|i}$ = $5482.17(11.434913) $\approx$ $62,688.14

The loan payoff after the first year is $62,688.14.

$120,000 - $62,688.14 = $57,311.86

$57,311.86 was paid in principal the first year.

$65,786.04 - $57,311.86 = $8474.18

$8474.18 was paid in interest the first year.

3.   As calculated above, the loan payoff after the first year is $62,688.14.
   Monthly payments - loan payoff = $65,786.04 - $62,688.14 = $3097.90

$3097.90 could be saved in interest payments if the loan were paid off after the first year.

Investment allowances + Gray's bonus + allocation of remaining profits =
($20,700 + $13,500 + $10,800) + $21,950 + $115,850
 = $45,000 + $21,950 + $115,850 = $182,800

$182,800 is greater than $62,688.14 (the loan payoff).
There is enough money to pay off the loan.

4. Answers may vary. For example:
   Paying off the loan would save the partnership interest payments.
   The purchase of the new press increased volume. Rather than pay off the loan, the money might be invested in the partnership for further expansion, which would further increase revenue.
   The partners may prefer to receive income from the partnership rather than use that money to pay off the loan.

Case 2   Stock Investments

1. Southwest Power Company:
   Annual dividend per share of preferred stock = 0.06(100) = $6
   Annual dividends for preferred stock = $6(5,000,000) = $30,000,000
   Net income - Annual dividends for preferred stock
   = $52,000,000 - $30,000,000 = $22,000,000
   Annual dividend per share of common stock = $22,000,000 ÷ 8,000,000 = $2.75

   Northeast Power Company:
   Annual dividend per share of preferred stock = 0.06(100) = $6
   Annual dividends for preferred stock = $6(2,000,000) = $12,000,000
   Net income - Annual dividends for preferred stock
   = $46,000,000 - $12,000,000 = $34,000,000
   Annual dividend per share of common stock = $34,000,000 ÷ 4,000,000 = $8.50

   Northeast Power Company's common stock should have the higher market value per share.

Review/Test, pages 547–548

1. Strategy
   To find the brokerage fee:
   • Multiply the number of shares (400) by the price per share $\left(45\frac{3}{8}\right)$ to find the selling price of the shares.
   • Multiply the selling price by 2.4%.
   To find the total amount paid for the shares, add the selling price and the brokerage fee.

   Solution
   $400\left(45\frac{3}{8}\right) = 18,150$
   $18,150(0.024) = 435.60$

   The brokerage fee is $435.60.

   $18,150 + 435.60 = 18,585.60$

   The total amount paid for the shares is $18,585.60.

2. Strategy
   To find the selling price, multiply the number of shares (240) by the price per share $\left(25\frac{3}{4}\right)$.
   To find the brokerage fee, multiply the selling price by 2.5%.
   To find the differential fee, multiply the number of shares in the odd lot (40) by $\frac{1}{8}$.
   To find the proceeds, subtract the brokerage fee and the differential fee from the selling price.

   Solution
   $240\left(25\frac{3}{4}\right) = 6180$

   The selling price is $6180.

   $6180(0.025) = 154.50$

   The brokerage fee is $154.50.

   $40\left(\frac{1}{8}\right) = 5$

   The differential fee is $5.

   $6180 - (154.50 + 5) = 6180 - 159.50$
   $ = 6020.50$

   The proceeds are $6020.50.

3. Strategy
   To find the dividend per share of common stock:
   • Find the dividend per share of preferred stock by multiplying the par value (100) by 5%.
   • Find the total amount paid in preferred dividends by multiplying the dividend per share by the number of shares (5000).
   • Subtract the total amount paid in preferred dividends from the total amount paid in dividends (120,000).
   • Divide the result by the number of shares of common stock (100,000).

   Solution
   Dividend per share of preferred stock = 100(0.05) = 5
   Total preferred dividends = 5(5000) = 25,000
   120,000 - 25,000 = 95,000
   95,000 ÷ 100,000 = 0.95

   The dividend per share of common stock was $.95.

4. Strategy
   To find the current percent yield, use the formula for the current percent yield.

   Solution
   Current percent yield = $\frac{2.40}{42.875} \times 100 \approx 5.6$

   The current percent yield is 5.6%.

5. Strategy
    To find the earnings per share, divide the earnings by the number of shares outstanding.
    To find the price-earnings ratio, use the P/E formula.

    Solution
    Earnings per share = 1,350,000 + 750,000 = 1.8

    The earnings per share is $1.80.

    P/E ratio = $\frac{21.50}{1.80}$ ≈ 12

    The price-earnings ratio is 12.

6. Strategy
    To find the annual interest, multiply the face value of the bond (15,000) by the interest rate (7%).
    To find the current price of the bond, multiply the face value by the quoted price $\left(92\frac{3}{4}\% = 0.9275\right)$.

    Solution
    15,000(0.07) = 1050

    The annual interest is $1050.

    15,000(0.9275) = 13,912.50

    The current price is $13,912.50.

7. Strategy
    To find the accrued interest:

    • Find the selling price by multiplying the quoted price as a percent $\left(87\frac{1}{4}\% = 0.8725\right)$ by the face value (12,000).
    • Find the number of days from June 1 to November 22.
    • Use the accrued interest formula to find the accrued interest.
    To find the proceeds, add the selling price and the accrued interest.

    Solution
    Selling price = 12,000(0.8725) = 10,470
    There are 174 days from June 1 to November 22.
    I = Prt
    I = 12,000(0.085)$\left(\frac{174}{360}\right)$ = 493

    The accrued interest is $493.

    10,470 + 493 = 10,963

    The proceeds are $10,963.

8. Strategy
    To find the annual interest, multiply the face value of the bond (20,000) by the interest rate (7.5%).
    To find the current price of the bond, multiply the face value by the quoted price $\left(105\frac{3}{4}\% = 1.0575\right)$.
    To find the current yield, use the formula for current yield.

    Solution
    20,000(0.075) = 1500

    The annual interest is $1500.

    20,000(1.0575) = 21,150

    The current price is $21,150.

    Current yield = $\dfrac{\text{annual interest}}{\text{current price}}$ x 100 = $\dfrac{1500}{21,150}$ x 100 ≈ 7.1

    The current yield is 7.1%.

9. Strategy
    To find the net asset value, divide the current value of the stocks in the mutual fund (4,375,000) by the number of shares issued by the fund (1,200,000).

    Solution
    NAV = $\dfrac{4,375,000}{1,200,000}$ ≈ 3.65

    The net asset value is $3.65.

10. Strategy
    To find the sales charge, subtract the NAV (11.35) from the offer price (11.97).
    To find the sales charge on the sale of 500 shares, multiply the sales charge by 500.
    To find what percent of the NAV is the sales charge, solve the basic percent equation for the rate.
    To find how many shares can be purchased for $4000, divide 4000 by the offer price.

    Solution
    Sales charge = offer price - NAV = 11.97 - 11.35 = 0.62

    The sales charge is $.62.

    500(0.62) = 310

    The sales charge on the sale of 500 shares is $310.

    Part = base x rate
    0.62 = 11.35 x rate
    $\dfrac{0.62}{11.35}$ = rate
    0.055 ≈ rate

    The sales charge is 5.5% of the NAV.

    4000 ÷ 11.97 ≈ 334.169

    334.169 shares can be purchased for $4000.

11. Strategy
    To find the annual income received by each partner:
    • Find Marshall's annual salary.
    • Find Smith's annual salary.
    • Find each partner's equal share of the profits by subtracting the total of the two annual salaries from the profits and dividing the result by 2.
    • Add each partner's equal share of the profits to the annual salary.

    Solution
    Marshall's annual salary = 12(2400) = 28,800
    Smith's annual salary = 12(2800) = 33,600

    84,000 - (28,800 + 33,600) = 84,000 - 62,400 = 21,600
    Each partner's equal share of the profits = 21,600 ÷ 2 = 10,800

    Marshall's annual income = 28,800 + 10,800 = 39,600
    Smith's annual income = 33,600 + 10,800 = 44,400

    Marshall's annual income is $39,600, and Smith's annual income is $44,400.

12. Strategy
    To find the amount received by each partner at the end of the year:
    • Find the interest earned on the investment by each partner by multiplying the investment by 8.5%.
    • Find the remaining profits by subtracting the sum of the four returns on investment from the profits (148,000).
    • Find each general partner's share of the remaining profits by dividing the remaining profits by 2.
    • For each general partner, add the return on investment and the share of the remaining profits and subtract the drawings.

    Solution
    Collins: 0.085(50,000) = 4250
    Stone: 0.085(70,000) = 5950
    Marcos: 0.085(140,000) = 11,900
    Peters: 0.085(180,000) = 15,300

    148,000 - (4250 + 5950 + 11,900 + 15,300) = 148,000 - 37,400 = 110,600

    110,600 ÷ 2 = 55,300

    Collins: 4250 + 55,300 - 32,000 = 27,550
    Stone: 5950 + 55,300 - 27,000 = 34,250

    Collins receives $27,550, Stone receives $34,250, Marcos receives $11,900, and Peters receives $15,300.

CHAPTER 18
Financial Statements

Section 18.1, pages 555–556

1. (a) 77,400 − 39,200 = (38,200)
   (b) 38,200 ÷ 77,400 ≈ 0.4935 = (49.35%)

2. (a) 707,200 − 413,000 = 294,200
   (b) 294,200 ÷ 413,000 ≈ 0.7123 = 71.23%

3. (a) 4200 − 4000 = (200)
   (b) 200 ÷ 4200 ≈ 0.0476 = (4.76%)

4. (a) 897,200 − 652,200 = 245,000
   (b) 245,000 ÷ 652,200 ≈ 0.3757 = 37.57%

5. (a) 131,600 − 130,400 = 1200
   (b) 1200 ÷ 130,400 ≈ 0.0092 = 0.92%

6. (a) 105,600 − 95,200 = (10,400)
   (b) 10,400 ÷ 105,600 ≈ 0.0985 = (9.85%)

7. (a) 234,800 − 206,400 = (28,400)
   (b) 28,400 ÷ 234,800 ≈ 0.1210 = (12.10%)

8. (a) 426,400 − 387,600 = (38,800)
   (b) 38,800 ÷ 426,400 ≈ 0.0910 = (9.10%)

9. (a) 1,416,400 − 1,209,000 = 207,400
   (b) 207,400 ÷ 1,209,000 ≈ 0.1715 = 17.15%

10. (a) 143,200 − 58,000 = 85,200
    (b) 85,200 ÷ 58,000 ≈ 1.4690 = 146.90%

11. (a) 201,200 − 85,200 = 116,000
    (b) 116,000 ÷ 85,200 ≈ 1.3615 = 136.15%

12. (a) 195,600 − 195,200 = 400
    (b) 400 ÷ 195,200 ≈ 0.0020 = 0.20%

13. (a) 396,800 − 280,400 = 116,400
    (b) 116,400 ÷ 280,400 ≈ 0.4151 = 41.51%

14. (a) 1,019,600 − 928,600 = 91,000
    (b) 91,000 ÷ 928,600 ≈ 0.0980 = 9.80%

15. (a) 1,416,400 - 1,209,000 = 207,400
    (b) 207,400 ÷ 1,209,000 ≈ 0.1715 = 17.15%

16. 146,800 ÷ 1,416,400 ≈ 0.1036 = 10.36%

17. 707,200 ÷ 1,416,400 ≈ 0.4993 = 49.93%

18. 897,200 ÷ 1,416,400 ≈ 0.6334 = 63.34%

19. 95,200 ÷ 1,416,400 ≈ 0.0672 = 6.72%

20. 206,400 ÷ 1,416,400 ≈ 0.1457 = 14.57%

21. 387,600 ÷ 1,416,400 ≈ 0.2737 = 27.37%

22. 143,200 ÷ 1,416,400 ≈ 0.1011 = 10.11%

23. 25,600 ÷ 1,416,400 ≈ 0.0181 = 1.81%

24. 24,000 ÷ 1,416,400 ≈ 0.0169 = 1.69%

25. 201,200 ÷ 1,416,400 ≈ 0.1421 = 14.21%

26. 396,800 ÷ 1,416,400 ≈ 0.2801 = 28.01%

27. 600,000 ÷ 1,416,400 ≈ 0.4236 = 42.36%

28. 247,200 ÷ 1,416,400 ≈ 0.1745 = 17.45%

29. 1,019,600 ÷ 1,416,400 ≈ 0.7199 = 71.99%

30. 1,416,400 ÷ 1,416,400 ≈ 1.0000 = 100.00%

Section 18.2, pages 561–562

1. (a) 215 - 198 = 17
   (b) 17 ÷ 198 ≈ 0.0859 = 8.59%

2. (a) 5 - 4 = 1
   (b) 1 ÷ 4 = 0.2500 = 25.00%

3. (a) 210 - 194 = 16
   (b) 16 ÷ 194 ≈ 0.0825 = 8.25%

4. (a) 35 - 30 = (5)
   (b) 5 ÷ 35 ≈ 0.1429 = (14.29%)

5. (a) 132 - 130 = 2
   (b) 2 ÷ 130 ≈ 0.0154 = 1.54%

6. (a) 163 - 160 = (3)
   (b) 3 ÷ 163 ≈ 0.0184 = (1.84%)

7. (a) 34 - 30 = 4
   (b) 4 ÷ 30 ≈ 0.1333 = 13.33%

8. (a) 133 - 126 = (7)
   (b) 7 ÷ 133 ≈ 0.0526 = (5.26%)

9. (a) 84 − 61 = 23
    (b) 23 ÷ 61 ≈ 0.3770 = 37.70%

10. (a) 9 − 8 = 1
    (b) 1 ÷ 8 = 0.1250 = 12.50%

11. (a) 37 − 33 = 4
    (b) 4 ÷ 33 ≈ 0.1212 = 12.12%

12. (a) 53 − 48 = 5
    (b) 5 ÷ 48 ≈ 0.1042 = 10.42%

13. (a) 31 − 13 = 18
    (b) 18 ÷ 13 ≈ 1.3846 = 138.46%

14. (a) 5 − 2 = 3
    (b) 3 ÷ 2 = 1.5000 = 150.00%

15. (a) 26 − 11 = 15
    (b) 15 ÷ 11 ≈ 1.3636 = 136.36%

16. 215 ÷ 210 ≈ 1.0238 = 102.38%

17. 5 ÷ 210 ≈ 0.0238 = 2.38%

18. 210 ÷ 210 = 1.0000 = 100.00%

19. 30 ÷ 210 ≈ 0.1429 = 14.29%

20. 132 ÷ 210 ≈ 0.6286 = 62.86%

21. 2 ÷ 210 ≈ 0.0095 = 0.95%

22. 160 ÷ 210 ≈ 0.7619 = 76.19%

23. 34 ÷ 210 ≈ 0.1619 = 16.19%

24. 126 ÷ 210 = 0.60 = 60%

25. 84 ÷ 210 = 0.40 = 40%

26. 9 ÷ 210 ≈ 0.0429 = 4.29%

27. 37 ÷ 210 ≈ 0.1762 = 17.62%

28. 53 ÷ 210 ≈ 0.2524 = 25.24%

29. 31 ÷ 210 ≈ 0.1476 = 14.76%

30. 26 ÷ 210 ≈ 0.1238 = 12.38%

Section 18.3, pages 567–568

1. Working capital = current assets − current liabilities = 887,100 − 488,400 = 398,700

    The working capital for 1993 was $398,700.

2. Working capital = current assets - current liabilities = 824,200 - 432,200 = 392,000

    The working capital for 1992 was $392,000.

3. Quick assets = current assets - inventories = 887,100 - 421,800 = 465,300

    The quick assets for 1993 were $465,300.

4. Quick assets = current assets - inventories = 824,200 - 373,300 = 450,900

    The quick assets for 1992 were $450,900.

5. Current ratio = $\dfrac{\text{current assets}}{\text{current liabilities}} = \dfrac{887{,}100}{488{,}400} \approx 1.82$

    The current ratio for 1993 was 1.82 to 1.

6. Current ratio = $\dfrac{\text{current assets}}{\text{current liabilities}} = \dfrac{824{,}200}{432{,}200} \approx 1.91$

    The current ratio for 1992 was 1.91 to 1.

7. Acid-test ratio = $\dfrac{\text{quick assets}}{\text{current liabilities}} = \dfrac{465{,}300}{488{,}400} \approx 0.95$

    The acid-test ratio for 1993 was 0.95 to 1.

8. Acid-test ratio = $\dfrac{\text{quick assets}}{\text{current liabilities}} = \dfrac{450{,}900}{432{,}200} \approx 1.04$

    The acid-test ratio for 1992 was 1.04 to 1.

9. Ratio of stockholders' equity to liabilities = $\dfrac{\text{total stockholders' equity}}{\text{total liabilities}}$
    $= \dfrac{868{,}000}{743{,}900} \approx 1.17$

    The ratio of stockholders' equity to liabilities in 1993 was 1.17 to 1.

10. Ratio of stockholders' equity to liabilities = $\dfrac{\text{total stockholders' equity}}{\text{total liabilities}}$
    $= \dfrac{763{,}700}{740{,}700} \approx 1.03$

    The ratio of stockholders' equity to liabilities in 1992 was 1.03 to 1.

11. Ratio of total debt to total assets = $\dfrac{\text{total liabilities}}{\text{total assets}} = \dfrac{743{,}900}{1{,}611{,}900} \approx 0.46$

    The ratio of total debt to total assets in 1993 was 0.46 to 1.

12. Ratio of total debt to total assets = $\dfrac{\text{total liabilities}}{\text{total assets}} = \dfrac{740{,}700}{1{,}504{,}400} \approx 0.49$

    The ratio of total debt to total assets in 1992 was 0.49 to 1.

13. Ratio of plant and equipment to long-term liabilities = $\dfrac{\text{plant and equipment}}{\text{long-term liabilities}}$
    $= \dfrac{377{,}100}{255{,}500} \approx 1.48$

    The ratio of plant and equipment to long-term liabilities in 1993 was 1.48 to 1.

14. Ratio of plant and equipment to long-term liabilities = $\dfrac{\text{plant and equipment}}{\text{long-term liabilities}}$

$$= \dfrac{373,400}{308,500} \approx 1.21$$

The ratio of plant and equipment to long-term liabilities in 1992 was 1.21 to 1.

15. $\dfrac{\text{acid-test ratio for 1992 - acid-test ratio for 1993}}{\text{acid-test ratio for 1992}} = \dfrac{1.04 - 0.95}{1.04} = \dfrac{0.09}{1.04}$

$$\approx 0.0865 = (8.65\%)$$

The percent change in the acid-test ratio from 1992 to 1993 was (8.65%).

16. $\dfrac{\text{current ratio for 1992 - current ratio for 1993}}{\text{current ratio for 1992}} = \dfrac{1.91 - 1.82}{1.91} = \dfrac{0.09}{1.91} \approx 0.0471 = (4.71\%)$

The percent change in the current ratio from 1992 to 1993 was (4.71%).

17. $\dfrac{\text{ratio of stockholders' equity to total liabilities for 1993 - ratio of stockholders' equity to total liabilities for 1992}}{\text{ratio of stockholders' equity to total liabilities for 1992}} =$

$$\dfrac{1.17 - 1.03}{1.03} = \dfrac{0.14}{1.03} \approx 0.1359 = 13.59\%$$

The percent change in the ratio of stockholders' equity to total liabilities from 1992 to 1993 was 13.59%.

18. $\dfrac{\text{ratio of total debt to total assets for 1992 - ratio of total debt to total assets for 1993}}{\text{ratio of total debt to total assets for 1992}} =$

$$\dfrac{0.49 - 0.46}{0.49} = \dfrac{0.03}{0.49} \approx 0.0612 = (6.12\%)$$

The percent change in the ratio of total debt to total assets from 1992 to 1993 was (6.12%).

19. Ratio of cash and investments to current assets = $\dfrac{\text{cash and investments}}{\text{current assets}}$

$$= \dfrac{218,800}{887,100} \approx 0.25$$

The ratio of cash and investments to current assets in 1993 was 0.25 to 1.

20. Ratio of cash and investments to current assets = $\dfrac{\text{cash and investments}}{\text{current assets}}$

$$= \dfrac{221,000}{824,200} \approx 0.27$$

The ratio of cash and investments to current assets in 1992 was 0.27 to 1.

21. (a) Current ratio = $\dfrac{\text{current assets}}{\text{current liabilities}} = \dfrac{1,857,000}{1,261,700} \approx 1.47$

The current ratio was 1.47 to 1.

(b) Quick assets = current assets - inventories = 1,857,000 - 657,900 = 1,199,100

Acid-test ratio = $\dfrac{\text{quick assets}}{\text{current liabilities}} = \dfrac{1,199,100}{1,261,700} \approx 0.95$

The acid-test ratio was 0.95 to 1.

22. (a) Current ratio = $\dfrac{\text{current assets}}{\text{current liabilities}} = \dfrac{663,999}{245,500} \approx 2.70$

    The current ratio was 2.70 to 1.

    (b) Quick assets = current assets - inventories = 663,999 - 225,243 = 438,756

    Acid-test ratio = $\dfrac{\text{quick assets}}{\text{current liabilities}} = \dfrac{438,756}{245,500} \approx 1.79$

    The acid-test ratio was 1.79 to 1.

Business Case Study

1. The Madison Company should be offered the loan because it has more assets in the form of cash and accounts receivable and fewer liabilities in the form of notes payable and accounts payable. The company would therefore be in a better financial position for repaying the loan.

Review/Test, pages 573–574

1. (a) 171 - 87 = 84
   (b) 84 ÷ 87 ≈ 0.9655 = 96.55%

2. (a) 861 - 808 = 53
   (b) 53 ÷ 808 ≈ 0.0656 = 6.56%

3. (a) 539 - 458 = 81
   (b) 81 ÷ 458 ≈ 0.1769 = 17.69%

4. (a) 47 - 46 = (1)
   (b) 1 ÷ 47 ≈ 0.0213 = (2.13%)

5. (a) 1617 - 1400 = 217
   (b) 217 ÷ 1400 = 0.1550 = 15.50%

6. (a) 1341 - 1315 = (26)
   (b) 26 ÷ 1341 ≈ 0.0194 = (1.94%)

7. (a) 965 - 869 = 96
   (b) 96 ÷ 869 ≈ 0.1105 = 11.05%

8. (a) 3897 - 3610 = 287
   (b) 287 ÷ 3610 ≈ 0.0795 = 7.95%

9. (a) 994 - 948 = (46)
   (b) 46 ÷ 994 ≈ 0.0463 = (4.63%)

10. 6075 ÷ 6075 = 1.0000 = 100.00%

11. 5538 ÷ 6075 ≈ 0.9116 = 91.16%

12. 537 ÷ 6075 ≈ 0.0884 = 8.84%

13. 117 ÷ 6075 ≈ 0.0193 = 1.93%

14. $420 \div 6075 \approx 0.0691 = 6.91\%$

15. $108 \div 6075 \approx 0.0178 = 1.78\%$

16. $312 \div 6075 \approx 0.0514 = 5.14\%$

17. Working capital = current assets - current liabilities = $1,617,000 - 948,000$
    $$= 669,000$$

    The working capital for 1993 was $669,000.

18. Quick assets = current assets - inventories = $1,400,000 - 458,000 = 942,000$

    The quick assets for 1992 were $942,000.

19. Acid-test ratio = $\dfrac{\text{quick assets}}{\text{current liabilities}} = \dfrac{942,000}{994,000} \approx 0.95$

    The acid-test ratio for 1992 was 0.95 to 1.

20. Current ratio = $\dfrac{\text{current assets}}{\text{current liabilities}} = \dfrac{1,617,000}{948,000} \approx 1.71$

    The current ratio for 1993 was 1.71 to 1.

21. Ratio of total debt to total assets = $\dfrac{\text{total liabilities}}{\text{total assets}} = \dfrac{2,069,000}{3,610,000} \approx 0.57$

    The ratio of total debt to total assets in 1992 was 0.57 to 1.

22. Ratio of plant and equipment to long-term liabilities = $\dfrac{\text{plant and equipment}}{\text{long-term liabilities}}$
    $= \dfrac{1,315,000}{1,145,000} \approx 1.15$

    The ratio of plant and equipment to long-term liabilities in 1993 was 1.15 to 1.

23. Current ratio for 1992 = $\dfrac{\text{current assets}}{\text{current liabilities}} = \dfrac{1,400,000}{994,000} \approx 1.41$

    Current ratio for 1993 = $\dfrac{\text{current assets}}{\text{current liabilities}} = \dfrac{1,617,000}{948,000} \approx 1.71$

    $\dfrac{\text{current ratio for 1993 - current ratio for 1992}}{\text{current ratio for 1992}} = \dfrac{1.71 - 1.41}{1.41} = \dfrac{0.30}{1.41} \approx 0.2128 = 21.28\%$

    The percent change in the current ratio from 1992 to 1993 was 21.28%.

24. Acid-test ratio for 1992 = $\dfrac{\text{quick assets}}{\text{current liabilities}} = \dfrac{942,000}{994,000} \approx 0.95$

    Acid-test ratio for 1993 = $\dfrac{\text{quick assets}}{\text{current liabilities}} = \dfrac{1,078,000}{948,000} \approx 1.14$

    $\dfrac{\text{acid-test ratio for 1993 - acid-test ratio for 1992}}{\text{acid-test ratio for 1992}} = \dfrac{1.14 - 0.95}{0.95} = \dfrac{0.19}{0.95} = 0.2 = 20\%$

    The percent change in the acid-test ratio from 1992 to 1993 was 20%.

25. (a) Current ratio = $\dfrac{\text{current assets}}{\text{current liabilities}} = \dfrac{965,020}{608,662} \approx 1.59$

The current ratio was 1.59 to 1.

(b) Quick assets = current assets - inventories = 965,020 - 277,968 = 687,052

Acid-test ratio = $\dfrac{\text{quick assets}}{\text{current liabilities}} = \dfrac{687,052}{608,662} \approx 1.13$

The acid-test ratio was 1.13 to 1.

CHAPTER 19
Statistics

Section 19.1, pages 583–588

1. Strategy
    To find the sector that represents the smallest number of firms, locate the smallest sector in the circle graph.

    Solution
    The smallest sector is Partnerships. Partnerships represent the smallest number of firms.

2. Strategy
    To find the number of corporations, solve the basic percent equation for part.

    Solution
    Part = base x rate
    Part = 17,000,000 x 0.194
    Part = 3,298,000

    3,298,000 of the firms are corporations.

3. Strategy
    To find the number of partnerships, solve the basic percent equation for part.

    Solution
    Part = base x rate
    Part = 17,000,000 x 0.101
    Part = 1,717,000

    1,717,000 of the firms are partnerships.

4. Strategy
    To find the percent of the firms that are partnerships or sole proprietorships, add the percent that is partnerships to the percent that is sole proprietorships.

    Solution
    10.1% + 70.5% = 80.6%

    80.6% of the firms are partnerships or sole proprietorships.

5. Strategy
    To find the percent of the firms that are partnerships or corporations, add the percent that is partnerships to the percent that is corporations.

    Solution
    10.1% + 19.4% = 29.5%

    29.5% of the firms are partnerships or corporations.

6. Strategy
    To find the sector that represents the largest fixed expense, locate the largest sector in the circle graph.

    Solution
    The largest sector is Depreciation and Amortization.

    Depreciation and amortization represent the largest fixed expense.

7. Strategy
    To find the amount spent for property
    tax, solve the basic percent equation
    for part.

    Solution
    Part = base x rate
         = 150,000 x 0.13
         = 19,500

    The amount spent for property tax is
    $19,500.

9. Strategy
    To find the percent of fixed expenses
    that are for rent and insurance, add
    the percent that is for rent and the
    percent that is for insurance.

    Solution
    8% + 8% = 16%

    16% of the fixed expenses are for rent
    and insurance.

11. Strategy
    To find the percent that is budgeted
    for administrative costs and teacher
    salaries, add the percent that is for
    administrative costs to the percent
    that is for teacher salaries.

    Solution
    4.8% + 50.2% = 55%

    55% of the money is budgeted for
    administrative costs and teacher
    salaries.

13. Strategy
    To find the amount of money budgeted
    for utilities, solve the basic percent
    equation for part.

    Solution
    Part = base x rate
         = 22,450,000 x 0.120
         = 2,694,000

    $2,694,000 is budgeted for utilities.

8. Strategy
    To find the interest expense for the
    hotel, solve the basic percent
    equation for part.

    Solution
    Part = base x rate
         = 150,000 x 0.31
         = 46,500

    The interest expense for the hotel is
    $46,500.

10. Strategy
    To find the total amount spent on
    property taxes and insurance:
    *   Add the percent that is for
        property taxes to the percent that
        is for insurance to find the total
        percent.
    *   Solve the basic percent equation
        for part.

    Solution
    13% + 8% = 21%

    Part = base x rate
         = 150,000 x 0.21
         = 31,500

    The total amount spent on property
    taxes and insurance is $31,500.

12. Strategy
    To find the percent that is budgeted
    for bonds and capital outlay, add the
    percent that is for bonds and the
    percent that is for capital outlay.

    Solution
    4.3% + 6.3% = 10.6%

    10.6% of the money is budgeted for
    bonds and capital outlay.

14. Strategy
    To find the amount of money budgeted
    for transportation, solve the basic
    percent equation for part.

    Solution
    Part = base x rate
         = 22,450,000 x 0.035
         = 785,750

    $785,750 is budgeted for
    transportation.

15. Strategy
     To find the amount of money budgeted for supplies and miscellaneous expenses:
     • Add the percent that is for supplies to the percent that is for miscellaneous expenses to find the total percent.
     • Solve the basic percent equation for part.

     Solution
     15.3% + 3.6% = 18.9%
     Part = base x rate
          = 22,450,000 x 0.189
          = 4,243,050

     $4,243,050 is budgeted for supplies and miscellaneous expenses.

16. Strategy
     To draw the circle graph:
     • Find what percent each segment is of the total operating expenses.
     • Multiply each of the percents by 360° to find the angle for each sector.
     • Draw a circle and use a protractor to draw sectors representing the percent each segment contributed to the total.

     Solution
     $\frac{3,140}{5,319} \approx 59.0\%$ 0.590 x 360° ≈ 212°

     $\frac{666}{5,319} \approx 12.5\%$ 0.125 x 360° = 45°

     $\frac{1,513}{5,319} \approx 28.4\%$ 0.284 x 360° ≈ 102°

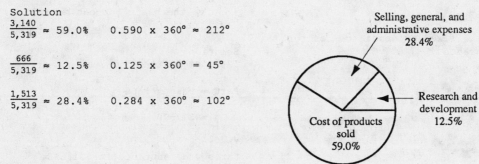

17. Strategy
     To draw the circle graph:
     • Find what percent each segment is of the total operating expenses.
     • Multiply each of the percents by 360° to find the angle for each sector.
     • Draw a circle and use a protractor to draw sectors representing the percent each segment contributed to the total.

     Solution
     $\frac{3,887}{4,401} \approx 88.3\%$ 0.883 X 360° ≈ 318°

     $\frac{447}{4,401} \approx 10.2\%$ 0.102 X 360° ≈ 37°

     $\frac{67}{4,401} \approx 1.5\%$ 0.015 X 360° ≈ 5°

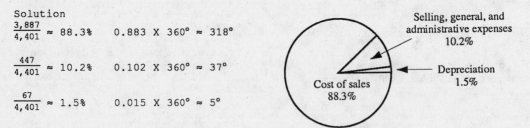

18. Strategy
    To draw the circle graph:
    • Find what percent each segment is of the total sales receipts.
    • Multiply each of the percents by 360° to find the angle for each sector.
    • Draw a circle and use a protractor to draw sectors representing the percent each segment contributed to the total.

    Solution
    $\frac{8,398}{9,306} \approx$ **90.2%**   0.902 x 360° ≈ 325°

    $\frac{368}{9,306} \approx 4.0\%$ 0.040 x 360° ≈ 14°

    $\frac{540}{9,306} \approx 5.8\%$ 0.058 x 360° ≈ 21°

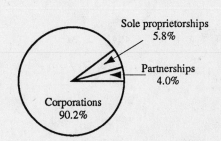

19. Strategy
    To draw the circle graph:
    • Add the three sales figures to find the total domestic motor vehicle sales.
    • Find what percent each segment is of the total sales.
    • Multiply each of the percents by 360° to find the angle for each sector.
    • Draw a circle and use a protractor to draw sectors representing the percent each segment contributed to the total.

    Solution
    10,626 + 4,608 + 710 = 15,944

    $\frac{10,626}{15,944} \approx 66.6\%$ 0.666 x 360° ≈ 240°

    $\frac{4,608}{15,944} \approx 28.9\%$ 0.289 x 360° ≈ 104°

    $\frac{710}{15,944} \approx 4.5\%$ 0.045 x 360° ≈ 16°

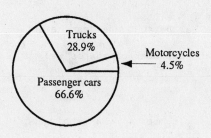

20. Strategy
    To draw the circle graph:
    • Add the four mortgage figures to find the total number of mortgage applications.
    • Find what percent each segment is of the total sales.
    • Multiply each of the percents by 360° to find the angle for each sector.
    • Draw a circle and use a protractor to draw sectors representing the percent each segment contributed to the total.

    Solution
    37 + 16 + 53 + 49 = 155

    $\frac{37}{155} \approx 23.9\%$ 0.239 x 360° ≈ 86°

    $\frac{16}{155} \approx 10.3\%$ 0.103 x 360° ≈ 37°

    $\frac{53}{155} \approx 34.2\%$ 0.342 x 360° ≈ 123°

    $\frac{49}{155} \approx 31.6\%$ 0.316 x 360° ≈ 114°

21. Strategy
    To draw the circle graph:
    • Add the four figures to find the total domestic freight shipped.
    • Find what percent each segment is of the total freight shipped.
    • Multiply each of the percents by 360° to find the angle for each sector.
    • Draw a circle and use a protractor to draw sectors representing the percent each
      segment contributed to the total.

    Solution
    1,048 + 712 + 597 + 454 = 2,811

    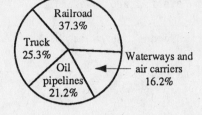

    $\frac{1,048}{2,811} \approx 37.3\%$ 0.373 x 360° ≈ 134°

    $\frac{712}{2,811} \approx 25.3\%$ 0.253 x 360° ≈ 91°

    $\frac{597}{2,811} \approx 21.2\%$ 0.212 x 360° ≈ 76°

    $\frac{454}{2,811} \approx 16.2\%$ 0.162 x 360° ≈ 58°

22. Strategy
    To find the day in which the greatest
    number of shares was traded, locate
    the bar with the greatest height.

    Solution
    Friday's bar has the greatest height.

    The greatest number of shares was
    traded on Friday.

23. Strategy
    To find the day in which the least
    number of shares was traded, locate
    the bar with the shortest height.

    Solution
    Wednesday's bar has the shortest
    height.

    The fewest shares were traded on
    Wednesday.

24. Strategy
    To find the number of shares of stock
    traded, read the bar graph to find the
    number traded on Monday.

    Solution
    On Monday, 3000 shares of stock were
    traded.

25. Strategy
    To find the number of shares of stock
    traded, read the bar graph to find the
    number traded on Thursday.

    Solution
    On Thursday, 4500 shares of stock were
    traded.

26. Strategy
    To find the difference, subtract the
    number of shares traded on Wednesday
    from the number of shares traded on
    Friday.

    Solution
    5000 - 2500 = 2500

    The difference between the number of
    shares traded on Wednesday and the
    number of shares traded on Friday is
    2500.

27. Strategy
    To find the difference, subtract the
    number of shares traded on Wednesday
    from the number of shares traded on
    Tuesday.

    Solution
    4000 - 2500 = 1500

    The difference between the number of
    shares traded on Tuesday and the
    number of shares traded on Wednesday
    is 1500.

28. Strategy
    To find which month in 1992 had the
    lowest sales, read the bar graph to
    find the shortest bar for 1992.

    Solution
    In 1992, February had the lowest
    sales.

29. Strategy
    To find which month in 1993 had the
    lowest sales, read the bar graph to
    find the shortest bar for 1993.

    Solution
    In 1993, March had the lowest sales.

30. Strategy
    To find the number of watches sold,
    read the bar graph to find the number
    sold in February 1993.

    Solution
    In February 1993, 300 watches were
    sold.

31. Strategy
    To find the number of watches sold,
    read the bar graph to find the number
    sold in May 1992.

    Solution
    In May 1992, 400 watches were sold.

32. Strategy
    To find the difference, subtract the
    January 1992 sales from the January
    1993 sales.

    Solution
    400 - 350 = 50

    The difference between the January
    sales for 1992 and 1993 is 50 watches.

33. Strategy
    To find the difference, subtract the
    April 1992 sales from the April 1993
    sales.

    Solution
    350 - 250 = 100

    The difference between the April sales
    for 1992 and 1993 is 100 watches.

34. Strategy
    To find the year in which benefits
    earned exceeded the premiums paid,
    read the bar graph to find the year in
    which the bar representing benefits
    paid is higher than the bar
    representing premiums earned.

    Solution
    In 1991 benefits paid exceeded
    premiums earned.

35. Strategy
    To find the amount of premiums earned
    in 1990, read the bar representing
    premiums earned for the year 1990.

    Solution
    In 1990, the amount of premiums earned
    was $45,000.

36. Strategy
    To find the amount of benefits paid in
    1992, read the bar representing
    benefits paid for the year 1992.

    Solution
    In 1992, the amount of benefits paid
    was $50,000.

37. Strategy
    To find the difference, subtract the
    amount of benefits paid in 1992 from
    the amount of premiums earned in 1992.

    Solution
    70,000 - 50,000 = 20,000

    The difference between the premiums
    earned and the benefits paid in 1992
    was $20,000.

38. Strategy
    To find the difference, subtract the
    amount of benefits paid in 1993 from
    the amount of premiums earned in 1993.

    Solution
    80,000 - 65,000 = 15,000

    The difference between the premiums
    earned and the benefits paid in 1993
    was $15,000.

39. Strategy
    To find the month in which profit was
    the highest, locate the highest dot in
    the graph.

    Solution
    Profit was the highest during June.

40. Strategy
    To find the month in which profit was
    the lowest, locate the lowest dot in
    the graph.

    Solution
    Profit was the lowest during February.

41. Strategy
    To find the profit, read the line
    graph to find the profit for March.

    Solution
    The company's profit for March was
    $4000.

42. Strategy
    To find the profit, read the line
    graph to find the profit for January.

    Solution
    The company's profit for January was
    $2500.

43. Strategy
    To find the difference, subtract the
    company's profits for February from
    the company's profits for May.

    Solution
    5000 - 2000 = 3000

    The difference between the company's
    profits for February and May is $3000.

44. Strategy
    To find the quarter in which the
    company had the highest income, locate
    the highest dot on the graph for 1992.

    Solution
    In 1992, the company had the highest
    income during the third quarter.

45. Strategy
    To find the quarter in which the
    company had the highest income, locate
    the highest dot on the graph for 1993.

    Solution
    In 1993, the company had the highest
    income during the fourth quarter.

46. Strategy
    To find the income, read the graph to
    find the income for the second quarter
    of 1992.

    Solution
    The income for the second quarter of
    1992 was $3,000,000.

47. Strategy
    To find the income, read the graph to
    find the income for the first quarter
    of 1993.

    Solution
    The income for the first quarter of
    1993 was $2,000,000.

48. Strategy
    To find the difference, subtract the
    third-quarter income for 1993 from the
    third-quarter income for 1992.

    Solution
    5,000,000 - 3,500,000 = 1,500,000

    The difference between the company's
    third-quarter incomes for 1992 and
    1993 was $1,500,000.

49. Strategy
    To find the hours during which the
    greatest number of residential calls
    was made, locate the highest dot on
    the graph for residential calls.

    Solution
    The greatest number of residential
    calls was made between 9 and 10 A.M.

50. Strategy
    To find the hours during which the least number of business calls was made, locate the lowest dot on the graph for business calls.

    Solution
    The least number of business calls was made between 3 and 4 P.M.

51. Strategy
    To find the difference, subtract the number of business calls made between 11 A.M. and noon from the number of residential calls made between 11 A.M. and noon.

    Solution
    55,000 - 30,000 = 25,000

    The difference between the number of business calls and the number of residential calls made between 11 A.M. and noon was 25,000.

52. Strategy
    To find the number of business calls made between 9 A.M. and noon, add the number made between 9 A.M. and 10 A.M., the number made between 10 A.M. and 11 A.M., and the number made between 11 A.M. and noon.

    Solution
    25,000 + 35,000 + 30,000 = 90,000

    Between 9 A.M. and noon, 90,000 business calls were made.

53. Strategy
    To find the difference:
    • Add the number of business calls made between 3 P.M. and 4 P.M. to the number made between 4 P.M. and 5 P.M.
    • Add the number of residential calls made between 3 P.M. and 4 P.M. to the number made between 4 P.M. and 5 P.M.
    • Subtract the first sum from the second sum.

    Solution
    20,000 + 25,000 = 45,000
    65,000 + 40,000 = 105,000
    105,000 - 45,000 = 60,000

    The difference between the number of business calls and the number of residential calls made between 3 and 5 P.M. was 60,000.

Section 19.2, pages 593–596

1. Strategy
   To make the frequency distribution:
   • Find the range by subtracting the smallest number from the largest.
   • Find the class width by dividing the range by 4 (the number of classes).
   • Form the classes.
   • Tabulate the data for each class.
   • Count the number of tallies in each class.

   Solution

   Range = 90 - 10 = 80

   Class width = $\frac{80}{4}$ = 20

Classes	Tally	Frequency
10-30	//////////	10
31-51	understand/////////	9
52-72	///////	7
73-93	////	4

2. Strategy
   To find the number of loans between $3100 and $5100, find the frequency for the class 31-51.

   Solution
   There were 9 loans between $3100 and $5100.

3. Strategy
   To find the number of loans that were for $5100 or less, add the frequencies for the classes 10-30 and 31-51.

   Solution
   10 + 9 = 19

   There were 19 loans that were for $5100 or less.

4. Strategy
   To find the percent of loans that were for between $1000 and $3000, solve the basic percent equation for rate. Base = 30, part = 10.

   Solution
   Part = base x rate
   10 = 30 x rate
   $\frac{10}{30}$ = rate
   $\frac{1}{3}$ = rate

   $33\frac{1}{3}$% of the loans were for between $1000 and $3000.

5. Strategy
   To make the frequency distribution:
   • Find the range by subtracting the smallest number from the largest.
   • Find the class width by dividing the range by 7 (the number of classes).
   • Form the classes.
   • Tabulate the data for each class.
   • Count the number of tallies in each class.

   Solution

   Range = 107 - 37 = 70

   Class width = $\frac{70}{7}$ = 10

Classes	Tally	Frequency
37-47	/////	5
48-58	//////////	10
59-69	///////	7
70-80	///////////	11
81-91	//////////	10
92-102	///////	6
103-113	/	1

6. Strategy
   To find the number that charge a corporate room rate that is between $59 and $69, find the frequency for the class 59-69.

   Solution
   There are 7 hotels that charge a corporate room rate that is between $59 and $69.

7. Strategy
   To find the number that charge a corporate room rate that is less than or equal to $80, add the frequencies for the classes 37-47, 48-58, 59-69, and 70-80.

   Solution
   5 + 10 + 7 + 11 = 33

   There are 33 hotels that charge a corporate room rate that is less than or equal to $80.

8. Strategy
   To find the percent of the hotels that
   charge between $70 and $80, solve the
   basic percent equation for rate.
   Base = 50, part = 11.

   Solution
   Part = base x rate
   $\quad$ 11 = 50 x rate
   $\quad \frac{11}{50}$ = rate
   0.22 = rate

   22% of the hotels charge a corporate
   room rate that is between $70 and $80.

9. Strategy
   To find the percent of the hotels that
   charge a corporate room rate that is
   greater than or equal to $81 per
   night:
   • Find the number that charge $81 or
     more per night by adding the
     frequencies for the classes 81-91,
     92-102, and 103-113.
   • Solve the basic percent equation
     for rate.

   Solution
   10 + 6 + 1 = 17
   Part = base x rate
   $\quad$ 17 = 50 x rate
   $\quad \frac{17}{50}$ = rate
   0.34 = rate

   34% of the hotels charge a corporate
   room rate that is greater than or
   equal to $81 per night.

10. Strategy
    To find the class interval with the
    highest frequency, locate the bar with
    the greatest height.

    Solution
    The class interval 20 to 30 claims has
    the highest frequency.

11. Strategy
    To find the number of branch offices,
    read the histogram to find the number
    of offices in which between 10 and 20
    claims were filed.

    Solution
    Between 10 and 20 claims were filed in
    4 branch offices.

12. Strategy
    To find the ratio:
    • Read the histogram to find the
      number of branch offices in which
      between 30 and 40 claims were
      filed.
    • Write the ratio of the number of
      branch offices in which between 30
      and 40 claims were filed to the
      total number of branch offices.

    Solution
    Number of branch offices: 6
    $\frac{6 \text{ offices}}{20 \text{ offices}} = \frac{3}{10}$

    The ratio is 3:10.

13. Strategy
    To find the ratio:
    • Read the histogram to find the
      number of branch offices in which
      less than 10 claims were filed.
    • Write the ratio of the number of
      branch offices in which less than
      10 claims were filed to the total
      number of branch offices.

    Solution
    Number of branch offices: 2
    $\frac{2 \text{ offices}}{20 \text{ offices}} = \frac{1}{10}$

    The ratio is 1:10.

14. Strategy
    To find the class interval that has
    the highest frequency, locate the bar
    with the greatest height.

    Solution
    The class interval $40,000 to $45,000
    has the highest frequency.

15. Strategy
    To find the number of employees, read
    the histogram to find the number of
    employees whose salary is between
    $45,000 and $50,000.

    Solution
    There are 11 employees whose salary is
    between $45,000 and $50,000.

16. Strategy
    To find the ratio:
    • Read the histogram to find the
      number of employees whose salary is
      between $50,000 and $55,000.
    • Write the ratio of the number of
      employees whose salary is between
      $50,000 and $55,000 to the total
      number of employees.

    Solution
    Number of employees: 6
    $$\frac{6 \text{ employees}}{51 \text{ employees}} = \frac{2}{17}$$

    The ratio is 2:17.

17. Strategy
    To find the number of employees who
    earn more than $55,000, add the number
    whose salary is between $45,000 and
    $50,000 to the number whose salary is
    between $50,000 and $55,000.

    Solution
    $3 + 1 = 4$

    There are 4 employees who earn more
    than $35,000.

18. Strategy
    To find the class interval that has
    the highest frequency, locate the bar
    with the greatest height.

    Solution
    The class interval $40 to $60 has the
    highest frequency.

19. Strategy
    To find the number of customers, read
    the histogram to find the number who
    made purchases between $120 and $140.

    Solution
    There were 9 customers who made
    purchases between $120 and $140.

20. Strategy
    To find the number of customers who
    made purchases of more than $80, add
    the number who made purchases between
    $80 and $100, the number who made
    purchases between $100 and $120, and
    the number who made purchases between
    $120 and $140.

    Solution
    $15 + 12 + 9 = 36$

    There were 36 customers who made
    purchases of more than $80.

21. Strategy
    To find the ratio:
    • Add the number whose purchases were
      between $0 and $20 to the number
      whose purchases were between $20
      and $40.
    • Write the ratio of the sum to the
      total number of customers.

    Solution
    $24 + 27 = 51$
    $$\frac{51 \text{ customers}}{153 \text{ customers}} = \frac{1}{3}$$

    The ratio is 1:3.

22. Strategy
    To find the percent of the customers
    who made purchases between $40 and
    $80:
    • Find the number of customers by
      adding the frequencies for the
      classes 40-60 and 60-80.
    • Solve the basic percent equation
      for rate.

    Solution
    $36 + 30 = 66$
     Part = base x rate
      $66 = 153$ x rate
     $\frac{66}{153}$ = rate
    $0.431 \approx$ rate

    Approximately 43.1% of the customers
    made purchases between $40 and $80.

23. Strategy
    To find the class interval that has
    the highest frequency, locate the
    highest dot in he frequency polygon.

    Solution
    The class interval 15 to 20 hours has
    the highest frequency.

24. Strategy
    To find the number of families, read
    the frequency polygon to find the
    number of families who watched between
    25 and 30 hours a week.

    Solution
    There were 5 families that watched
    between 25 and 30 hours a week.

25. Strategy
    To find the number of families, add
    the number who watched between 10 and
    15 hours to the number who watched
    between 15 and 20 hours per week.

    Solution
    $20 + 30 = 50$

    There were 50 families that watched
    between 10 and 20 hours per week.

26. Strategy
    To find the percent that watched
    between 0 and 5 hours a week, solve
    the basic percent equation for rate.
    Base = 100, part = 5.

    Solution
    Part = base x rate
      $5 = 100$ x rate
     $\frac{5}{100}$ = rate
    0.05 = rate

    5% of the families watched between 0
    and 5 hours a week.

27. Strategy
    To find the class interval that has
    the lowest frequency, locate the
    lowest dot in the frequency polygon.

    Solution
    The class interval $0 to $15 has the
    lowest frequency.

28. Strategy
    To find the number of customers, read
    the frequency polygon to find the
    number of customers whose bills were
    between $75 and $90.

    Solution
    7 customers had bills between $75 and
    $90.

29. Strategy
    To find the number of customers, add
    the number who had bills between $0
    and $15, the number who had bills
    between $15 and $30, and the number
    who had bills between $30 and $45.

    Solution
    $1 + 7 + 12 = 20$

    20 customers had bills between $0 and
    $45.

30. Strategy
     To find the percent that had bills
     between $15 and $30, solve the basic
     percent equation for rate.

     Solution
     Part = base x rate
       7 = 50 x rate
       $\frac{7}{50}$ = rate
     0.14 = rate

     14% of the customers had bills between
     $15 and $30.

31. Strategy
     To find the class interval that has
     the highest frequency, locate the
     highest dot in the frequency polygon.

     Solution
     The class interval 4% to 6% has the
     highest frequency.

32. Strategy
     To find the number of families, read
     the frequency polygon to find the
     number that spent between 2% and 4% of
     their income on vacations.

     Solution
     4 families spent between 2% and 4% of
     their income on vacations.

33. Strategy
     To find the number of families, add
     the number that spent 8% to 10% and
     the number that spent 10% to 12%.

     Solution
     3 + 2 = 5

     5 families spent more than 8% of their
     income on vacations.

34. Strategy
     To find the ratio, write the ratio of
     the number that spent between 10% and
     12% of their incomes on vacations (2)
     to the total number of families (50).

     Solution
     $\frac{2 \text{ families}}{50 \text{ families}} = \frac{1}{25}$

     The ratio is 1:25.

35. Strategy
     To find the ratio:
     • Find the total number that spent
       less than 4% of their income on
       vacations by adding the number that
       spent between 0% and 2% and the
       number that spent between 2% and
       4%.
     • Find the total number that spent
       more than 8% of their income on
       vacations by adding the number that
       spent between 8% and 10% and the
       number that spent between 10% and
       12%.
     • Write the ratio of the number that
       spent 0% to 4% of their incomes on
       vacations to the number that spent
       8% to 12%.

     Solution
     11 + 4 = 15
     3 + 2 = 5
     $\frac{15 \text{ families}}{5 \text{ families}} = \frac{3}{1}$

     The ratio is 3:1.

Section 19.3, pages 599–600

1. Strategy
   To find the mean number of hamburgers
   sold, divide the sum of the numbers
   sold by the number of lunch hours (5).

   Solution
   $$\frac{252 + 286 + 245 + 292 + 285}{5} = \frac{1360}{5} = 272$$

   The mean number of hamburgers sold per
   lunch hour was 272.

2. Strategy
   To find the mean braking distance,
   divide the sum of the braking
   distances by the number of trials (5).

   Solution
   $$\frac{220 + 208 + 216 + 219 + 227}{5} = \frac{1090}{5} = 218$$

   The mean braking distance was 218
   feet.

3. Strategy
   To find the median age, arrange the
   ages in order from smallest to
   largest. The median is the middle
   number.

   Solution
   22   24   25 $\boxed{26}$ 30   34   45
   $\uparrow$
   middle number

   The median age is 26.

4. Strategy
   To find the median utility bill,
   arrange the bills in order from
   smallest to largest and calculate the
   mean of the two middle numbers.

   Solution
   48.92
   61.92
   74.16
   86.48 ⎤
   87.48 ⎦ ← middle numbers
   92.81
   97.92
   112.53

   $$\frac{86.48 + 87.48}{2} = \frac{173.96}{2} = 86.98$$

   The median utility bill is $86.98.

5. Strategy
   To find the mean, divide the sum of
   the numbers by the number of days (5).
   To find the median, arrange the
   numbers in order from smallest to
   largest. The median is the middle
   number.
   To find the mode, find the number that
   occurs more frequently than any other
   number in the list.

   Solution
   $$\frac{8 + 9 + 9 + 7 + 6}{5} = \frac{39}{5} = 7.8$$

   The mean is 7.8 applications.

   6   7 $\boxed{8}$ 9   9
   $\uparrow$
   middle number

   The median is 8.
   The mode is 9 applications.

6. Strategy
   To find the mean, divide the sum of
   the numbers by the number of days (6).
   To find the median, arrange the
   numbers in order from smallest to
   largest. The median is the middle
   number.
   To find the mode, find the number that
   occurs more frequently than any other
   number in the list.

   Solution
   $$\frac{24 + 30 + 28 + 24 + 36 + 38}{6} = \frac{180}{6} = 30$$

   The mean is 30.

   24   24 $\boxed{28\quad 30}$ 36   38
   $\uparrow$
   middle numbers

   $$\frac{28 + 30}{2} = \frac{58}{2} = 29$$

   The median is 29.
   The mode is 24 requests.

7. Strategy
   To find the mean number of miles,
   divide the sum of all the miles driven
   by the number of days (5).
   To find the median, arrange the miles
   driven in order from smallest to
   largest. The median is the middle
   number.

   Solution
   $$\frac{96 + 85 + 140 + 92 + 88}{5} = \frac{501}{5} = 100.2$$

   The mean is 100.2 miles.

   85   88 $\boxed{92}$ 96   140
   $\uparrow$
   middle number

   The median is 92 miles.

8. Strategy
   To find the mean number of requests,
   divide the sum of the requests by the
   number of days (6).
   To find the median, arrange the
   numbers in order from smallest to
   largest and calculate the mean of the
   two middle numbers.

   Solution
   $$\frac{46 + 18 + 29 + 49 + 38 + 24}{6} = \frac{204}{6} = 34$$

   The mean is 34 requests.

   18   24 $\boxed{29 \quad 38}$ 46   49
   $\uparrow$
   middle numbers

   $$\frac{29 + 38}{2} = \frac{67}{2} = 33.5$$

   The median is 33.5 requests.

9. Strategy
   To find the mean price, divide the sum
   of the prices by the number of prices
   (5).
   To find the median, arrange the prices
   in order from smallest to largest. The
   median is the middle number.

   Solution
   $$\frac{38.75 + 44.50 + 42.95 + 41.00 + 48.00}{5}$$
   $$= \frac{215.20}{5} = 43.04$$

   The mean is $43.04.

   38.75   41.00 $\boxed{42.95}$ 44.50   48.00
   $\uparrow$
   middle number

   The median is $42.95.

10. Strategy
    To find the mean, divide the sum of
    the gallons by the number of purchases
    (5).
    To find the median, arrange the
    numbers in order from smallest to
    largest. The median is the middle
    number.

    Solution
    $$\frac{9.4 + 9.3 + 11.8 + 10.3 + 9.7}{5} = \frac{50.5}{5} = 10.1$$

    The mean number of gallons purchased
    is 10.1.

    9.3   9.4 $\boxed{9.7}$ 10.3   11.8
    $\uparrow$
    middle number

    The median is 9.7 gallons.

11. Strategy
    To find the mean, divide the sum of
    the paychecks by the number of checks
    (6).
    To find the median, arrange the
    paychecks in order from smallest to
    largest and calculate the mean of the
    two middle numbers.
    To find the mode, find the number that
    occurs more frequently than any other
    number in the list.

    Solution
    $$\frac{4400 + 4700 + 4550 + 4850 + 4700 + 4250}{6}$$

    $$= \frac{27,450}{6} = 4575$$

    The mean is $4575.

    4250   4400 $\boxed{4550 \quad 4700}$ 4700   4850
                      ↑
              middle numbers

    $$\frac{4550 + 4700}{2} = \frac{9250}{2} = 4625$$

    The median is $4625.
    The mode is $4700.

12. Strategy
    To find the mean, divide the sum of
    the prices by the number of days.
    To find the median, arrange the
    numbers in order from smallest to
    largest. The median is the middle
    number.
    To find the mode, find the number that
    occurs more frequently than any other
    number in the list.

    Solution
    $$\frac{36.25 + 35.75 + 36.50 + 36 + 36.25}{5}$$

    $$= \frac{180.75}{5} = 36.15$$

    The mean is $36.15.

    35.75   36 $\boxed{36.25}$ 36.25   36.50
                     ↑
              middle number

    The median is $36.25.
    The mode is $36.25.

13. Strategy
    To find the mean profit, divide the sum of the profits by the number of quarters
    (4).

    Solution
    $$\frac{278,630 + 315,470 + 296,910 + 304,820}{4} = \frac{1,195,830}{4} = 298,957.50$$

    The mean quarterly profit was $298,957.50.

14. Strategy
    To find the mean, divide the sum of the sales by the number of months (12).

    Solution
    $$\frac{387 + 346 + 295 + 281 + 308 + 332 + 409 + 415 + 398 + 376 + 297 + 388}{12} = \frac{4232}{12} \approx 352.66667$$

    The mean monthly sales were $352,666.67.

15. Strategy

     To find the mean length, divide the sum of the lengths by the number measured (50).
     To find the median, find the middle numbers.
     To find the mode, find the number that occurs more frequently than any other number in the list.

     Solution

$$\frac{5(100.02) + 10(100.01) + 20(100.00) + 10(99.99) + 5(99.98)}{50}$$

$$= \frac{500.1 + 1000.1 + 2000 + 999.9 + 499.9}{50} = \frac{5000}{50} = 100$$

     The mean length is 100 m.

```
 5    100.02's
10    100.01's
20    100.00's ] ← middle number
10     99.99's
 5     99.98's
```

     The median is 100 m.
     The mode is 100 m.

16. Strategy

     To find the mean lifetime, divide the sum of the lifetimes of the 50 batteries by the number of batteries tested (50).
     To find the median, find the middle numbers.
     To find the mode, find the number that occurs more frequently than any other number in the list.

     Solution

$$\frac{5(10) + 10(15) + 20(20) + 10(25) + 5(30)}{50} = \frac{50 + 150 + 400 + 250 + 150}{50} = \frac{1000}{50} = 20$$

     The mean is 20 hours.

```
 5    10's
10    15's
20    20's ] ← middle number
10    25's
 5    30's
```

     The median is 20 hours.
     The mode is 20 hours.

Business Case Study

1.

	Cash Sales	Credit Sales	Collections on Credit Sales	Total Cash Payments Received	Accounts Receivable at End of Period	Total Sales for Period
1st 6 months	30,000	70,000	30,000	60,000	40,000	100,000
2nd 6 months	35,000	35,000	45,000	80,000	30,000	70,000
3rd 6 months	60,000	0	30,000	90,000	0	60,000

2. No, the business is not experiencing growth. Total sales have declined from $100,000 during the first six months, to $70,000 during the second six months, to $60,000 during the third six months of operation.

Review/Test, pages 605–606

1. Strategy
   To find the amount spent on newspaper
   advertising, solve the basic percent
   equation for part.

   Solution
   Part = base x rate
        = 1,500,000 x 0.12
        = 180,000

   $180,000 is spent on newspaper
   advertising.

2. Strategy
   To find the amount spent on television
   and radio advertising:
   • Add the percent spent on television
     advertising and the amount spent on
     radio advertising.
   • Solve the basic percent equation
     for part.

   Solution
   45% + 25% = 70%
   Part = base x rate
        = 1,500,000 x 0.70
        = 1,050,000

   $1,050,000 is spent on television and
   radio advertising.

3. Strategy
   To draw the circle graph:
   • Find what percent each segment is of the total revenue of $4700 (2200 + 1800 +
     700). Round to the nearest tenth of a percent.
   • Find the measure of the angle for each sector. Round to the nearest whole number.
   • Draw a circle and use a protractor to draw the sectors representing the percent
     each segment contributed to the total revenue from the three segments.

   Solution

   Car sales: $\frac{2200}{4700}$ = 46.8%

   Car leasing: $\frac{1800}{4700}$ = 38.3%

   Parts and service: $\frac{700}{4700}$ = 14.9%

   New car sales: 0.468 x 360° = 168°
   Car leasing: 0.383 x 369 = 138°
   Parts and service: 0.149 x 360° = 54°

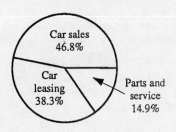

4. Strategy
   To find which month in 1992 had the
   lowest sales, read the bar graph to
   find the shortest bar for 1992.

   Solution
   In 1992, October had the lowest sales.

5. Strategy
   To find the difference, subtract the
   October 1992 sales from the October
   1993 sales.

   Solution
   13,000 - 7000 = 6000

   The difference between the October
   sales for 1992 and 1993 was 6000 cars.

6. Strategy
   To find the quarter during which sales
   were highest during the first year,
   locate the highest dot on the graph
   for Year 1.

   Solution
   Sales were highest during the first
   year during the fourth quarter.

7. Strategy
   To find the difference, subtract the
   third quarter sales for Year 1 from
   the third quarter sales for Year 2.

   Solution
   10,000 - 4000 = 6000

   The difference between the third
   quarter sales for Year 1 and Year 2
   was 6000 issues.

8. Strategy
   To make the frequency distribution:
   • Find the range by subtracting the smallest number from the largest number.
   • Find the class width by dividing the range by 5 (the number of classes).
   • Form the classes.
   • Tabulate the data for each class.
   • Count the number of tallies in each group.

   Solution

   Range = 124 - 52 = 72

   Class width = $\frac{72}{5} \approx 14$

Classes	Tally	Frequency
52-66	////	4
67-81	/////	5
82-96	/////	5
97-111	///	3
112-126	///	3

9. Strategy
   To find the number of sales representatives that spent between 82 and 96 days on the road, find the frequency for the class 82-96.

   Solution
   5 sales representatives spent between 82 and 96 days on the road.

10. Strategy
    To find the number of employees over 45 years of age, add the number between 45 and 55 (8) to the number between 55 and 65 (4).

    Solution
    8 + 4 = 12

    12 employees are over 45 years of age.

11. Strategy
    To find the ratio:
    • Read the histogram to find the number of employees between 25 and 35 years of age.
    • Write the ratio of the number of employees between 25 and 35 years of age to the total number of employees.

    Solution
    Number of employees 25 - 35: 6
    $\frac{6 \text{ employees}}{30 \text{ employees}} = \frac{1}{5}$

    The ratio is 1:5.

12. Strategy
    To find the number of cars, read the frequency polygon to find the number of cars that get between 30 and 40 miles per gallon.

    Solution
    12 cars get between 30 and 40 miles per gallon.

13. Strategy
    To find the percent of cars that get between 40 and 50 miles per gallon, solve the basic percent equation for rate.

    Solution
    Part = base x rate
    $\quad$ 8 = 50 x rate
    $\quad \dfrac{8}{50}$ = rate
    0.16 = rate

    16% of the cars get between 40 and 50 miles per gallon.

14. Strategy
    To find the mean occupancy, divide the sum of the occupancies by the number of nights (7).
    To find the median, arrange the numbers of occupancies in order from smallest to largest. The median is the middle number.
    To find the mode, find the number that occurs more frequently than any other number in the list.

    Solution
    $$\dfrac{55 + 60 + 58 + 60 + 52 + 48 + 47}{7} = \dfrac{380}{7} \approx 54.3$$

    The mean is 54.3 occupancies.

    47$\quad$48$\quad$52$\quad$55$\quad$58$\quad$60$\quad$60
    $\qquad\qquad\qquad$↑
    $\qquad\quad$middle number

    The median is 55 occupancies.
    The mode is 60 occupancies.